D1107315

The Geological Society of America
Memoir 70

FENESTELLA FROM THE PERMIAN OF WEST TEXAS

By
M. K. Elias and G. E. Condra
University of Nebraska, Lincoln, Nebraska

July 19, 1957

Made in the United States of America

PRINTED BY WAVERLY PRESS, INC.
BALTIMORE, MD.

PUBLISHED BY THE GEOLOGICAL SOCIETY OF AMERICA
Address all communications to the Geological Society of America
419 West 117 Street, New York 27, N. Y.

The Memoir Series
of
The Geological Society of America
is made possible
through the bequest of
Richard Alexander Fullerton Penrose, Jr.

"Paleontologists have now universally conceded that in the determination of such difficult groups of organisms as the fossil Bryozoa the microscopic structure is the most essential element."

"To get a correct idea of the structure of Paleozoic Bryozoa, it is absolutely necessary that they be studied with the aid of thin sections."

E. O. Ulrich. Paleozoic Bryozoa. 1890.

To the memory of the great student of Paleozoic Bryozoa, E. Oscar Ulrich, this memoir is respectfully dedicated.

FOREWORD AND ACKNOWLEDGMENTS

This is the first part of a report on the King and King collection of Permian bryozoans made in Glass Mountains of Texas. The collection was stored in the Peabody Museum at Yale University and forwarded by Dr. Carl O. Dunbar to Condra for study and description. Condra also collected specimens from the area worked by the King brothers as did Dr. Charles Schuchert of Yale University. Etched bryozoans from this source were forwarded to us by Dunbar, but they are mostly specimens of bryozoans other than *Fenestella.*

The fistuliporoids of the collections, turned over to Dr. Raymond C. Moore of the Kansas Geological Survey for investigation and description, were described in part by Moore and Dudley (1944). Some progress was made in the study of the main part of the collection, but soon it was decided that intensive study should be made of certain genera, as with *Fenestella, Polypora, Thamniscus,* and others, and that each field of investigation should be expanded to include the description and comparison of related species obtained from formations of correlative age in other areas and regions. This change in procedure resulted in the present report on the *Fenestella.* The rest of the Glass Mountains collections is to be described later, some genera by the Kansas Geological Survey, and others by the Nebraska Survey.

Some late Pennsylvanian species of *Fenestella* described by Condra (1903) from Nebraska and from northern Texas by Moore (1929) are here revised and compared with the related Permian forms from the Glass Mountains and from Russia. We also described a few new species collected in Russia by Condra in 1937. The types of these species are in the collection of Carboniferous and Permian fossils he brought from Russia. Lists of the species of *Fenestella* in the Russian collection are supplemented.

The lifelong studies by Borg on living Cyclostomata have been utilized in a new approach toward understanding of microstructure of *Fenestella,* and technique was improved by study of thinnest possible thin sections under polarized light.

One of the results was the discovery in *Fenestella* and other fenestrate Cryptostomata of a structural equivalent to the common bud or colonial bud (Smitt, 1866; Borg, 1926; 1933) in Cyclostomata, here named colonial plexus. This means repudiation of Shulga-Nesterenko's theory of a "capillary system" in these same fenestrate forms, because her "system" is actually made of two unrelated elements: dorsal part of the colonial plexus originating primarily and the spicules ("capillaries") originating secondarily.

CONTENTS

ILLUSTRATIONS

PLATES

FIGURES

TABLES

ABSTRACT

The 38 species and varieties, 27 new ones of *Fenestella*, described are mainly from the Permian of the Glass Mountains, West Texas. Four are from material collected by Condra in 1937 from the lower Permian of the western Urals in Russia. Identified associated Bryozoa are also listed.

The described species of *Fenestella* are recognized by external and internal zooecial features, and in some consideration is given also to zoarial characters. Secondary encrustation and various appendages are described but not considered specifically diagnostic.

Variability of meshwork in a species has been determined wherever possible. Spacing of branches in the same zoarium is more irregularly varied than the spacing of dissepiments, which determines the length of fenestrules. Variability of length of fenestrules thus determined is not haphazard, but in most species is either correlated with the position of fenestrules in a zoarium or is determined by regular spacing of dissepiments at fixed intermittent shorter and longer intervals. The development of carinae and carinal nodes is of specific importance and is used in grouping of higher rank: subgeneric and next below, which is called group or section. Twelve groups or sections of the genus *Fenestella* are recognized and defined. Four of these are distinguished within *Minilia* Crockford, which is characterized by a double row of nodes, and treated as a subgenus of *Fenestella*. A newly introduced polyphyletic subgenus *Loculiporina* is characterized by superstructure similar to that in the Silurian and Devonian *Loculipora*. *Cervella* Chronic is also considered a polyphyletic subgenus of *Fenestella*.

The stratigraphy of the Permian of the Mid-Continent of America and of European Russia is reviewed in so far as it concerns the described Bryozoa, and the intercontinental correlation of the formations to which they belong is tabulated.

The identification and description of Permian species of *Fenestella* has necessitated a revision of the identical or closely related Pennsylvanian forms previously described by Ulrich, Rogers, Condra, Moore, and Elias, but no overall revision of all known Pennsylvanian species of the genus has been attempted.

Microstructure of the wall in *Fenestella* has been studied in polarized light on the specially prepared thin (1 to 2 μ thick) sections. A complex zoarial inner skeleton in *Fenestella* and other fenestrate Cryptostomata is differentiated and named the colonial plexus; it distinguishes this new order, named Fenestrata, from order Cryptostomata Vine, not Ulrich. Comparative study of the microstructure of extant and fossil Cheilostomata and Cyclostomata shows that Fenestrata are closer to the latter order in the following respect: the common bud or colonial bud of Cyclostomata, as understood by Smitt and Borg, is found to be homologous to the *colonial plexus*, but the latter is a more extensive and complex structure than the common bud. Laminated sclerenchyma is developed secondarily on the outer and inner sides of these homologous structures in Fenestrata and in Cyclostomata. The transverse minute spicules (so-called capillaries) in the outer sclerenchyma of Fenestrata do not compare well with either pores or pseudopores of Cyclostomata, and new evidence indicates that they are calcareous entities not openings subsequently filled by calcium carbonate. They apparently originated simultaneous with the sclerenchyma, and are interpreted as calcified bases of a simple filamentous alga, much like the similarly calcified minute epiphytic *Pleurocladia lacustris* of northwestern Europe.

I. STRATIGRAPHY AND FOSSIL LOCALITIES

INTRODUCTION

The major subdivisions of the Permian in the Glass Mountains (Tomlinson *et al.*, 1940), from which most of the described Bryozoa were collected, are Wolfcamp Series, Leonard Series, and Guadalupe Series as shown in Table 1.

The bryozoans described from the Glass Mountains were collected from only a few horizons, whose characteristics are as follows:

WOLFCAMP SERIES

The Wolfcamp is mostly shales and thin limestones with a massive basal limestone 37 feet thick; maximum thickness about 600 feet. In some sections it is underlain with apparent conformity by shale of the Gaptank Series that contains the *Uddenites* fauna, but in other sections the contact with the Gaptank is a sharp angular unconformity. The Wolfcamp is overlain by basal conglomerates of the Leonard Series.

The principal large fauna was obtained by dissolution of fossiliferous specimens of gray limestone from interval 9 in the middle of the section at Wolf Camp (P. B. King, 1930, p. 54–55, sec. 24; P. B. King, 1937, p. 94; R. E. King, 1930, p. 134, loc. 93). A few species originally labeled from the *Uddenites* zone of the Wolfcamp are described here as uppermost Pennsylvanian forms in the *Uddenites* beds.

LEONARD SERIES

Three facies of the Leonard are recognized in the Glass Mountains: mostly thin-bedded limestones in the northeast (lower part called Hess); mostly massive limestone in the central part, believed to be reefs; and interbedded siliceous shales, clay shales, sandstones, limestones, and conglomerates in the west. The Leonard is more or less uniformly thick with a maximum thickness of about 2000 feet.

The two principal collections studied were obtained by the dissolution of brown fossiliferous limestones from the upper half of the series characterized by *Perrinites vidriensis*. There are two zones within the series where this ammonite commonly occurs: at the top of the "Fourth limestone" of the western facies of the Leonard, about the middle of the section at Sullivan Peak, and the shaly limestones at the base of the upper fourth of the series at Clay Slide, (P. B. King, 1930, p. 65). In the section at Dugout Mountain *P. vidrienses* was collected near the top of the Leonard (P. B. King, 1930, p. 133; 1937. p. 98). One collection of bryozoans from R. E. King's locality 123 (1930, p. 135) is from a brown limestone 3 feet thick (bed 14) about 1100 feet above the base of the measured section and an estimated 500 feet below the "First limestone" of the Word, which contains *Waagenoceras* (P. B. King, 1930, p. 139). The second collection of bryozoans came from similar limestone from R. E. King locality 119 (1930, p. 135) at Clay Slide, believed to be in the upper fourth of the Leonard section (P. B. King, 1930, p. 65). The species of *Fenestella* described from the two collections are listed on Table 2. Other fossils identified from the Leonard are discussed in the chapter on ecology.

TABLE 1.—*Correlation of biostratigraphic zones**

Standard sequence	Eastern Europe and Ural Mountains: Biostratigraphic zones: Based on fusulines	Eastern Europe and Ural Mountains: Biostratigraphic zones: Based on Bryozoa	Eastern Europe and Ural Mountains: Biostratigraphic zones: Based on ammonites	Mid-Continent and South-central North America: Biostratigraphic zones: Based on ammonites	Mid-Continent and South-central North America: Biostratigraphic zones: Based on Bryozoa	Mid-Continent and South-central North America: Biostratigraphic zones: Based on fusulines	Mid-Continent and South-central North America: Standard sequence: West Texas	Mid-Continent and South-central North America: Standard sequence: Northern Mid-Continent
Tartarian				*Cyclolobus*	*Fenestella strukovi* var. *vidrioensis*	*Polydiexodina shumardi* and others	Ochoa	
Kazanian							Capitan Vidrio (Guadalupian)	
Kungurian		*Fenestella tschernovi* var. *usiensis* (In Tschernov's P² or Usinsk fm. of northern Urals)		*Waagenoceras*	*Fenestella strukovi* var. *tenuissima* *Fenestella binodata* var. *wordensis* *Fenestella tschernovi* var. *usiensis*	*Parafusulina sellardsi* and others	Word (Guadalupian)	Cimarron
Artinskian: Sarga Irgina	*Pseudofusulina* (*Schwagerina*)	*Fenestella tschernovi*	*Medlicottia orbignyana*	*Perrinites vidriensis*	*Fenestella binodata* var. *leonardensis*	*Parafusulina schucherti* and others	Leonard	
Artinskian: Burtzevka	(*Parafusulina?*) *lutugini* *Pseudofusulina* (*Schwagerina*) *juresanensis*	*Hexagonella ischimbaica* *Lyrocladia*	*Artisnkia artiensis* *Sakmarites vulgaris*		*Fenestella binodata* var. *leonardensis*			
	Pseudofusulina (*Schwagerina*) *concavutas*				*Fenestella tschernovi*			
Artinskian: Sterlitamak	*Pseudofusulina* (*Schwagerina*) *anderssoni*	*Fenestella permica* *Fenestella nikiforovae* *Archimedes* *Lyrocladia*	*Waagenina* *Propinacoceras*	*Medlicottia copei* *Perrinites cummingsi*	*Fenestella* cf. *parviuscula* *Fenestella nikiforovae* var. *crusiformis*	*Pseudofusulina* (*Schwagerina*) *hessensis* and others		

Sakmarian	Kasmarka (Tastuba)	*Pseudofusulina* (*Schwagerina*) *mölleri*	*Ascopora nodosa* var. *sterlitamakensis* *Timanodictya dichotoma* *Archimedes*	*Artinskia nalivkini* *Epipronorites schucherti*	*Artinskia adkinsi* *Properrinites bosei*	*Fenestella binodata* var. *wolfcampensis* *Fenestella archimediformis* *Fenestella nikiforovae*	*Schwagerina* (*Pseudoschwagerina*) *uddeni* *Pseudofusulina* (*Schwagerina*) *emaciata* and *longissimoidea* *Schwagerina* (*Paraschwagerina*) *kansasensis* *Schwagerina* sp.	Wolfcamp		Wellington Big Blue
	Kurmaia	*Pseudofusulina* (*Schwagerina*) *uralica* *Schwagerina ciceroidea*	*Fenestella tuberculifera*	*Sakmarites postcarbonarius* *Artinskia* sp.	*Artinskia wortheni* *Properrinites plummeri*					
	Assel	*Pseudofusulina* (*Schwagerina krotovi* *Schwagerina* (*Paraschwagerina*) *princeps* (= *molleri* Rauser) *Triticites* cf. *beedei*	*Fenestella quadratoporaeformis*							
Gjelian		*Pseudofusulina* (*Schwagerina*) *sokensis* *Schwagerina fusulinoides* *Triticites* cf. *beedei* *Triticites* cf. *plummeri* *Triticites montiparus* *Triticites schwageriniformis*	*Ascopora* *Fenestella novlinsky*	*Uddenites* *Prouddenites* *Shumardites* *Neodimorphoceras*	*Uddenites schucherti* *Schumardites simmondsi*	*Fenestella binodata* *Fenestella geminanoda*	*Triticites beedei* *Triticites plummeri*	Gaptank	Cisco	Virgil
					Prouddenites bosei *Shumardites fornicatus*	*Fenestella kansasensis*	*Triticites oriziformis*		Canyon	Missouri
	Teguliferina beds	*Rugosofusulina prisca*	*Ascopora nodosa* *Rhabdomeson rhombiferum*	*Parashumardites mosquensis*						
Moscovian		*Fusulina* *Fusulinella* *Wedekindellina*	*Fenestella veneris* *Ascopora nodosa*		*Anthracoceras* *Glaphyrites* *Dimorphoceras*	*Prismopora*	*Fusulina* *Fusulinella* *Wedekindellina*		Strawn	Des Moines

* Unconformities not shown except above and below the Wolfcamp of Glass Mountains. This is to indicate its correlation with the middle part of the Big Blue of northern Mid-continent, which is believed to represent a larger time interval correlative to the Sakmarian of Urals.

Permian-Pennsylvanian boundary not shown because it is undecided internationally. Base of Permian is now usually placed at the base of the Big Blue in America, which is generally believed to correspond to the base of the Sakmarian in Urals. However, most Russian authors place the base of the Permian at the base of the Artinskian, which correlates with the base of the Leonard in Texas. A few geologists place the boundary at other horizons within and beyond the Sakmarian.

GUADALUPE SERIES: WORD GROUP

The Word, which starts with a "persistant limestone bed", overlies the Leonard with apparent conformity, but it is believed that there is a sharp faunal change at the boundary, from the fauna with *Perrinites vidriensis* below to the fauna with *Waagenoceras* above (P. B. King 1937, p. 98). In the southeastern Glass Mountains the Word is about 1500 feet thick and consists of siliceous shales, clay shales, and sandstones with almost no limestone except that at the base. Eastward other limestones wedge into the section (the principal ones are named Second, Third, and Fourth, from bottom up), while the shales between them become insignificant. At the Word Ranch the separate limestones merge into a solid cherty fossiliferous dolomite 500 feet thick.

The principal faunules of bryozoans were obtained by the dissolution from the light gray massive Fourth limestone specimens, but a few good ones were obtained from limestones in the middle and basal parts of the Word.

GUADALUPE SERIES: CAPITAN GROUP

The Capitan is a massive dolomitic limestone about 1800 feet thick; the lower half is differentiated in the east as the massive Vidrio member. Only a few fragments of *Fenestella* were obtained from the samples of the latter, and none from higher horizons of the Capitan.

Prominent unconformities above and below the Wolfcamp in Texas have been recognized for some time, but the nature of corresponding boundaries in the northern Mid-Continent area was not established until detailed surface and subsurface stratigraphic work was done in Oklahoma, Nebraska, and Kansas. In 1931 Condra and Upp included in the Big Blue Series the beds above the Cottonwood limestone in the area from Oklahoma to Nebraska. Later Moore and Condra added to the series the older formations down to the Brownville limestone. Recent detailed correlation charts across Nebraska (Condra and Reed, 1943) and Kansas (Edson, 1945) demonstrate clearly that the unconformity between the Big Blue and Cimarron is more prominent in the northern Mid-Continent than the unconformity between the Virgil and the Big Blue.

Some recent correlations from Texas across Oklahoma and Kansas to Nebraska resulted in projecting the Wolfcamp-Leonard boundary at about the middle of the Big Blue, just above the Herrington limestone (Edson, 1945; Mohr, 1939). If correct, it means that the important Wolfcamp-Leonard stratigraphic break of Texas has no significant equivalent in the northern Mid-Continent and that the important Big Blue-Cimarron break of the north has no corresponding break in Texas. It seems more likely, however, that there is an error in the correlation over the 500-mile distance and that beds which belong in the upper Wolfcamp have been added erroneously to the Leonard.

CORRELATION WITH THE PERMIAN OF RUSSIA

In Table 1 the Permian series of the Glass Mountains are correlated with the divisions of the Permian in Russia, from which some related bryozoans have been recently described. Also incorporated in this table are the principal data and conclusions on American and Russian Carboniferous ann Permian rocks which were discussed at the 17th International Geological Congress held in Russia in 1937 (in which Condra had an active part), and which are expressed in a series of papers on the Russian Permian published in the Bulletin of the American Association of Petroleum Geologists (Miller, 1938; Dunbar, 1940; Moore, 1940, Knight, 1940; Kay, 1941). These data and conclusions are augmented by some important stratigraphic and paleontologic information published in Russia since 1937 (Nikiforova, 1938a; Grozdilova, 1938; Nalivkin and Dmitriev, 1939; Nikiforova 1939; Trizna, 1939; Alexandrova, 1939, Shulga-Nesterenko, 1941; Yakovlev, 1945). These publications indicate that Russian geologists draw the Carboniferous-Permian boundary at the base of the Artinskian as before and not at the base of the Sakmarian where most American geologists place it. It appears that this is geologically expedient for the Russians, particularly in subsurface correlations; and it is important to remember that fossils from the Sakmarian, which is equivalent to our Big Blue-Wolfcamp, are considered latest Carboniferous by most Russians while we consider them earliest Permian.

Some Russian geologists claim that the Sakmarian of Russia is separated by unconformities from the Orenburgian (or upper Uralian) below, and the Artinskian (in the restricted stratigraphic sense) above. Although the magnitude and even the existence of these unconformities are still disputed, an undoubted faunal change at both boundaries is recognized. This change corresponds in general to that above and below the Wolfcamp or the Big Blue Series.

The following facts have a direct bearing on evaluating the position, stratigraphic significance, and use in correlations of the described fossils: (1) No international agreement has been reached on the boundary between the Carboniferous and Permian, (2) the principal dispute is whether the initiation of Permian time is the unconformity between the Orenburgian and the Sakmarian, the same or about the same as between the Cisco (Virgil) and the Wolfcamp (Big Blue) in America, or the unconformity between the Sakmarian and the Artinskian, the same or about the same as between the Wolfcamp (Big Blue) and the Leonard (Cimarron.) The latter is followed officially by Russian geologists. This general statement is true if the correlation of the Sakmarian and the Wolfcamp is approximately correct, which seems to be well agreed to by both Americans and Russians. American concept of the Permian is used consistently in this paper.

II. STRATIGRAPHY AND FOSSILS FROM RUSSIA

LOCALITIES OF PERMIAN AND UPPER CARBONIFEROUS

The stratigraphy of the upper Carboniferous and Permian in Russia is generally well established, but there are many problems concerning the boundaries and the correlation of the subdivisions. The standard sequence from bottom up of the stratigraphic units, corresponding to Series in American terminology, is Moscovian, Uralian (with lower part or the Gjelian, and upper part or Orenburgian), Sakmarian, Artinskian, Kungurian, Kazanian, and Tartarian. Their approximate correlation with American divisions of Upper Carboniferous and Permian rocks is now well understood.

In the current stratigraphic work in Russia there is a general tendency in recognition of these units to rely more and more on paleontological evidence in preference to lithologic evidence; hence the division of the fossiliferous part of the Permian into biostratigraphic zones is usually indicated (*see* Table 1).

The fusulines are now used in the correlation of the units with the sequence of the zones from bottom up as follows: *Schwagerina* (= "*Pseudoschwagerina*"), *Pseudofusulina* ("*Schwagerina*") *moelleri:* and *Pseudofusulina* ("*Schwagerina*") *lutugini*. The first of these corresponds approximately to the Sakmarian, which corresponds to the Big Blue, and the last three combined correspond approximately to the Artinskian, which corresponds to the Leonard.

On the evidence of bryozoans Nikiforova suggested dividing the Artinskian into three biostratigraphic units from bottom up: the *Askopora sterlitamakensis* zone; the transitional zone with some characteristic species of *Fenestella* ("*Fenestella* zone"); and the *Hexagonella ishimbaica* zone. Naturally, the zones based on bryozoans do not coincide precisely with those based on fusulines but both zonings are locally valid. In sequences where fusulines are absent and bryozoans present, Nikiforova's zoning is the only usable one. Unlike the lithologic or erosional boundaries of rock units biostratigraphic zones are never divided by sharp, linear boundaries and cannot be expected to coincide with them. Hence the boundaries of the biostratigraphic zones, shown on Table 1 are approximations, not rigid physical boundaries of the lithologic units.

Lists of the bryozoans described and identified from the subdivisions of Russian Permian rocks are herewith appended, and those which are identical or closely related to the American forms described are also entered in Table 2.

BRYOZOANS COLLECTED ALONG THE ROUTE OF THE PERMIAN EXCURSION, 16TH INTERNATIONAL GEOLOGICAL CONGRESS

The specimens collected by Condra from some exposures included in the permian Excursion of 1937 have been prepared and identified by Elias chiefly through comparison with the Russian forms revised and described by Nikiforova, Shulga-Nesterenko, and Trizna. In establishing the precise age of the beds from which the collections were made, various Russian sources were consulted, mostly those published at and after the 1937 Congress. Following are the lists of identifications grouped by localities to facilitate possible revision of the ages of the respective beds. The names of the fenestrate

TABLE 2.—*Species of* Fenestella *from the Permian of West Texas*

Species \ Age	Wolfcamp		Leonard			Word		Capitan	Mesh work formula			
	lower	und.*	lower	middle	upper	lower	und.	Vidrio member	branches	fenestrules	zooecia	nodes
Group I												
F. gaptankensis n. sp.	+	...	...	...	...	...	...	...	12	6–7	16–17	6–7
F. austini n. sp.	...	+	...	...	...	...	...	...	10.5–11	5.5–6	14	6
F. petschorica Shulga	...	...	...	...	+?	...	...	...	10–12	6.5–7	16–17.5	5.5
F. varifenestrata n. sp.	...	...	...	...	+	...	...	...	12	10	16	7–8
Group II												
F. schucherti n. sp.	...	...	...	...	...	...	...	+	10	8	13–14	abt. 12–13
Group III												
F. stocktonensis var. *magnolobata*, n. var.	...	+	...	...	...	...	...	...	18–23	13–15	20–23	16–23
F. (*Loculiporina*) *pavonia* n. sp.	...	...	...	...	...	+	...	...	15–19	11	19–20	...
Group IV												
F. kingi n. sp.	...	...	...	...	...	+	...	+	20	15	17	7
Group V												
F. inornata n. sp.	...	...	...	...	...	...	...	+	19–20	17–17.5	23	...
F. strukovi Trizna var. *tenuissima* n. var.	...	...	...	...	...	...	+	...	17–18	12–13	14.5–16.5	9
F. strukovi Trizna var. *vidrioensis* n. var.	...	...	...	...	...	...	...	+	15–18	12–13	15	15
Group VI												
F. virgosa var. *dubia* n. var.	+	...	...	...	...	...	...	...	15	9–10	16	8
Group VII												
F. binodata var. *wolfcampensis* n. var.	...	+	...	...	...	...	...	...	13–20	11–13	17–18	34–36
F. binodata var. *leonardensis* n. var.	...	...	...	+	...	...	...	...	15–20	12–13.3	17–20	34–40
F. binodata var. *leonardensis* n. var.	...	...	...	...	+	...	...	...	16–17	11–12	18	36
F. binodata var. *wordensis* n. var.	...	...	...	...	...	...	+	...	13	10.5	16	32

Group VIII												
F. infranodosa n. sp.	...	...	...	...	+	...	...	...	20	19	19	38
F. infranodosa (?) var.	...	...	...	...	...	...	+	...	20–21	18.5–19	19	38
Group IX												
F. clinospina n. sp.	...	...	...	...	+	...	...	...	16	17–19	17–19	30–40
F. quadratopora Shulga	...	+	...	...	...	...	...	...	14–19	16–16.5	16–16.5	32
Group X												
F. cylindrica n. sp.	+	...	...	...	...	...	...	...	26	19.5–21	22–24	27–30
Group XI												
F. permica Shulga em.	...	+	...	...	...	...	...	...	18–20	16.5–20	17.5–22	17.5–22
F. girtyi, (?) Elias	...	...	...	+	...	...	...	...	20–21	16–17	17–18	16–17
F. girtyi, (?) Elias var.	...	...	...	...	...	...	+	...	16–25	16–17	15–16	16–17
F. plicata n. sp.	...	...	...	+	...	...	...	...	20	18–20	21–23	abt. 20
F. (*Loculiporina*) *muscus* (n. subg.), n. sp.	...	...	...	...	...	...	+	...	20	16–17	abt. 20	abt. 10
F. tenax var.	...	...	+	...	...	...	...	...	32	28	26–27	35–40
Group XII												
F. spinulosa Condra	...	+	...	...	...	...	...	...	19–20	19.5–21.5	19.5–21.5	21–25
F. nikiforovae Shulga	...	+	...	...	...	...	...	...	20	19–20	20	17–18
F. (*Cervella*) *cruciformis* n. sp.	...	...	+	...	...	...	...	...	24–25	21–22	21–22	25–28
F. (*Cervella*) *cornuta* n. sp.	...	+	...	...	...	...	...	...	21–23	18–20	18–20	18–20
F. archimediformis n. sp.	...	+	...	...	...	...	...	...	15–17	17–18.5	17–18.5	11–18
F. cf. *parviuscula* Bassler	...	...	+	...	...	...	...	...	20–24	17–18	18	19–23
F. parviuscula var. *libellus* n. var.	...	+	...	...	...	...	...	...	17	15.5–17	16–17	19–21
F. teschernovi Shulga	...	...	...	+	...	...	...	...	13–15	15.4–16	14.5–16	11–14
F. tschernovi var. *usiensis* Shulga	...	...	...	...	...	...	+	...	15	14–15	14–15	13–14

* und.—undifferentiated.

forms are accompanied by meshwork formulae, which are established by measurements on the identified specimens. The forms which are indicated as new species are either being described here, were described in 1944 (Condra and Elias), or will be described in forthcoming papers. For these latter species no new names are introduced here, and they are merely marked by a capital letter in place of specific name.

Bryozoans from the lower Artinskian of Shak-Tau limestone massive, near Ishimbaeva (Condra's locality R-4, 5), include the following:

Fenestella tenuiseptata Shulga (14/7//19–20/12–15)
Fenestella basloensis var. *shaktauensis* Elias and Condra, n. var.
Fenestella vischerensis Nikiforova (20/16//15–17/15–17)
Fenestella ornata Shulga (16/13–14//17–18/)
Polypora cf. *goldfussi* Eichwald (4–6/2.5–3//?)
Polypora (*Polyporella*) n. sp. (12–14/8–8.5//15)
Penniretepora cf. *invisa* Trizna (8//12–13)
Reteporidra cf. *eichwaldi* Nikiforova (4.5/2.5//abt. 12–13)
Goniocladia sp. (3/1.5//?)

Trizna (1939) and Nikiforova (1939) describe from the same Shak-Tau the following species of the "Fenestella zone" (exposures 2, 5, 6, 7, and 12; and exposures 8 and 9 of its basal part) and of the underlying "*Ascopora nodosa* var. *sterlitamakensis* zone" (exposures 1, 4, 10, and 11).

Fenestella virgosa var. *tumulosa* Trizna (exposure 9)
Fenestella ornata var. *propinqua* Trizna (exposure 5)
Fenestella bifida var. *repudiosa* Trizna (exposure 5)
Polypora torosa Trizna (exposure 5)
Penniretepora invisa Trizna (exposures 10 and 1)
Fistulipora amplia Nikiforova (exposure 9)
Rhombotrypella composita Nikiforova (exposures 8 and 9)
Ascopora nodosa var. *sterlitamakensis* Nikiforova (exposures 1, 4, 10, and 11)
Ascopora mixta Nikiforova (exposures 1, 2, 5, 9, and 11)

Bryozoans of the zone of *Pseudofusulina anderssoni* (Chernaiarechka zone) at Kazarmennyi Kamen (Condra's locality R-7) are:

Archimedes nikiforovae Condra and Elias
Fenestella cf. *tenuis* Trizna (19–20/12–13//about 18–19) (zone of *Pseudofusulina lutugini*, Ishimbaeva)
F. multiporataeformis Shulga (9–10/4–4.5//14)
F. permica Shulga (19–20/19/about 19) (P_1^1 and P_1^2) (zone of *P. lutugini*)
F. rhomboidea Nikiforova (22–23/19//19/38)
F. cf. *macella* Trizna (Zmeinaia Gora) (9–10/4–4.5//12–13)
F. stocktonensis var. *magnolobata* Elias and Condra, n. var. (16/14//20)
Polypora cyclopora Eichwald (6–7/4//14–15) (C_3^s or $_3^1$) = zone of *P. lutugini*
P. cf. *goldfussi* Eichwald (4–5/1.5–2//10) (C_3^i)
Reteporidra eichwaldi Nikiforova (4/2–2.25//?) (P_1A)
R. n. sp. B (2–2.5/1.5//?)
Rhombopora cf. *lepindodendroides* Meek

Trizna (1939) and Nikiforova (1939) describe the following forms from locality 13, Kazarmennyi Kamen, of the *Ascopora nodosa* var. *sterlitamakensis* zone:

Fenestella basloensis var. *strukovi Trizna, F. cavifera* var. *gregalis* Trizna, and *Ascopora mixta* Nikiforova

Bryozoans from the limestone in the lower part of the *Pseudofusulina lutugina* zone (Irgina zone or "*Fenestella zone*") at Lipovaia Gora, near Vavilovo include:

(Condra's locality R-9).

Fenestella shulgae Elias and Condra n. sp. (12–14/12//12–13/12–13)
Fenestella cf. *macella* Trizna (10/4//11–12/10)
Penniretepora trilineata var. *disposita* Trizna (7.5–9.5//10–12)
Penniretepora n. sp. (13–14//5)

(Condra's locality R-975)

Fenestella schischovae Shulga (17–18/11–13//14–16/few, strong)
Fenestella licharevi Shulga (9–12/6//18–19/3)
Fenestella macella Trizna (9/3.5–4//14)
Fenestella specifica Shulga (8–11/7–8/13–15/7–8)
Fenestella bifida Eichwald (14/10//16–17/abt. 5)
Polypora cf. *goldfussi* Eichwald (4–5/1.5–2//6.5–9)
Polypora n. sp. A (10/7.5//abt. 20)
Penniretepora cf. *quaesita* Trizna (6–7//10)
Rhombopora n. sp.

Trizna (1939) and Nikiforova (1939) describe from Lipovaia Gora the following forms from the "Fenestella zone" (exposures 5, 6, and 7; and exposure 3 representing its basal part) and from the overlying "*Hexagonella ishimbaica* zone," which is in the uppermost part of the *Pseudofusulina lutugina* zone corresponding approximately to the Sarga zone.

Fenestella parvula Trizna (exposure 7)
Fenestella pseudoveneris var. *tolerata* Trizna (exposures 3 and 5)
Fenestella cavifera var. *gregalis* Trizna (exposure 7)
Fenestella bifida var. *tuberosa* Trizna (exposure 5)
Fenestella ("*Archimedes*")[1] *mendax* Trizna (exposure 5)
Fenestella ("*Archimedes*")[1] *perpetrabilis* Trizna (exposure 6)
Fenestella ("*Archimedes*")[1] *melusovi* Trizna (exposure 6)
Polypora repens Trizna, (exposure 6)
Polypora variocellata var. *extenta* Trizna (exposures 5 and 6)
Penniretepora subtila var. *major* Trizna (exposure 1)
Penniretepora subtila var. *temeraria* Trizna (exposure 6)
Penniretepora trilineata var. *disposita* Trizna (exposure 5)
Dictyocladia (?) *schichanensis* var. *major* Trizna (exposure 5)
Cyclotrypa (?) *longacella* Nikiforova (exposures 3 and 5)
Hexagonella ischimbaica Nikiforova (exposure 10)
Stenopora disparilis Nikiforova (exposures 2 and 3)
Rhombotrypella composita Nikiforova (exposures 2 and 3)
Chainodictyon bashkirikus Nikiforova (exposure 7)
Chainodictyon simensis Nikiforova (exposure 3)

---

[1] Trizna does not describe or mention the screws of what she describes as a new species of *Archimedes*, but classifies the much encrusted fenestrate zoaria with *Archimedes* on the evidence of the microstructure of the encrusting tissue, apparently following the concept of genus *Archimedes* held by Shulga-Nesterenka (see Condra and Elias, 1944, p. 63–64). We hold however, that a much encrusted fenestellid meshwork cannot be referred to *Archimedes* unless proved an expansion from a screw. Hence, we reclassify the species of "*Archimedes*" described by Trizna as *Fenestella* (Condra and Elias, 1944, p. 172).

Chainodictyon kasayakensis Nikiforova (exposures 3, 5 and 6)
Ascopora nodosa var. *sterlitamakensis* Nikiforova (exposures 3, 5, and 7).

Bryozoans in shale of the lower part of the Artinskian Series at Simsk Industrial Plants (Condra's locality R-14) are:

Fenestella foraminosa Eichwald (8–9/7//15/3–4)
Fenestella nalivkini Elias andCondra n. sp. (21–25/21–24//25–27)
Fenestella lunariostellata Shulga (13–14/8//abt. 16?)
Fenestella heterocellata Shulga (8–14/3–3.5//12–16/none)
Fenestella virgosa var. *macella* Trizna (7–10/4-7//11–12)
Polypora tschernyschevi Nikiforova n. var. ? (4–6/2.5–3/14)
Polypora n. sp. *K* (6–7/3–3.5//14; 4 rows of apertures)
Polypora nadinae Shulga (7–8/5–6//15; 4–5 rows of apertures)
Polypora cf. *orbicribrata* Keyserling (5.5–6/5//15)
cf. *Septopora paradoxa* Nikiforova
Reteporidra eichwaldi Nikiforova (4–6/abt. 3//abt. 10)
Rhombotrypella arbuscula (Eichwald)
Rhabdomeson n. sp. ?
Rhombopora n. sp.

Bryozoans from the Permian (probably Lower Artinskian) in the massive reefs at Chikaly siding, near Kishert Station (Condra's locality R-15) are:

Fenestella pulcherrima Shulga (15–16/15//15/15?)
Fenestella cf. *strukovi* Trizna (16–20/13–16//15–18/15–18?)
Fenestella juraktauensis Shulga (16/12//abt. 23–24)
Polypora n. sp. *L* (14/8–9//15)
Polypora cf. *martis* Fisher (8–10/6//abt. 15)

Bryozoans from the middle Carboniferous at Kizel, up Kosva River from Gubakha Station, Central Urals include:

(Condra's locality R-18)
Fenestella elegantissima Eichwald (22–23/21//abt. 20)
Polypora orientalis Eichwald (14/10–11//abt. 15)
(Condra's locality R-19)
Batostomella sp.
Fenestella polyporata var. *orlovskensis* Nikiforova (11–13/5.5–6//abt. 15)
Fenestella cf. *beschevensiformis* Nikiforova (14/11–12//abt. 15)
Fenestella J n. sp. (7–8/10–11//abt. 17)
Fenestella T n. sp. (14/16//16)
Penniretepora uralica (?) (Stuckenberg) (8//14)
Rhombopora cf. *armata* var. *ovalis* Nikiforova

Brvozoans from the upper Carboniferous, upper Moscovian?, include:

(Condra's locality R-22)
Fenestella veneris Fisher (20/15//22)
Fenestella elegantissima Eichwald (20–22/20–22//23–25)
Polypora martis Fisher (9/6.5//14)
Rhombotrypella arbuscula var. *distincta* Nikiforova
Ptiloporella n. sp.; cf. *irregularis* Nikiforova (abt. 10/8//16)

III. HISTORY OF MICROSCOPIC INVESTIGATIONS

INTRODUCTION

For a long time the genus *Fenestella* and its species have been recognized primarily or wholly on external features. The genus is customarily characterized by a netlike fenestrate expanse, which is made by regularly spaced, gradually spreading, and occasionally bifurcating branches, interconnected by short and regularly spaced transverse links called dissepiments. The dissepiments in *Fenestella* and other Fenestellidae are "sterile," that is containing no zooecia, while the branches contain two rows (seldom sporadically three) of adherent zooecia. Each zooecium has one opening called the aperture, and all apertures open on one side of the expanse, called the obverse, "celluliferous", or front side. On this side there is usually a central longitudinal carina, which in most species is ornamented by nodes. The opposite side of the expanse is called the reverse or dorsal side and has no appertures. In most species the branches on the reverse bear longitudinal grooves or "striae" and may be adorned by nodes or spines.

The species of *Fenestella* customarily are recognized by measurements of spacing of the branches, apertures, and dissepiments, and by the size and ornamentation of these structures. The importance of the internal structure has been gradually recognized, however, especially by Russian paleontologists who pointed out the importance of the outline of the zooecial chamber as a specific character (Nekhoroshev, 1932, p. 35). The microstructure of the wall, including its encrusting tissue, also has been added to characteristics of species (particularly by Shulga-Nesterenko). The structure of the "zooecial cavity" in Fenestellidae, especially *Fenestella,* was elucidated by Ulrich (1890, p. 350–351), who also found in many species superior and inferior hemisepta located respectively on the roof and the floor of the zooecial cavity or chamber at or near the base of its vertical shaft or vestibulum. The rarely developed inferior hemiseptum has proved useful in the recognition of some species (Ulrich, 1890; Shulga-Nesterenko, 1941; Condra and Elias, 1944).

The detailed studies of the microstructure of the wall and of the encrusting tissue in *Fenestella* and related genera by Russian paleontologists and their attempts to use microscopic characters for recognition of genera and species from thin sections, commonly obtained by cutting cores from some deep bore-holes, added much to the knowledge of these Bryozoa and revived interest in their biology. Understanding of these and many other Paleozoic Bryozoa is still imperfect, however, and their relationship to the living and post-Paleozoic Bryozoa is an unsolved problem. The status of knowledge is illustrated by the following historical review of the more recent principal contributions to the morphology and anatomy of Fenestellidae and related families of Paleozoic Bryozoa and of the biological explanations suggested.

Direct quotations from the investigations are used here as frequently as possible, especially the contributions translated from Russian because they are generally not easily available.

INVESTIGATIONS BY NICHOLSON

Evidently Nicholson was the first to section fossil Bryozoa, and he published the earliest illustration of microstructure of the wall of a fenestellid (Nicholson and Lydekker, 1889, Fig. 453, p. 608). He observed that:

"In various of the Paleozoic Polyzoa, and particularly in the family of the Fenestellidae, a portion of the polyzoary consists of dense calcareous tissue, which exhibits under the microscope a finely punctate appearance. When a sufficiently thin section of this punctate layer is prepared, and examined with a sufficiently high magnitude, the tissue is seen to be penetrated by innumerable exceedingly minute tubuli (Fig. 453), which run at right angles to the surface of the polyzoary. Nothing certain has, however, been ascertained as to the nature and function of these tubuli."

The illustrated section is that of *Phyllopora* sp. from the Devonian of Canada.

Elsewhere he states (p. 623) that the "cells" (zooecia) in the Fenestellidae are filled with "perfectly homogenous compact calcite, which is strengthened by a basal striated membrane," or what Ulrich subsequently called striated "germinal plate."

INVESTIGATIONS BY ULRICH

Ulrich sectioned many species of *Fenestella* and related genera, although he published only brief statements about their microstructure and made only general references to the series of microscopic sketches, none of which was magnified more than 18 times (Ulrich, 1890, Pls. 54, 55). Ulrich clearly recognized two principal elements in the tissue of a *Fenestella* zoarium: "the original basal or germinal plate," and "the subsequently added layers of calcareous tissue" (1890, p. 352). He pointed out that the two are generally quite distinct from each other, especially when viewed in transverse thin sections of the branches.

Ulrich did not describe comprehensively the structure which he called the germinal plate, but remarked that "almost invariably the lower side of the plate presents a number of tooth-like projections that represent transverse sections of former longitudinal striations," and adds that "many fenestellids show strong striae on very young examples, which are wanting or nearly obsolete on old specimens." On the latter they are covered by the subsequent deposition of the layered sclerenchyma.

Although Ulrich said nothing about the upper side of the "germinal plate" he shows on the drawings (Pls. 54, 55) that it continues from the middle upward in the form of a central vertical plate, whose crest extends above the zooecial apertures and is usually called the carina.

The tissue that covers the "striae" of the germinal plate is variously referred to by Ulrich as sclerenchyma, layers of calcareous tissue, dense portions of zoarium, stony deposit, and secondary deposit. He describes it briefly thus: "A finely laminated composition prevails throughout, and very delicate vertical tubuli, penetrating the laminae, can, as a rule, be demonstrated. The tubuli again are generally arranged in series, and though varying in number are always abundant" (Ulrich, 1890, p. 353).

The subject of the secondary deposit is considered by Ulrich in the arguments regarding the classification of Fenestellidae and other families of his Cryptostomata. He mentions that Vine compares the presence of "the minute tubuli which penetrate the dense deposits of laminated sclerenchyma on both the front of the zooecia and the basal plate on the reverse side of the zoarium" with "the foraminated condition of the walls of the Tubuliporidae" of the suborder Cyclostomata (now elevated to the rank of order). But Ulrich argues that "the structure of the secondary deposit over the cells and basal plate differs in no essential manner from that of the dense tissue which forms the nonporiferous margins and pointed base in *Ptilodictya* and the deposit over the basal portions of the zoaria in many Cystodictyonidae" (Ulrich, 1890, p. 360–361). This statement serves as one of the four arguments used by Ulrich in favor of adding the families Fenestellidae and Acanthocladiidae to Cryptostomata Vine. However, the presence in these families of the colonial plexus (here described), seems to indicate their differentiation from the Cryptostomata Vine (not Ulrich).

INVESTIGATIONS BY SHRUBSOLE

Shrubsole (1880, p. 242–253), who was much impressed by considerable difference in appearance between the proximal and the distal parts of some zoaria of *Fenestella*, believed that it was caused by "encrusting organisms that disfigure and obscure the base of *Fenestella*" and also other parts of its zoarium.

INVESTIGATIONS BY VINE

Although Vine did not study microstructure of fossil bryozoans, he did much in organizing them taxonomically, and his differentiation of Paleozoic suborder Cryptostomata (1884) from comprehensive order Cyclostomata stood well the test of time. He also made some interesting observations (1879) on the peculiarities of various fenestellid zoaria and their "appendages" (*see* Figs. 6, 7).

INVESTIGATIONS BY WHIDBORNE

The following remark made by Whidborne in describing *Fenestella arthritica* shows him a good observer of minute details in the structure of fossil bryozoans and a predecessor to Shulga-Nesterenko in visualizing as "canals" the longitudinal ribs on the reverse: "Non-poriferous face of branches . . . covered with several irregular rows of tubercles or nodes, and in section showing a thick coat of dense tissue permeated by some very minute irregular longitudinal veins or canals." His further remarks make clear that he meant by the latter the ribbed reverse of Ulrich's "germinal plate," (considered here a part of the colonial plexus), as he found none on the obverse: "Poriferous face having a similar but thinner coat, which differs from the other by being without venation and in having numerous, small, tubular processes permeating it almost perpendicular and rising above its surface" (Whidborne, 1895, p. 170). The latter correspond to spicules here.

INVESTIGATIONS BY SIMPSON

Simpson (1895, p. 434) describes "tubuli" visible in thin sections of the encrustation on the reverse of *Fenestella* but considers them merely part of the ornamentation. He observes, however, that "the deposit of calcareous matter continues after the animals in the immediate vicinity are dead, and all ornamentations of the surface are obliterated." So great, he says, may be the difference in appearance between the younger, sculptured portions and the older, smoother portions of a fenestellid frond "that seen in different fragments they would be considered as belonging to two species".

INVESTIGATIONS BY CUMINGS

Cumings devotes considerable attention to the interrelationship between the "basal plate," budding of zooecia, and development of the carina and secondary calcareous deposits in *Fenestella* and related Fenestellidae from the Devonian of New York. The focus of his investigation is the manner of budding in the earliest stages of the zoarium; and not the histology of the wall, as he was undoubtedly somewhat handicapped by silicification of the bryozoans. Nevertheless Cumings sectioned some young stages of zoaria and studied them in sufficient detail for external and internal differentiation of their fundamental parts, such as the basal plate, primary carina, sclerenchyma, and vesicular tissue. Perhaps most important from the histological point of view is the description of the Morphology of the Carinae, to which he devotes a special chapter (1904, p. 64, 65). He states that:

> "The primary carinae first make their appearance in the metanepiastic stage (when the initial circle of zooecia is completed), and are intimately related to the basal plate (Figs. 47–54). In fact the carina seems to originate as an upgrowth or fold of the basal plate."

He also points out that the carina is a "triple" structure, the core of which is a "thin median plate or wall continuous with the axial wall". The axial wall is a cylindrical structure around an inner core or axis made of a "dense deposit of punctate sclerenchyma" (1904, p. 63). On both sides of the median plate of the carina are outer layers of "dense punctate sclerenchyma" (1904, p. 64) causing the carinae to attain "great size and prominence" (1904, p. 61, description of Figs. 47–54) at an early stage, only slightly older than metanepiastic stage. Apparently the primary carina, the axial wall, and the sclerenchyma around them appeared and developed rapidly at a brief interval near completion of the initial circle of zooecia or at the end of metanepiastic state, (*see* Cumings, 1904, Figs. 44–46, p. 58). As Cumings explains, "near the close of the paranepiastic state, the axis of the zoarium thickens preparatory to the expansion of the cone" (1904, p. 63).

INVESTIGATIONS BY LIKHAREV

Likharev studied minutely some exceptionally well-preserved specimens of *Fenestella* from the Permian of Russia and found that the skeleton of *Fenestella retiformis* and *F. wjatkaensis* consists of outer and inner parts; the inner being lighter-colored and divided from the outer by a sharp dark line of contact (1926, p. 1031). In *F. wjatkaensis* the inner layer is from 40 μ to nearly 80 μ thick and is generally solid; but traces of faint laminar structure are observable in it when the section is thin (p. 1029). The light substance forming the base of the zooecia envelops them from the sides and forms their roof. It also forms the dissepiments. The tubercles and outgrowths upon a carcina (in *F. retiformis*) are also composed of a "light substance comparable to that which surrounds the zooecia; and they are covered by a darker peripheral layer (p. 1025). In *F. wjatkaensis* the outer layer up to 40 μ thick is sharply layered, and is distinguished by porous structure (p. 1030). Likharev's "inner" layer of "light substance" corresponds to what is here called colonial plexus of Fenestellidae, and his "outer", darker or porous layer corresponds to the sclerenchyma penetrated by spicules or filaments.

Likharev's observation that the carinal spines have the same microstructure as the inner skeleton around the zooecia and as that of the dissepiments is in harmony with the conclusion of Cumings and ours that the carinal spines are part of the primary skeleton or colonial plexus in Fenestellidae.

INVESTIGATIONS BY SHULGA AND BY CONDRA AND ELIAS

Shulga-Nesterenko undertook a special detailed investigation of the microstructure of the encrusting tissue in *Fenestella* and related genera, and her findings constitute important contributions toward its understanding.

A well-preserved Permian bryozoan from Pechora Land, which looks much like the American Mississippian genus *Lyropora* and for which Shulga-Nesterenko erected new genus *Lyrocladia* (1931), provided excellent material for microscopic study of compact encrusting tissue. Her subsequent work on other genera of the family Fenestellidae and of the family Acanthocladiidae convinced her that they all possess the same or nearly the same microstructure, but differ in degree of development and size and distribution of structural elements (Shulga-Nesterenko, 1941). Her published accounts present a lucid and well-illustrated description and explanation of her observations.

She recognized in the compact "skeleton" of *Fenestella* and related Bryozoa a "capillary system" of canals and tubules, whose purpose is purportedly to convey the "skeletal substance" from inside to the periphery where it is "deposited in the form of foliaceous undulating layers constituting the tissue of branches and dissepiments" (Shulga-Nesterenko, 1931, p. 77). Her account presents a combination of factual description of the "capillary system" and of its inferred function, her figures, our Figures 2–4, illustrating her concepts and terminology.

"The skeletal substance, which consists seemingly of amorphous calcium carbonate, penetrate the thin walls of the zooecia and envelops them by a uniform layer (Pl. 35, figs. 3, 4). Possibly the secretion and circulation of the skeletal substance are connected with the presence of the connecting pores in the walls of the zooecia (Fig. 83), ,in favor of which is the presence of these pores not only between the neighboring zooecia, but also on the side of the wall facing fenestrules, where no doubling of wall exists. This granular calcareous secretion, which has been named granular layer (Pl. 35, fig. 5), is being received in the capillary canals. They adhere externally to the zooecial walls, and stretch along the branches of the bryozoans and parallel to the rows of the zooecia. They resemble the folds of the hydrospires in the ambulacral fields of the blastoids."

This allusion to the hydrospiral folds of the blastoids seems to emphasize the fact that no similar system of "capillary canals" has been observed in living bryozoans. Shulga-Nesterenko was apparently aware of this fact as she expressed hope to discover in them something like her "capillary system." To her knowledge and belief "even the structure of the thin skeletal developments in the modern bryozoans has not been studied by the zoologists, because their microscopic investigations usually begin with decalcification and the character of the zooecial skeleton is hardly taken into account" (Shulga-Nesterenko, 1941, p. 32–33); then she states that "a good verification of the views just outlined on the function of the capillary system would be a corresponding investigation of the skeleton of living bryozoans, a problem which I set for myself in the future" (Shulga-Nesterenko, 1941, p. 37, in Russian).

In her report on the subsequent investigations of the living bryozoans (1949b) Shulga-Nesterenko states that she did not find anything like her skeleton-building "capillary system." This was anticipated by Condra and Elias who pointed out that "no corresponding system of 'tubules' is known in the living bryozoans," whose "calcareous encrustation . . . is penetrated by nothing like 'capillary system' of the fossil Cryptostomata, and the lime is precipitated by 'a delicate organic membrane' raised above the surface of the primary skeleton," as per investigations by Harmer (Condra and Elias, 1944, p. 26, 27). Shulga-Nesterenko states that she "abandoned her thesis that the capillary tubules are conveyors of lime from the zooecial chamber to the periphery of the branches" (1946b, p. 38), and admits that "the elements of the capillary system perhaps could have conveyed nutrition to the peripheral ectodermal epithelium, the latter precipitating the outer skeleton of the colony" (p. 38), as in living bryozoans (p. 6, 31, 32). Thus, while modifying the idea of its function, she maintains her morphologic concept of the "capillary system" which is rejected here.

She also criticizes severely our ideas on the nature of *Archimedes* (1944), calling it "fantastic"; but she ignores our remark that she produced no evidence supporting the inferred connection of the longitudinal "capillary canals" with the transverse "capillaries" (Condra and Elias, 1944, p. 26). There is now sufficient evidence to prove that the "capillary canals" and "capillaries" were never hollow. They are not like pores or pseudopores of living bryozoans; but are structural entities, always calcareous and originating as transverse uprights so indicated by the distinct outward drag of the laminated sclerenchyma around them. Probably Shulga-Nesterenko erroneously assumed that the "capillaries" were openings in the wall of Fenestellidae because all previous investigators of these structures, except Condra and Elias (1944), considered them exceedingly "minute tubuli" (Nicholson, 1889), or "delicate vertical tubuli" (Ulrich, 1890), or "capillaries" (Nekhoroshev, 1926). It is a credit to Shulga-Nesterenko's power of observation that in spite of her acceptance of this erroneous assumption, she correctly sketched the terminals of the "capillaries" protruding as small pimples upon the surface of the branches (Shulga-Nesterenko, 1941, Fig. 43, p. 86; Fig. 87, p. 128; Fig. 89, p. 132; and others, one of which is republished here, Fig. 3). Thus, as shown by her, as well as observed by us, the "capillaries" never appear as depressions on the surface, which would be the case if they were hollow pores (capillaries), even if subsequently sealed by calcification.

Pores comparable in diameter to the "capillaries" in the wall of Fenestellidae are known in exoskeletons of several groups of fossil and living invertebrates—the punctate brachiopods; the system of delicate canals in the columnals and plates of crinoids and in the plates and spines of echinoids; and the pores or alveoli in the keriotheca of some fusulines. Under certain conditions of burial and preservation these openings are filled with limonite. Thus, Henbest reports limonitic filling of the pores in the keriotheca of *Triticites* (1937, Pl. 35), and Burma and Elias have occasionally observed it in the same genus of fusulines. In Elias' extensive collections of molds of various invertebrates from the Redoak Hollow sandstone of the Ardmore Basin, Oklahoma, the limonitic fillings of the "punctae" in brachiopod *Eumetria* make a delicate brush on the outer and inner molds of valves, as the calcareous substance is fully leached out; similar leaching of the calcareous substance from the crinoidal columnals and echinoid spines in these same collections exposes the limonite-filled minute openings in the form of a delicate lattice within the molds.

In all these examples, the size of the openings ranges from about 6 to 15 μ, which is also the approximate range of the diameter in the so-called "capillaries" of Fenestellidae. However, none of the abundant and well-preserved limonitic molds of many species of *Fenestella*, *Polypora*, and *Archimedes* in Elias' collection have any trace of limonitic filling of the "capillaries".

In view of all evidence and because of the erroneous implications connected with the terms, it seems advisable to discontinue to call the minute, (transverse to the laminated sclerenchyma) uprights in the wall of Fenestellidae "pores" or "capillaries". Instead, a term such as spicule or filament should be used (Fig. 1) which will denote that they are structural entities and not merely openings.

When Condra and Elias (1944) investigated and revised the genus *Archimedes*, particularly in its relation to *Fenestella*, they concluded that *Archimedes* is a consortium of *Fenestella* and phytomorph, an enigmatic organism broadly related to algae. To phytomorph belongs part of what was usually described as sclerenchyma, the tissue which builds the shaft and flanges of the *Archimedes* screw. They also recognized needlelike structures, which arise perpendicularly from the grooved dorsal side of the fenestellid meshwork of the flanges and penetrate the phytomorph, and considered them to be a filamentous alga. They recognized in the flanges and expanse of *Archimedes* the types of meshwork characteristic of contemporaneous species of *Fenestella*, most of which were found in strata where *Archimedes* occur. The phytomorph consists of densely packed, parallel thin laminae, within which are minute fibers or tubuli; originally it was flexible, as indicated by the variable degree of twisting in the screws. The screws of *Archimedes* frequently develop from the edge of *Fenestella* fronds singly or in symmetrical pairs, the twist in one being opposite that in the other. The fenestellid frond from which *Archimedes* arises remains thin, with only slight and even encrustation, and the phytomorphic tissue starts at the bases of *Archimedes* screws and thickens upward, or distad, until it reaches the thickness characteristic of each *Archimedes* "species." Toward the apex of a screw the phytomorph gradually thins again. This distribution of the tissue contradicts its correlation with the so-called "stony deposit" or sclerenchyma of fenestellids that thickens toward their base and indicates old age of a zoarium.

Perhaps Russian authors misunderstood the microstructural differences between the encrusting tissues in *Fenestella* and *Archimedes* partly because of the scarcity of *Archimedes* in Russia. Nearly all the few local species have been described on single specimens and, therefore, thin-sectioning from satisfactorily preserved material has been limited. Nikiforova (1938a, p. 109) was aware of her deficient knowledge of the microstructure of *Archimedes:* "In view of the scarcity of the material [in *Archimedes*] we have not been able to undertake a more detailed study of its thin sections. When further finds of *Archimedes* are made it would be much desirable to study in more detail the structure of the axial part of its zoarium." Although a few specimens have been secured in Russia since Nikiforova's monograph, no axial sections have been illustrated or described either by Shulga-Nesterenko (1941; 1949a) or Trizna (1939).

Obviously their knowledge of the microstructure of the encrusting tissue in *Archimedes* is as meager as when Nikiforova admitted it.

Opportunity for study of *Archimedes* microstructure is greater in the United States, the only country where this bryozoan occurs profusely in many formations of the upper Mississippian and lower Pennsylvanian, and where nearly all the numerous localities are practically inexhaustible. Because of this most American species are richly represented in our collections, and choice material is readily available for as many sections as desired. Even so, the microstructure of the encrusting tissue presents a difficult problem for research as shown in the detailed description and numerous photomicrographs by Condra and Elias (1944). It is difficult to describe the microstructure in *Archimedes* because it is made of several elements intimately interwoven into a dense tissue. Its differences from the somewhat similar encrusting tissue in *Fenestella* are not those noted by Nikiforova and Shulga-Nesterenko. The phytomorphic or foliaceous fibrous structure within the *Archimedes* shaft that "resemble, especially when weathered, the system of gill-like partitions of the cup in mushroom fungi" (Condra and Elias, 1944, p. 30) set Archimedes aside from *Fenestella.* The fibers of the foliaceous fibrous aggregate are oriented so that in cross section they appear as regularly alternating radial equidimensional dark and light bands (*see* Condra and Elias, 1944, Pl. 1, fig. 1; Pl. 27, fig. 4; Pl. 29, fig. 27). Filamentous needlelike structures (called now spicules) penetrate more or less along the contacts of the alternating bands, and the whole is fused into a compact deposit. Among the microstructures illustrated by Russian authors the one nearest to this foliaceous fibrous structure is that in the heavily encrusted lateral "supports" of *Lyrocladia* (Shulga-Nesterenko, 1931, Pl. 5, fig. 11; 1941, Pl. 35, figs. 1, 4), which also shows equidimensional alternate dark and light bands. The thickness of the bands averages 30 μ (Elias' measurement on Shulga-Nesterenko's photographs). This is comparable to the thickness of the bands in American *Archimedes*, which range from 25 μ n *A. wortheni* (genotype), *A. intermedius*, and *A. invaginatus* to 30 μ in *A. swallovanus*, and to 30–40 μ in *A. perminimus*. *Archimedes nikiforovae* collected by Condra from the Artinskian of Kasarmenny Kamen of Urals (Condra and Elias, 1944, p. 181–182, Pl. 39, figs. 2–5) shows this type of structure, but it is not as well developed as in the thicker shafts characteristic of nearly all American species of *Archimedes.*

IV. PREPARATION AND STUDY OF SILICIFIED BRYOZOANS

Dilute hydrochloric (or other) acid has been used successfully to etch silicified fossils from unsilicified or partially silicified rock matrix, particularly of Devonian and Permian limestones. Such etching of the Permian limestones of Glass Mountains revealed numerous delicate bryozoan species, far exceeding the few that could be observed on the naturally weathered collected specimens. Nearly all species here described are based on such etched specimens, which are much better for study than their weathered equivalents.

Etching has one shortcoming which should be taken into account both technically and scientifically. The etched zoaria are often so fragile that they almost collapse under their own weight and are easily broken by touching. Some paleontologists use transparent cement as a reinforcing substance; however, despite its glasslike transparency it obscures important delicate details, and hinders study and photographing. On the other hand, breaking of uncemented zoaria can be prevented by storing in a covered container, the lid of which can be provided with transparent celluloid window[2]. The most fragile zoaria have only an incomplete thin silicified skeleton, as the unsilicified part dissolves in acid. Such etched material is unsatisfactory, and the original material should be studied without resorting to etching, or acid should be applied only moderately and locally. In other specimens only the inner skeleton of *Fenestella*, called here colonial plexus, is silicified, while the outer encrusting tissue is not, or only partially silicified. Such specimens have some value in the study of the nature and relationship between these two structures, but most important for such study are nonsilicified calcareous specimens, which are scarce among the Permian bryozoans of western Texas. In the etched siliceous bryozoans the degree of preservation of structural details differs, depending on the size of grains or crystals of the secondary silica which replaces the original calcium carbonate. In some bryozoans studied the replacement is in the form of quartz, which is occasionally so well crystallized that individual crystals can be recognized even under slight magnification. Under these conditions of silicification the structural features of the bryozoans suffer greatest destruction, as even such prominent features as zooecial apertures or larger carinal nodes become only roughly indicated. Perhaps fossil material like this could be discarded; but, when it is the only kind representing a species and if it is possible to detect and measure on it the principal zoarial and zooecial features by which species are customarily recognized, the material is useful. Some such material is described in this report: see *Fenestella plicata* n. sp. (Pl. 33, figs. 3–6).

Under equal conditions of silicification the finer the original structure the more likely it is to be blurred or obliterated by crystallization. Therefore, fine details like those in the structure of the wall can seldom be observed in silicified specimens. The progress in understanding the microstructure of the wall reported here is based largely on the study of nonsilicified related forms from Nebraska and elsewhere.

Observation of the fine structural details, the importance of which is being gradu-

[2] Use of cotton to support etched zoaria is more trouble than help, because fine threads entangle with zoaria, and their removal requires much patience and skill, lest it results in breaking the fossil.

ally realized, depends not only on the degree of preservation but also on the technique of orientation for most advantageous observation. The standard method is study of thin transparent sections under the microscope[3]; just how thin a section should be depends on size of microscopic structure to be studied and magnification employed. Ordinary petrographic sections range from 0.02 to 0.04 mm. in thickness. The thickness of thin sections of fossil bryozoans, foraminifers, corals, and other invertebrates is not discussed or even mentioned in most treatises on them, or even in articles devoted to the technique of preparation, perhaps because it is taken for granted that they are about as thick as petrographic slides. In ordinary mechanical grinding the thinnest section possible is circa 0.01 mm, but this is seldom approached. Fragility of material, lack of skill, and defective equipment reduce the possibility of attaining this thinness, and doubtlessly the majority of the investigations of wall structure in Paleozoic bryozoans has been on sections 0.02–0.04 mm thick. However, considering that the various structural elements recognizable in the wall are a few microns to a fraction of a micron thick and because there are substantial differences in the coefficient of refraction (and also birefringence) of the elements (spicules, laminae) in the wall of fenestrate Cryptostomata, the picture seen in a section 20–40 μ thick is not sufficiently clear to allow differentiation of the boundaries of the laminae and the transverse spicules. When this was noted a determined effort was made to reduce the thickness of sections, (or at least of their edges) to within the thickness of the elements studied. Thickness desired was attained by finishing mechanically ground sections by etching with dilute hydrochloric acid.

The main difficulty of this method is to determine when to stop the action of acid so that the thin section is not lost by dissolution. The present method consists of smearing acid over the thin section by finger tip (the dilute hydrochloric does not hurt the skin, unless left on it to evaporate or unless there are cracks or sore spots). The smearing is done instantly, and the section is immediately washed in water and placed under the microscope to see how far the etching advanced and whether it affected the section evenly. The process is repeated until desired thinness is obtained. However, because commonly thin sections are not uniformly thick, a slightly more intense smearing from a fine camels hair brush over thicker parts of the section helps attain more nearly equal thickness. The thinner the section, the more obvious are the various defects of mechanical grinding on the bottom side, which is glued to the glass by Canada balsam or Lakeside cement. Because of this and because of unequal susceptibility to dissolution of various elements in the fossil, it is impossible to attain an evenly thin section, and the effect of uneven thickness becomes more pronounced with decreased thickness. However, it is possible to obtain sufficiently large areas of equal thickness to allow observation and measurement of the finest structural details.

[3] Differential weathering sometimes reveals delicate structural details (see Condra and Elias, 1944, Pl. 11, figs. 4–7); also, some secondary differential chemical replacements and subsequent etching may reveal these details without preparation of thin sections.

V. WALL STRUCTURE

INTRODUCTION

Because of the enigmatic character of some details in the wall structure and in the appendages of *Fenestella* and related Paleozoic bryozoans, a comparative study of the nature and origin of the calcareous structures in the related living and post-Paleozoic bryozoans has been undertaken. Although considerable work on the structure and calcification of the wall in living bryozoans has been done by several bryozoologists, notably Smitt, Waters, Calvet, Levinsen, Lang, Harmer, Canu, Borg, and others, there are many obscure points concerning the general process of calcification and the meaning of the various "pores". The results obtained by the scientists mentioned, and those obtained from the present microscope study of some critical living and post-Paleozoic forms permit a better understanding of the wall of *Fenestella* and the differentiation of its main parts.

Ulrich (1890, p. 333) believed that Cryptostomata, to which he assigned *Fenestella,* were Paleozoic representatives of Cheilostomata. However, some structures in certain groups of living and post-Paleozoic Cyclostomata correspond to similar structures in the Paleozoic fenestrate bryozoans and are unrecognizable in Cheilostomata. Likewise, Reteporae of Cheilostomata, whose zoarial growth form so resembles *Fenestella* that they were once placed with *Fenestella* in a comprehensive genus *Retepora,* are now believed different from it (Waters, 1896). Indeed, the dissepiments in *Fenestella* are structurally quite different from the analogous connecting bars, which are called trabeculae in Reteporae (Fig. 12–14). Thus the structure of the calcareous skeleton of this and other living *Fenestella*-like Cheilostomata (Harmer, 1934) provides no starting point for a comparative study with *Fenestella,* as here undertaken. On the other hand Cyclostomata which are about as ancient as Cryptostomata and apparently of common origin (Borg, 1926, p. 490) are similar to them in the manner of calcification and in the sculpture, particularly on the reverse of their branches.

ELEMENTS OF WALL STRUCTURE

In the light of the present investigation the structure of the wall of fenestrate Cryptostomata is differentiated into three fundamental parts (Fig. 1):

(1) Colonial or germinal plexus (new term) includes the "striated membrane" of Nicholson or striated "germinal plate" of Ulrich; it also includes the "primary carina" of Cumings and the "capillary canals" of Shulga-Nesterenko (but not her "capillary tubules"). The proposed term is not synonymous with the "coenoecium" or "polyzoarium," which Nicholson understood to be the external investment "of the colony . . . formed by the combined ectocists of the various polypides, and . . . varies greatly both in form and actual composition," and "the only element of the *Polyzoa* with which the paleontologist is concerned" (Nicholson, 1872, p. 192). Colonial plexus is the primary part of the coenoecium if the latter is understood in this broad sense.

(2) Laminated sclerenchyma is a secondary calcareous deposit, whose laminae

correspond to the rhythmic growth lines of the brachiopods, mollusks, and other invertebrates.

(3) Transverse spicules or filaments are uprights which traverse the laminated sclerenchyma, usually producing distinct drag of the laminae around them in the direction of their growth. They were called minute tubuli by Nicholson and Ulrich, capillaries by Russian authors, and needlelike structures by Condra and Elias (1944).

COLONIAL OR GERMINAL PLEXUS

The new term colonial plexus is applied to the part of the colony continuous from the base of fenestrate zoaria to the tips of their branches. The earliest hints about the existence of such colonial plexus in Fenestellidae may be the brief references to "basal plate" or "germinal plate," a supposed equivalent of "lame germinale" of D'Orbigny, by Ulrich (1882, p. 129, 130; 1890, p. 352), Waagen and Pichl (1887, p. 777), and Nicholson and Lydekker (1889, p. 623). Important observations on the same structure have been made in England. The significance of "basal plate composed of vertical capillary tubes" was recognized by King (1849, p. 388), who states that on this plate are "planted" the zooecia. He ascribes the discovery of this relationship to Lonsdale. It seems clear that the "vertical capillary tubes" described by King are the "striae" of the authors, and the ribs of the colonial plexus here illustrated, which are situated along the reverse of a branch. These do not correspond to the "capillary tubules" described by Russian authors.

Vine perhaps studied *Fenestella* and related genera in greater detail (though not in thin sections) than most of his contemporaries. He came close to recognizing the vital role of the colonial plexus in the family Fenestellidae in holding together the zooecia (1884, p. 190):

"The cells in all *Fenestellae* are arranged bi-serially, and between the cells there are very delicate interspaces, the walls of the cells in the opposite sides of the branches being separate and distinct.

FIGURES 1–7.—STRUCTURAL DETAILS OF *FENESTELLA*

Figure

1. Diagrammatic view showing the structure of a branch of *Fenestella*.

2–4. Generalized drawings to illustrate Shulga-Nesterenko's terminology and concept of the same structure, including her "capillary system" (Fig. 2) (Shulga-Nesterenko, 1941; 1949a; 1949b).

5. Ontogenetic stages of development of a zoarium in late Paleozoic *Fenestella*.
   a. Nepiastic or infantile stage characterized by development of initial circle of zooecia or zoids and initiation of zoarial branches.
   b. Neanastic or adolescent stage characterized by rapid spreading of branches accompanied by frequent bifurcation.
   c. Ephebastic or adult stage characterized by slowly spreading to subparallel branches and occasional bifurcation. In the lateral parts of a zoarium branches may curve to the right and to the left, and many of them may bifurcate simultaneously.
   d. Geronastic or senile stage characterized by parallel to converging branches and occasional termination of a few.

6. Detail of *Fenestella banyana* Prout showing supporting pillars of the zoarium (from St. Louis Acad. Sci. Trans., 1, 1859, p. 450; republished by Vine, 1879, Fig. 204). [To show supporting pillars of the zoarium.]

7. Base of Palaeocoryne-like pillar, parasitically attached to *Fenestella* sp. (from Vine, 1879 fig. 203).

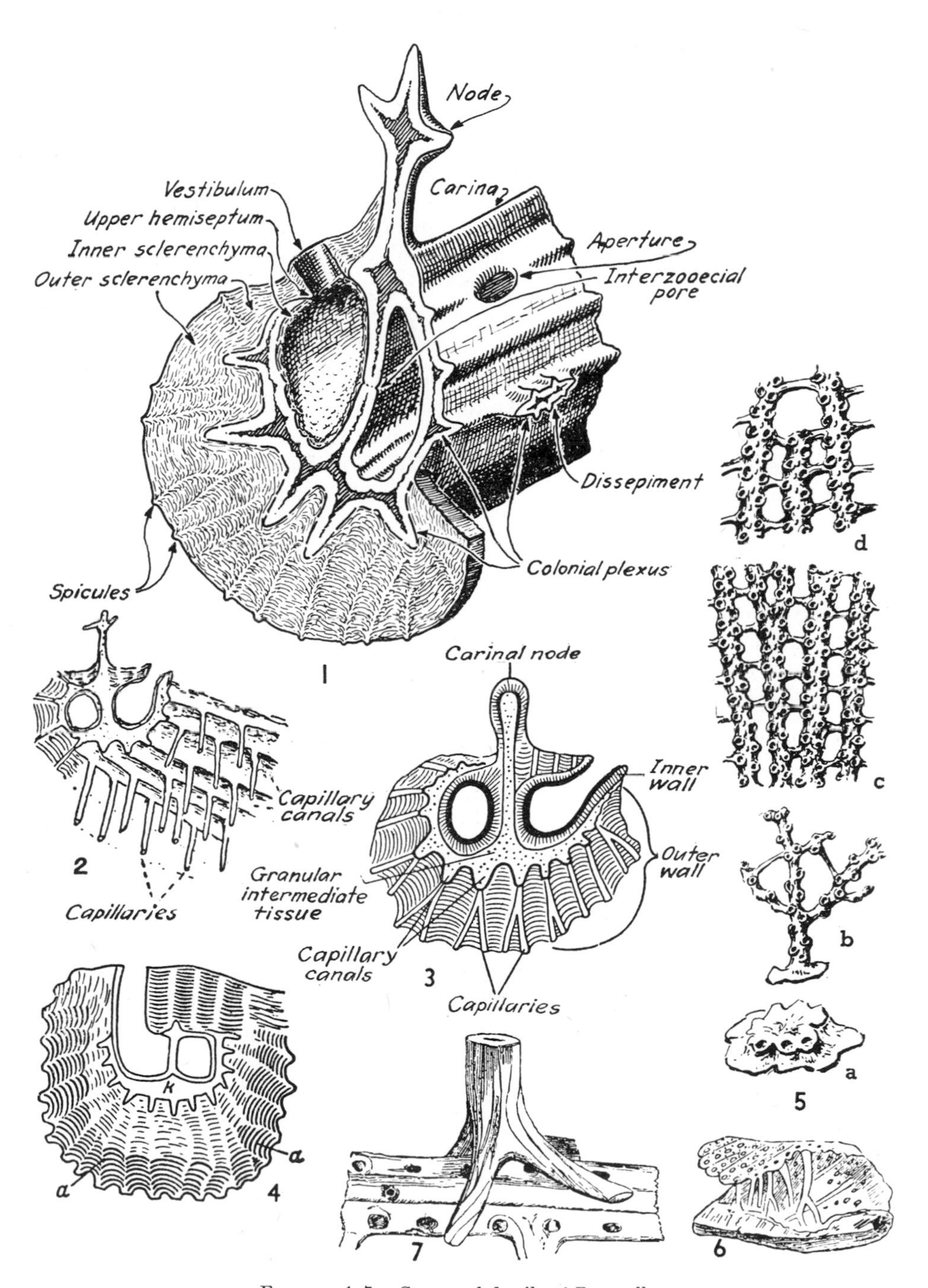

FIGURES 1–7.—*Structural details of Fenestella*

Yet by means of this interspace the whole of the cells of the colony appear to be linked together. Have we here the passages through which the endosarc passed from cell to cell? If so, then the unity of the cells in the colony, and also the distinct surroundings of the cell by its own wall, and the purpose of the interspace, are easily explained."

He found the same interspaces in "*Pinnatopora*" (*Penniretepora*) and further observed that similar "very delicate hollow space," apparently of significance, exists in *Ptilodictya* "all along the so-called 'laminar axis' ". . . .

The principal observation on which the present concept of a continuous colonial plexus is based is the manner of crystallization of calcium carbonate that fills the inside or core in Fenestellidae. The calcium carbonate in the core of the plexus acts as a single crystalline unit in polarized light: viewed under crossed nichols it shows uniform birefringence and extinguishes uniformly (Pl. 1, figs. 4, 6; Pl. 2, figs. 2, 4). Because the colonial plexus is thin, a few microns to 20–25 microns across, and because calcium carbonate has high birefringence, observation of the structure and boundaries of the colonial plexus is more difficult in thicker slides. The thinner sections also allow clearer observation of complete extinction of light.

The presence of the plexus has been established in many tangential and cross sections prepared from various species of *Fenestella*, *Archimedes*, *Hemitrypa*, and *Polypora*, ranging in geological age from Mississippian to Permian. In tangential sections the crystalline unit that fills the plexus, usually blacks out when the plane of polarization parallels the axis of a zoarial branch. There the axis lies in the plane of the optical ellipsoid in the crystal; in view of this and also because the branches in a fenestrate zoarium are usually more or less radiating, the polarized light, which passes through the plexus in two neighboring branches, does not extinguish in both at exactly the same position, even though it may seem to at a first glance. Unless these branches are perfectly parallel (which is occasionally the case), when either the nicols or the slide is rotated, the light in the plexus of each branch blacks out at a slightly different position—when the axis of each branch in its turn parallels the plane of polarization. Because the branches are not strictly parallel, this slight but clearly observable lag of extinction of one branch as compared with a neighboring branch, permits delineation of the limits of the plexus in one branch from the limits in a neighboring branch (*see* the description of microstructure of dissepiments).

The structure, composition, and extent of the plexus became gradually understood through systematic study of thin sections of fenestrate Bryozoa in polarized light. The decisive evidence for the inclusion or exclusion of any particular structure in the plexus was the manner of crystallization: if acting as a crystalline unit together with other parts of the plexus, it was considered its part, except where a unit of crystallization extended beyond clearly indicated physical boundaries. As a slide is rotated, some comparatively large crystalline grains within the zooecial cavities black out simultaneously with the plexus; they obviously do not belong with it, though in some way apparently connected with it at the time of crystallization (Pl. 1, fig. 6; Pl. 2).

The particular part of the colonial plexus which was the subject of some attention by Waagen and Pichl (1885), Ulrich (1890), and Shulga-Nesterenko (1931; 1941) consists of distinctive subparallel ribs or folds that arise from the basal plate or the common base on the dorsal side or the reverse of branches (Fig. 17; Pl. 4, fig. 1).

They can be observed best in transverse sections (Pl. 1, figs. 4–8; Pl. 4, fig. 1), and Ulrich (1890, p. 352) says: "Almost invariably the lower side of the [basal or germinal] plate presents a number of tooth-like projections. . . ." Shulga-Nesterenko (1941, p. 35) calls them capillary canals, which resemble the "folds of the hydrospire in blastoids, and stretch along the zoarial branches." Condra and Elias (1944, p. 23) describe these structures as prominent parallel ribs on the reverse of branches in *Fenestella* and *Archimedes*. The present investigation shows that each wedge-shaped rib has a thin platy core, and several ribs radiate from a common cylindrically rolled plate, next to and parallel to the base of a row of zooecial chambers. The calcium carbonate that fills the interconnected cylindrical and radiating plates reacts as a crystalline unit in polarized light (Pl. 1, figs. 3–6; Pl. 2). In many well-preserved specimens the platy cores contain some fine dark granules (Pl. 2, figs. 1, 2) that sometimes concentrate in their middle. In some cross sections the concentration of the granules permits differentiation (without polarized light) of the internal platy cores from the thin external walls into which the dark particles do not enter. These walls consist of one or more indistinct concentric laminations, whose light boundaries are generally lighter than the similar bands in the adjacent laminated sclerenchyma external to the plexus. The same structure can usually be recognized in the other parts of the plexus: (1) inner platy core, a concentration of fine dark particles whose calcification results in a single crystalline unit; and (2) thin outer walls, generally optically different and usually somewhat laminated.

A cross section of the zoarial branch shows that the principal (or basal) cylindrically rolled germinal plate extends upward over all external surface of the zooecial chambers and also sends out a thin central wall into the narrow space between them. Radial ribs rise from it along the reverse of a branch and along its sides, although the lateral ribs are not as tall as the dorsal ribs. The central platy wall that meanders between the two rows of zooecia usually expands above the latter and furnishes the core of the structure known as carina (Pl. 1, fig. 6).

Although Shulga-Nesterenko (1941) apparently did not study her thin sections in polarized light (no reference to such procedure can be found), she correctly detected the perfect continuity of the dark substance that builds the dorsal ribs of the plexus (her "capillary canals") and fills the narrow space "which divides the two rows of zooecia, the carina, and the cores of tubercles and outgrowths" (Shulga-Nesterenko, 1941, p. 35). Besides confirming most of her observations this study shows also the extension of the colonial plexus into the dissepiments.

DISSEPIMENTS

Although the dissepiments in the fenestrate Paleozoic bryozoans are often described, their nature is not explained, except that it is understood that their purpose is to connect the branches into a continuous netlike expanse. Observations based on the tangential thin sections of several species of *Fenestella* show that the dissepiment usually starts as a direct outgrowth from one of the lateral ribs that comes out of the rolled germinal plate. The core of the plate extends through the core of this rib to the core of the dissepiment. Usually it extends no farther than about half way to the neighboring branch, where it fuses with a similar outgrowth from the opposite branch. Observations under polarized light show that although the two outgrowths are fused, their cores are often separated by a narrow interval that does not black out when the cores do (Pl. 2, figs. 1, 2). The usual flattening of the dissepimental cores in the plane of the meshwork results in more or less flattened dissepiments in most species of *Fenestella,* while their "striated" or finely grooved sculpture is due to the development of the minute low ribs along the dissepimental cores.

This manner of growth of the dissepiments of *Fenestella* has not been previously reported, but the fact that each dissepiment is made of two opposite outgrowths fused at their point of contact harmonizes with the bilateral symmetry of each dissepiment. Taking this into account the conclusion seems inevitable that the plexus sprouted lateral outgrowths at rhythmically spaced intervals, the length of which is highly characteristic of species. In most species the spacing of dissepiments is independent of the disposition of the zooecia in the branches. This is particularly so in the primitive or less-specialized Fenestellidae of the earlier Paleozoic. Stabilized correlation between the spacing of the zooecia and the spacing of the dissepiments began to develop in Mississippian, became more stable and common toward the end of Pennsylvania, and reached its acme in Permian time.

In *Fenestella, Septopora,* and a few other genera, which are characterized by the arrangement of zooecia into two rows only, the meandering medial partition tends to straighten toward the face of the obverse of a zoarium. It is often extended farther upward as separate spines, or more frequently as a continued wall-like carina, usually terminating in spines or more complex superstructures. Regularly spaced lateral outgrowths from swelled crests of the wall-like carinas fuse into elevated meshwork characteristic of *Hemitrypa* and similar genera and subgenera. The spacing of the meshes in such elevated meshwork is apparently controlled by the underlying zooecia, because in the number and position the small meshes in the superstructures correspond strictly to them. However, the lateral outgrowths of the superstructure that produce the elevated meshwork in the other genera, *Isotrypa, Loculipora,* and *Loculiporina* n.g., are apparently controlled only by the colonial plexus, because their transverse connecting bars constitute the upward extension of the underlying dissepiments.

REDUCTION OF COLONIAL PLEXUS

Not all species and genera of Fenestellidae have all parts of the plexus developed. For instance, a few of them have no carina, while others have no dissepiments, and have their branches connected either by their own rhythmic lateral undulations (*Subretepora, Phyllopora, Reteporina*), or not connected at all (*Diplopora*). The most reduced plexus is noted in the latest Pennsylvanian and Permian representatives of the genera *Thamniscus* (Pl. 1, fig. 2) and *Acanthocladia,* which will be described in a forthcoming paper. However, all fenestrate Cryptostomata possess a colonial skeleton (plexus), a continuous, foil-like structure, which is variously corrugated and expanded to produce a platy lattice, the honeycomblike meshes of which determine the individual zooecia. While the shape of the zooecial chambers (excluding vestibulum) may influence the shape of these meshes, some properties of the plexus seem to have greater control over the meshes: (1) the foil-like nature, (2) tendency to produce more or less parallel, radiating ribs, and (3) tendency to produce regularly spaced, narrow, short, lateral outgrowths, the dissepiments.

EARLY STAGES OF COLONIAL PLEXUS

The classical work of Cumings (1904; 1905) on the structure of the initial stages in the colony development in some fenestrate Cryptostomata, coupled with the work by Borg (1926) on the development of the earliest colonial stages in the living Cyclostomata provide important data that help in understanding the nature of the plexus in fenestrate Cryptostomata.

Cumings (1904; 1905) described the early stages in the development of carina in some Devonian fenestrate bryozoans. He was aware of the morphological and anatomical distinction between the secondary deposit and the inner skeletal structure in the early stages of zoarial development of *Fenestella.* The former is distinguished as "punctate deposit," in whose "copious deposit" the basal part of zoarium is "submerged" (1905, p. 170); elsewhere he recognizes in it "concentric zones" (p. 171). The "skeletal structure" is made of thin walls of zooecia, which are made of "non-punctuate substance" (p. 171). The carina, originating early during the metanepiastic stage "as an upgrowth or fold of the basal plate" (Cumings, 1904, p. 64) is "probably the true first zooecium" (p. 170). It consists of a thin plate or wall "continuous with the axial wall" and is augmented on both sides by the outer layers of "dense punctate sclerenchyma." In the drawings (1904, Fig. 61, p. 64) this sclerenchyma is more densely shaded than the subsequent deposit of "secondary sclerenchyma" in which all basal part is "submerged." Cumings regards the outer layers of dense punctate sclerenchyma as parts of carina, which is considered a "double or more properly triple" structure (1904, p. 64). About half a millimeter above the zooecia carina expands laterally and terminates in a perpendicular plate, the whole resembling a structural beam. In later stages carinae may "by secondary deposits . . . be greatly increased in height and breadth."[4]

Cuming's description and sketches of the primary carina that extends like a fold from the basal plate, the "true first zooecium," correspond well to Smitt and Borg's concepts of the "common bud" or "samknopp" in the initial zoaria of all Bryozoa, and to D'Orbigny's "lame germinale." What is not quite clear in the concept of the common bud or germinal plate, however, is its exact structure, limits, and extent within a zoarium. No wonder, then, that paleontologists were not able to recognize it satisfactorily in fossil Bryozoa and could not establish its extent in their zoaria. Borg's detailed investigations (1926; 1942) of the inception and development of the zoaria of living Cyclostomata helps in understanding the nature and function of the common bud in these Bryozoa.

---

[4] These characters of the carina, described by Cumings from the early stages of a zoarium indicate that it belongs to *Fenestrapora* or a related genus with excessively developed carina rather than to *Fenestella.* Cuming's remark (1904, footnote, p. 70) that "thin sections indicate that the early nepiastic stages of *Hemitrypa* are identical with those of *Fenestella*" seems to indicate that this was *Fenestrapora, Hemitrypa,* or another genus with complex carina, whose early stages he thought belonged to *Fenestella.*

COMMON BUD OF CYCLOSTOMATA AND ITS HOMOLOGY TO THE COLONIAL PLEXUS

Smitt's publications (1865; 1867; 1872) contain the foundational knowledge of the origin and development of the zoarium. He states that in all Bryozoa the developing margin of the zoarium is to be regarded "as a colonial bud, a common bud (samknopp), which separates itself by means of fission and develops into separate zoids" (Borg, 1926, p. 254, quoted from Smitt, 1866, p. 6). However, subsequent investigations proved that it is not true in either Cheilostomata or Ctenostomata (Nitsche, 1871, p. 445), and Barrois (1877) denies that it is so even in the Cyclostomata which he studied—of *Crisia* and *Phalangella flabellaris*, the latter now classified as *Tubulipora phalangea* and partly *T. plumosa* (Harmer, 1898, p. 75). Barrois found no evidence in these species "that the zoids are formed through fission of the septa in a common bud, and, furthermore, he thinks it impossible to speak of any common bud at all" (Borg, 1926, p. 254, quoted from Barrois, 1877). In view of this Borg paid particular attention to the process of development of zoaria in Cyclostomata and to the recognition of the structure Smitt called "colonial bud" or "common bud" (in English translation).

Borg found that in all Cyclostomatous Bryozoa the zoarium originates in a primary disk, "a semicircular hollow formation with calcareous walls." The common bud originates before this disk is "completely calcified," and from the common bud the whole zoarium gradually develops. The bud is an approximately cylindrical structure, and "its lateral wall consists of a cuticle, a calcified layer, ectoderm, and mesoderm, thus showing the same structure as the body wall of a zoid. The calcified layer of the wall of the bud is thickest nearest the primary disk and becomes distally thinner and thinner until it finally ceases at the edge of the terminal membrane of the bud, which is made up of a thin cuticle only with underlying ectoderm and mesoderm," the structure observed in Crisiidae (Borg, 1926, p. 255); but he found it also typical for all Cyclostomata. As the bud grows in length the calcified layer also "grows through apposition," new particles being added at the edge of the terminal membrane and on the inner side of the wall of the bud, which results in an increase in thickness of the calcified layer. An important structural character of the calcified layer, revealed by examination in polarized light is "that the minute particles composing it are located in a certain direction; namely, parallel to the longitudinal axis of the bud. The same is true also of the calcified walls of the zoids" (Borg, 1926, p. 254). That Borg does not record that in an adult stage of calcification the particles fuse and make a uniformly oriented continuous crystalline substance seems to indicate that the substance of the common bud between the calcified particles remains largely soft during the life of zoarium, but obviously the oriented calcareous particles may serve as centers for further calcification, during the life and in post-mortem petrifaction, so that eventually they fuse into a uniformly oriented crystalline unit.

In describing "secondary calcification," best observed in *Hornera*, Borg does not mention orientation of the calcareous particles in it, but describes it as a "calcareous layer . . . around the entire circumference." It takes the form of "a slight thickening of the wall of each zoid during the entire life of the zoarium through the gathering of new calcareous matter from the inside," but "it is, however, absolutely overshadowed by the formation of new calcareous matter from the outer side. . . . This process is of course made possible owing to the presence of soft tissues outside the calcareous layers. During the entire life of the zoarium the ectodermal epithelium which is the most immediate covering of the calcareous layer seems to continue to secrete new calcareous matter" (Borg, 1926, p. 307).

This description implies that the secondary calcification is added layer after layer, and, therefore, is apt to be laminated. When decalcified, the wall shows "distinctly separated layers" (Borg, 1926, Pl. 7, fig. 45). The present examination of the wall in fossil *Hornera jacksonica* discloses its finely laminated character. In the same fossil material one can find indications of an inner calcareous layer which reacts optically as a crystalline unit and makes a foil-like skeleton around the zooecia. It lies between the thinly laminated to druse-forming crust which covers the inner surface of zooecial chambers and the thick outer laminated tissue. This layer is not as clearly indicated and as uniformly optically oriented as the colonial plexus in *Fenestella* but is near that in the Permian species of *Thamniscus* where the plexus is poorly developed.

In his matured concept of the zoarium of *Crisina*, Cyclostomata, and of the part played by the common bud, Borg state, (1942, p. 38–40): "The zoids all originate within the common bud and are, consequently, all covered by its terminal membrane. . . . These zoids are thus never constricted off from the common bud but remain permanently covered by its terminal membrane just as do the kenozoids. The whole zoarium in *Crisina* is thus to be considered as much widened and strongly complicated common bud. This easily explains the secretion of calcareous matter from the outside, *e.g.*, the secondary thickening." The discussed observations indicate that the structure, location, and zoarial extent of the colonial plexus in fenestrate Cryptostomata correspond so well with Borg's description of the common bud in Cyclostomata that the two structures may be considered homologous. If so, this is strong evidence of close relationship between the living Cyclostomata and the late-Paleozoic fenestrate Cryptostomata. The following observations on other colonial structures known in some Bryozoa indicate lesser development of similar structure.

POSSIBLE COMMON BUD DEVELOPMENT IN OTHER BRYOZOA

Busk observes that in the face of the living cheilostomatous *Salicornaria* (now known as *Cellaria*) and *Melicerita* collected by CHALLENGER Expedition there is a "delicate chitinous hollow filament, which . . . follows the contour of the frontal areas, and is possibly continuous throughout the entire zoarium" (1884, p. 75). He also states that this is "probably a channel through which the extension and calcification of the septa are effected," and that "the network formed by it should be regarded as zoarial rather than appertaining to the individual zooecia enclosed in its meshes" (1884, p. 84). Although Waters (1889) published a supplementary report on the same Bryozoa of the CHALLENGER Expedition and investigated in detail the microstructure of some, he did not comment on the above observations by Busk. However, Harmer expressed disbelief in the existence of the "hollow filaments" described by Busk and pointed out that what he observed was merely a narrow chitinous elevation between the calcareous walls of the adjacent zooecia; he observed that when the Bryozoa are burned, in place of the chitin appears a "narrow slit;" thus the chitinous elevation is an upper edge of "a chitinous layer separating continuous zooecia" and prolonged into the membranaceous epitheca" in the front of the zooecia (Harmer, 1900, p. 227). Although Harmer nowhere rejects the fundamental concept of the continuity and zoarial extent of this chitinous layer (supposed by Busk to be a network of filaments), he apparently did not make it a subject of special investigation.

It seems of some significance that these observations were made in the living Cheilostomata that are nearest to Cretaceous Melicerititidae, which according to Waters (1891, p. 49) and Marcus (1924, p. 158) combine the characteristic features of Cheilostomata and Cyclostomata. They are classified with Cyclostomata by many paleontologists and zoologists, but Waters disagrees with this classification. He claims that some have avicularia and hence belong with Cheilostomata (same argument repeated by Borg, 1926, p. 488), but suggests a revision of the whole group. However, in accord with the further investigation by Levinsen (1925), *Meliceritites*, *Meliceratella*, and other related Jurassic and Cretaceous genera are now classified with Cyclostomata (Bassler, 1935, p. 14). Waters (1891) hoped that members of the group would prove to be links between some Paleozoic forms and post-Mesozoic Cheilostomata, and even anticipated that future investigations might prove applicability of some generic cheilostome names to Paleozoic ancestors. It seems that the concept of the plexus in fenestrate Cryptostomata suggested by us provides a new incentive toward reinvestigation of Mesozoic Melicerititidae and the living and Paleozoic forms which may be related to them.

DOUBLE WALL IN SOME RECENT CYCLOSTOMATA

The discovery of a special kind of "double wall", as Borg calls it, in recent Horneridae and Lichenoporiidae sets them aside from the other Cyclostomata. Borg, who investigated the wall in Cyclostomata in more detail than its previous investigators, describes in these two families a "slitlike cavity" along the outer surface of the primary wall, which is bordered on both sides by mesodermic layers and ectodermal epithelium. He regards it a caelomic cavity and says that "the slitlike cavity is frequently invisible, because the two mesodermic layers have been pressed together" (Borg, 1926, p. 196); but in other places it is quite distinct, and in *Hornera violacea* "there is secreted a layer of calcareous matter immediately underneath the cuticle, so that the wall of the cystid thus contains two entirely separated calcareous layers" (p. 197). The inner calcareous layer is the ordinary wall common to all Horneridae and other Cyclostomata, but the outer layer makes "a finely granulated, nontransparent film . . . much thicker on the basal (reverse) than on the frontal (obverse) side; it reaches all around the stem in the proximal and middle parts of the zoaria only" (Borg, 1926, p. 197). This description and the indicated position of these structures are somewhat like the plexus, but the mentioned layer adheres to the outside of the thick laminated wall in Horneridae and Lichenoporidae, while the layer of the plexus lies under or *inside* the thick laminated sclerenchyma of fenestrate Cryptostomata.

Doubling of wall in Cheilostomata is caused by coalescence of the walls of the neighboring zooecia, but doubling of the wall in Horneridae and Lichenoporidae takes place not at the contact between neighboring zooecia but in the outer or zoarial wall that embraces them all.

NEW BRYOZOAN ORDER: FENESTRATA[5]

The homology of the colonial plexus of fenestrate Cryptostomata to the common bud in extant Cyclostomata throws new light on their position among other orders of the phylum.

All Cryptostomata were originally classified in comprehensive suborder Cyclostomata (Ulrich, 1882, p. 149–151). In 1883 Vine removed from Cyclostomata the bifoliate and a few closely allied ramose forms, for which he erected suborder Cryptostomata. In 1890 Ulrich expanded it by adding the fenestrate forms. Thus, the fenestrate forms were the last removed from Cyclostomata. The fact that they possess zoarial plexus, apparently homologous to the common bud of Cyclostomata, and the fact that comparable structures are absent in other Cryptostomata suggest a return to Vine's concept of Cryptostomata and segregation of fenestrate forms into the new order Fenestrata to be added to Borg's class Stenolaemata at a par with orders Trepostomata and Cyclostomata.

It seems that Fenestrata are ancestral to at least part of Cheilostomata, the evolution expressed in the reduction to eventual suppression of the colonial plexus in Cheilostomata. Because of this, and in accord with Dollo's law of loss, the dissepimentlike trabeculae in the *Fenestella*-like cheilostome *Palmicellaria parallelata* (Fig. 12–14) are tubular extensions of zooecial walls and not a part of a colonial plexus (as true dissepiments are). A rare case of a single hollow node making similar nondissepimental connection in *Fenestella binodata* (Fig. 16) seems to represent an early attempt to produce a trabecula. The fact that *F. binodata* and *P. parallelata* have similarly intermittent longer and shorter fenestrules is additional evidence of probable direct ancestry of the former to the latter.

LAMINATED SCLERENCHYMA

The laminated texture of the sclerenchyma in Fenestrata has been known since these Bryozoa were first sectioned. It did not attract particular attention, however, because it is so like the lamination in the walls of Trepostomata, which were specially studied because their classification with Bryozoa was seriously disputed. Excellent drawings from thin sections, magnified 50 to 80 times, of the Trepostomata from the Salt Range of India (Waagen and Wentzel, 1887) illustrate clearly the various plications, twists, and drags of the laminae in the walls. Discounting some statements made by Waagen and Wentzel contrasting the wall structure in Monticuliporidae (believed by them to be corals) with that in other Bryozoa, most of their observations about Monticuliporidae are acceptable. "The secondary thickenings are always composed of successive reversal conical layers of sclerencyhma, as has been observed already by Nicholson;" and furthermore, "the reversal conical layers . . . are again

[5] Term Fenestratae was used by Busk (1859, p. 96, 97) as a group name for the species of *Hornera* from the Crag of England, the rest of the species of *Hornera* designated as Ramosae. These two designations could be of subgeneric rank, but obviously the author had no intention to give them taxonomic status; none was given by subsequent authors, and the division is not generally recognized.

themselves composed of little fibers, which extend parallel to the layers" (Waagen and Wentzel, 1887, p. 864–865). They also correctly observe that in the sclerenchyma of Monticuliporidae there are no "capillary tubes by which the walls of the Bryozoa seem always to be pierced in great numbers" (p. 863), a statement apparently based on observations of some fenestrate Cryptostomata of the Salt Range, although only when describing *Thamniscus serialis* do they state that "the non-poriferous side is . . . pierced at intervals by very small pores" (p. 810).

Cumings and Galloway (1915) made a more detailed investigation of laminated sclerenchyma in Trepostomata (=Monticuliporoids) from the earlier Paleozoic, as they observed the "histology of the trepostome walls under much higher magnification [up to ×400] than has hitherto been employed and in longitudinal rather than in tangential sections" (1915, p. 359). They describe the laminae as being composed of "minute granules" (p. 360), which can be distinctly seen under magnification of ×287, for instance, in *Bythopora gracilis* (Pl. 14, fig. 42). They state that in this bryozoan "the granules are larger than in most other forms, and hence can be seen distributed in more or less concentric bands." In some walls they "are more closely concentrated in the axial region of the wall, and, when bands of granules from either side of the wall are present, they are often offset instead of continuing uninterruptedly across the median region of the wall" (p. 360). The same authors correct the supposition of Waagen and Wentzel about acanthopores in Trepostomata, stating that they cannot possibly be young zooecia (or corallites, if Trepostomata were corals) as they are slender spines that extend far beyond the surface of zoarium (about 2½ zooecial diameter above it), and are occasionally found imbedded in the surrounding sediments (Pl. 15, figs. 51 and 52). The illustrations show considerable deposition of laminated tissue around the thin central core of the spines and a sharp draglike upward turn of laminae along the spines similar to drag of laminae around the spicules in Fenestrata.

Waagen and Wentzel apparently overlooked the similar laminated tissue in Fenestrata from India because it is overshadowed by the prolific transverse spicules in the Permian Cryptostomata they studied. Likewise, Nicholson and Lydekker (1889) do not mention the lamination of the sclerenchyma. However, Ulrich states that in fenestrate Cryptostomata the reverse is "being covered by a dense layer of striated or minutely granulose sclerenchyma" (1890, p. 344–345). The laminated character of the sclerenchyma is shown on many of his sketches (Pl. 53, figs. 4b–c, 7). Cumings is not concerned with the texture of the "profuse deposits of secondary sclerenchyma" in the basal part of the zoarium of *Fenestella* but indicates roughly its laminated character in some of his sketches (1904, p. 59, Figs. 55, 56, p. 52). Only Shulga-Nesterenko (1931; 1941) devoted special attention to the lamination of sclerenchyma in Fenestrata as she studied it in *Lyrocladia* from the Permian of Russia. She showed distinctly in her sketches (1941, Figs. 99, 100, p. 142, 143) that the "capillary tubules" are clearly seen only when against the dark laminated background. She observes that there is slight undulation of the laminae, which becomes more intense at the edges of the "capillary tubules" where the tissue is "denser." But in the lighter-colored tissue, deeper inside the zoarium (Fig. 4) than the darker tissue, the "capillary tubules are barely discernible" (Shulga-Nesterenko,

1941, p. 143). The present observations fully confirm Shulga-Nesterenko's idea that the "capillary tubules", that is the spicules, are usually discernible only because of the lamination of the tissue which they traverse.

The lamination is made of numerous thin, continuous or interrupted, straight to wavy to plicated barlike laminae. The laminae are less transparent than the structureless substance in which they are embedded because of their apparent higher index of refraction. The intervals where present between the successive laminae range up to several times the laminal width. The width of the laminae is usually 0.8–0.9 μ.

Under polarized light the structureless substance between the laminae tends to resolve into large irregular patches, each acting more or less as a crystalline unit and embracing several laminae. But the laminae do not act optically with the enclosing substance and remain light, usually pale orange colored, when the medium blacks out.

Borg describes similar texture of the calcareous layer (after its "careful decalcification") in the wall in living *Hornera lichenoides*. It is a "network of fine threads" forming several "distinctly separated layers, probably indicating that the deposition of calcareous matter has taken place during several different periods" (Borg, 1926, p. 196–197). He does not give the thickness of the "fine threads" that make the wall, but judging from the single photomicrograph (Borg, 1926, Pl. 7, fig. 45, ×150; 1926b, Fig. 4, p. 591) they are about 3 μ thick.

Borg's description is apparently the only published information about the threads of the wall in living *Hornera*, but similar threads can be observed on ×100 photomicrograph of the frontal tangential section of *Hornera jacksonica* (lower Eocene) in Canu and Bassler (1920, Pl. 143, fig. 14)[6]. Through the courtesy of Dr. Bassler the topotypes of *H. jacksonica* and *Idmidronea maxillaris* were made available to us for additional study. In thin section (Pl. 3) the wall structure of these fossil bryozoans appears to be fundamentally the same as in Paleozoic Fenestrata, except in *H. jacksonica* the spicules are absent. The texture of the laminated tissue of its wall looks like that in Fenestrata. It is made of thin long laminae that are immersed in structureless substance and appear darker because of their higher coefficient of refraction. The laminae are about 1 μ thick in *H. jacksonica*, and where laminae are not in contact the intervals between them range up to 3 or 4 times their thickness. In polarized light the substance around the laminae blacks out along the larger patches, and the short laminae stand out as light-orange bars. The laminae produce folds, drags, and loops at the edge of zooecial chambers and pores (or pseudopores) and especially in the narrow intervals between these openings.

In view of these observations, it seems inevitable to conclude that the sclerenchyma in Fenestrata is of the same nature as that in the group of living Cyclostomata represented by the genus *Hornera*, as that in Paleozoic Trepostomata, and perhaps as that in some Cheilostomata (*see* Fig. 11).

If this conclusion is accepted, then it follows that the sclerenchyma in Fenestrata (and in Trepostomata) apparently was secreted and deposited in the same manner as that in the living *Hornera* and related *Cyclostomata;* this means that it was secreted by the ectoderm that stretched externally over the whole zoarium, not by a

[6] By a typographical error the explanation of Plate 143, p. 144 reads *Filisparsa fallax*, but the description of *Hornera jacksonica* in the text, p. 797, correctly indicates that its illustrations are on Plate 143, figs. 1–26.

special "capillary system." In fact, no equivalent of the latter is known in *Hornera* or any living bryozoans that have the same or similar secondary calcification of the wall.

Furthermore, the laminated tissue in the walls of some Trepostomata, shown in detailed sketches and mentioned in descriptions by Cumings and Galloway (1915), seems to differ from that in Fenestrata by a much denser spacing of the smaller laminae: circa 1 micron thick in *Bythopora gracilis* in which the granules of the laminae are "larger than in most other forms." Our comparative observations on some Trepostomata from the Cincinnatian of Ohio confirm those by Cumings and Galloway. In the "dark zones" the fine laminae are commonly spaced with no intervals of ground substance. In the lighter-colored zones the laminae are separated by narrow intervals, which usually average laminal thickness. Some laminae are made of small dashlike bars, or even shorter "granules," just as Cumings and Galloway show on their sketches; other, perhaps most, laminae remain continuous for long stretches, as seen in both longitudinal and transverse sections of the zoaria. Hence it is the closer spacing of thinner laminae and weaker development of the enclosing structureless substance that distinguishes the wall of Trepostomata from that in Fenestrata.

COMMON PRIMARY WALL IN FENESTRATA AND CYCLOSTOMATA

The colonial plexus in Fenestrata is apparently homologous to the common bud or the colonial bud in the living Cyclostomata. It may be further pointed out that

---

FIGURES 8–17.—DETAILS IN LIVING AND FOSSIL BRYOZOA

Figure

8, 9. Living *Hornera antarctica,* order Cyclostomata (after Borg, 1926, Figs. 52, 53). Showing the early stages of secondary calcification and the position of pores in relation to the incipient ridges on the reverse (Fig. 9) and the more complex sculpture on the obverse (Fig. 8). Fig. 8, ×36; fig. 9, ×31.

10. Fossil *Entalophora raripora* D'Orbigny, order Cyclostomata (after Beissel, 1865, Pl. 10, fig. 127, upper part only). Showing the multitude of pores perpendicular to zooecial tubes, ×60.

11. Living *Retepora* order Cheilostomata (after Harmer, 1934, Pl. 38, fig. 4) showing coarsely laminated calcification and the pattern made by the impressions of the basal parts of walls, ×36.

12–14. Living *Palmicellaria parallelata* Waters (after Waters, 1896, Pl. 6, figs. 19, 12, 13).

12. The obverse or anterior of part of full grown zoarium, ×2. Showing variable spacing of tubular trabeculae, which join neighboring branches. In the fenestrules thus formed there are usually two but occasionally also one or three zooecia per fenestrule. See Pl. 9, fig. 5. For same kind of variable spacing of dissepiments in *Fenestella binodata.*

13. Detail of the same zoarium, showing the regular position of the connecting trabeculae whose bases are invariably at or near zooecial apertures, ×10.

14. Detail of the same zoarium, view diagonal showing "rozette plate *a*" from which the connecting trabeculae usually develop at every other zooecium, ×10.

15. *Fenestella compactilis* var. *plattsmouthensis* n. var., showing calcite cleavage in the basal part of the colonial plexus, ×25.

16. *Fenestella binodata* var. *leonardensis* n. var. Detail of the specimen shown on Plate 9, figure 8, showing a trabeculalike development linking the opposite sides of the two zoarial branches, ×60.

17. *Fenestella plebeia* McCoy (after McCoy, 1844 [1862], Pl. 29, fig. 3, right side). Lower Carboniferous of Ireland, abt. ×8. Showing ribs or folds on the basal side of the colonial plexus

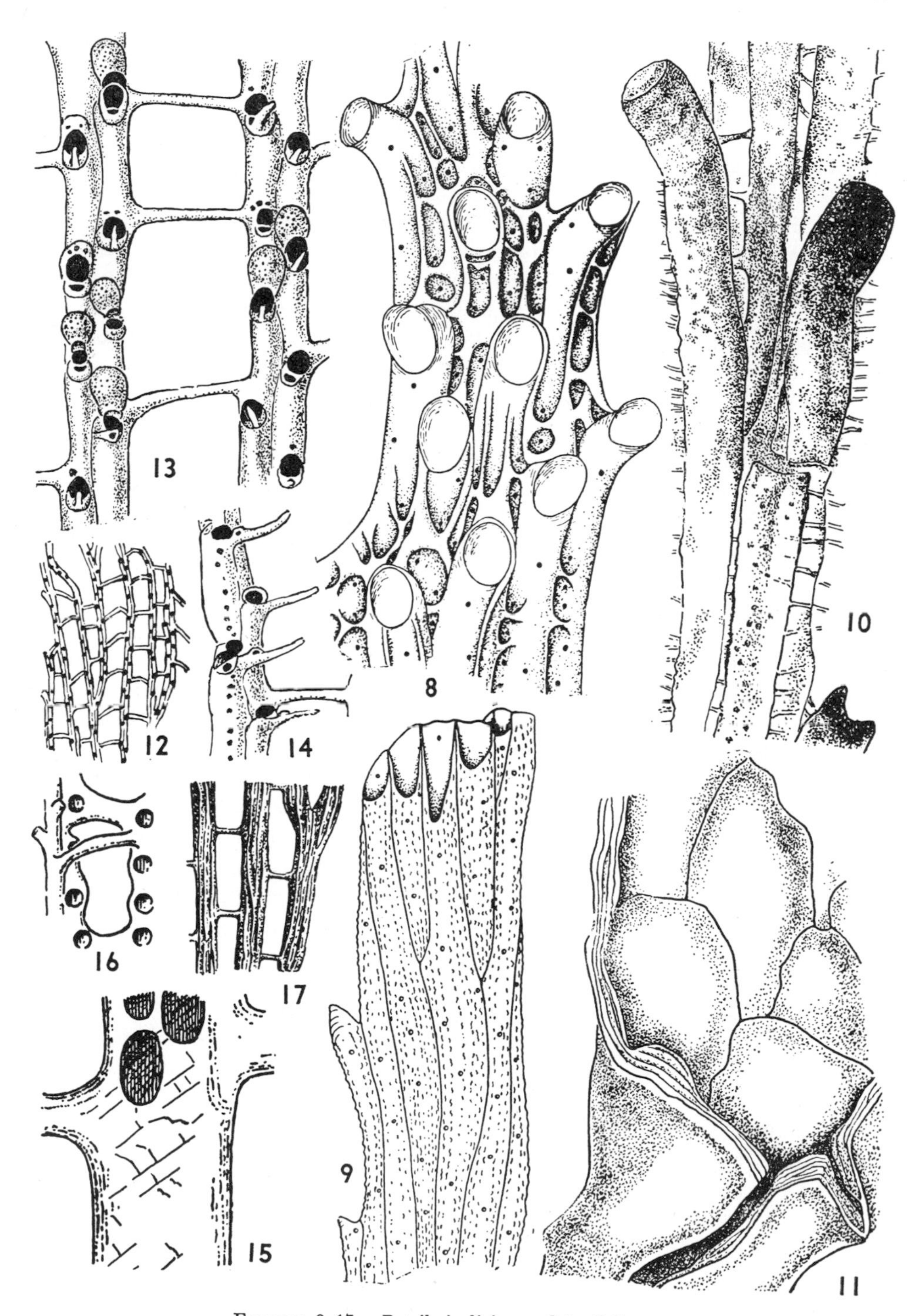

FIGURES 8–17.—*Details in living and fossil Bryozoa*

the laminated sclerenchyma of Fenestrata has the same texture and occupies the same position relative to the plexus as the secondary calcification relative to the primary calcareous common bud in Cyclostomata. In both there is little secondary calcareous deposition over the primary wall inside the zooecial chambers, but by far the greatest secondary deposit is added from the outside. This deposition forms the thick laminated crust.

From these considerations follows that in Fenestrata the neighboring zooecia share a common primary wall. This conclusion is at variance with the expressed belief by Ulrich that "Theoretically it may be said that the zooecia of all the Paleozoic Bryozoa had perfectly independent and complete wall." Thus, the composite wall between two zooecia would be doubled, and the "primitive duplex character of the zooecial walls of the Fenestellidae and Acanthocladidae is generally shown in deep tangential sections of the early stages of zoaria" (Ulrich, 1890, p. 308, 312). No illustrations were published to support this observation, however, and it seems that it is the secondary sclerenchymatous crusts on both sides of the thin primary wall that correspond to what Ulrich called the "primitive duplex" wall. Such understanding is harmonious with Shulga-Nesterenko's observations. She published a good illustration of communicating pores between two zooecia in *Fenestella bifida* var. *cyclotriangulata* (1941, Fig. 83, p. 121), and remarked that "in many examples there are unusually clearly differentiated individual walls of each zooecium (Fig. 83; Pl. 29, fig. 4), these walls being separated by a thin band of a dark amorphous granular tissue, which is the primary skeletal secretion of the zooids." Although she speaks, just as Ulrich does about the separate walls in each zooecium, she recognized in the "thin band" the true primary wall common to both neighboring zooecia. What she calls the individual zooecial walls are the inner layers of the sclerenchyma secondarily deposited over the common wall. These layers on each side of the sclerenchyma face inside each zooecium. It seems permissible to conclude, therefore, that the zooecia in Fenestrata have a *common primary wall*, another point of similarity between these fossil Bryozoa and the living Cyclostomata. Among living Bryozoa only in Cyclostomata and Phylactolaemata is the primary wall shared by neighboring zooecia (Borg, 1926, p. 192). In Cheilostomata and Ctenostomata each zooecium has its own primary wall.

SPICULES OR FILAMENTS

The relationship between the colonial plexus, the spicules or filaments, and the laminated tissue has not been clearly understood. Shulga-Nesterenko implies that the "capillary canals" are organically connected with the "capillary tubules," here called spicules or filaments, when she states that the "calcareous substance", after secretion by zooids, is "entering into the folds of the capillary canals" and from there enters "farther into the capillary tubules." She does not explain or illustrate how this connection is accomplished. In her most detailed account about these implied connections (Shulga-Nesterenko, 1941, p. 35) she states that "the distal edge of a capillary canal or its bottom, which is filled with granular tissue, sends off the capillary tubules toward the periphery of the zoarial branches," and that the "capillaries may be arranged along the canal in one row, or come out in bunches. . . ."

Ulrich (1890, p. 306) only questionably supposes the direct connection of these structures with the zooecial chamber when he states that in Fenestellidae "the nonporiferous side of the branches, as well as the spaces between the zooecia apertures, are pierced (?) by very minute vertical tubes, which compare with the surface pores of both the Cyclostomata and Cheilostomata". In order to find out how far the "tubes" extend and whether they pierce the wall and act as connecting pores it is necessary to understand the structure of the "tubes" and their relationship to other zoarial structures that they supposedly connect. In Fenestrata the existence of the extensive plexus stretching between the zooecial chambers necessitates a revision of Ulrich's belief that the "minute tubes" are comparable to the "surface pores" of the living Bryozoa. Because the plexus is enveloping the zooecia, the "minute tubes," in order to serve them, must pierce not only the encrusting laminated tissue but also the plexus. The fact that the latter can actually be pierced by some sort of pores is proved by Shulga-Nesterenko's observation on *Fenestella bifida* var. *cyclotriangulata*, where such piercing connections are clearly shown (1941, Fig. 83, p. 121). Ability of the "capillary tubules" to penetrate to the inner surface of a zooecial chamber has not been shown. Not fully acceptable is her observation that "the capillary tubules" start as the branches of the "capillary canals," the ribs of the plexus as here described. She further states that the point of origin of the "capillary tubules" is commonly the distal edge of these "canals." Our investigations, although in general agreement with Shulga-Nesterenko's description of the place where the "capillary tubules" start, show that the majority start from the flanks rather than from the crests ("bottom") of the ribs. From some crests of the ribs occasionally rise a few larger tubular outgrowths that enter into the curved spines. These may be true outgrowths of the ribs, and if so they belong to the plexus.

Shulga-Nesterenko's and our observations indicate the absence of "capillary tubules" in the grooves between the radiating ribs. This and the inability of the "tubules" to pierce the plexus furnish strong evidence against the identity of the "capillary tubules" with either true pores or pseudopores (Levinsen, 1909; Borg, 1926) of living Cyclostomata (Pl. 3), whose thick, finely laminated, calcareous wall is like that in Fenestrata. "External pores" or "pseudopores" observed by Levinsen and Borg traverse the wall exclusively and precisely within the grooves or the depressions (*see* Figs. 7, 8). Some true pores that occur commonly in *Septopora* (Pl. 4, fig. 4) and other genera of Acanthocladiidae are called "accessory pores" (Ulrich, 1890, p. 627). They are invariably in the grooves or bottoms between the ribs of the plexus, not on the slopes or crests, and thus correspond to the pores and the pseudopores of living Cyclostomata.

To recapitulate: our observations are in agreement with those of Shulga-Nesterenko in regard to the general location of the bases of the "capillary tubules" *outside the grooves*, but do not support her contention that they reach inside the "folds" to the "bottom" of the "capillary canals," from which the "capillary tubules" are supposed to "branch off." There is no evidence that the *walls of the "folds"* were crossed by the "capillary tubules" or by their possible prolongations.

DETAILS OBSERVABLE IN THINNER SECTIONS

It seems that desirable thinness was not reached in any of Shulga-Nesterenko's sections. This conclusion is deduced from the fact that she speaks of the "dark" border or halo around the "light compact core" seen under magnification of ×100 in the cross sections of the "capillary tubules" in the best-preserved fossil material (Shulga-Nesterenko, 1941, p. 35; Pl. 35, fig. 3). Our observations, using about the same magnification but on much thinner slides, show that the dark border or halo around the "capillary tubules" is produced by a sharp drag of the laminae in the laminated tissue around the "piercing capillary tubules." Shulga-Nesterenko states (1941, p. 35) that "the diameter of capillaries is always measured with the halo," which means that she considered the halo to be the wall of the capillaries. However, the evidence that the drag produces the halo indicates that it is not so. In some "tubules" individual laminae nearest them occasionally turn parallel to their axis. But even then it seems hardly possible to consider these laminae as elements of the wall, because they extend along the edges of the tubes for a short distance only.

In a few places there is no drag of laminated tissue around the "capillary tubules" and they cross the laminae at about a 90-degree angle, but in most the drag is either moderate, with an angle circa 45°, or so intense that the laminae become subparallel to the "tubules" at their contact. The latter is reminiscent of the previously mentioned more intense drag of laminated tissue around acanthopores in Trepostomata (*see* Cumings and Galloway, 1915, Pl. 15, figs. 51–54). Although among all tubular structures known in Trepostomata the acanthopores are nearest the spicules in Fenestrata, they are much larger in size and seemingly correctly compared with the immersed basal parts of avicularia in Cheilostomata. Cumings and Galloway show the unusually well-preserved acanthopores of *Decayia maculata* (1915, Pl. 15, fig. 53) whose light-colored lumen, circa 15 μ in diameter, is encircled by finely laminated walls circa 10 μ thick. Only the "inner fascicle of laminae" (1915, Pl. 15, explanation to fig. 54) is considered "the primary wall of the acanthopore," and the dragged "fascicles of laminae outside of this are secondary deposits, probably laid down by the surrounding zooecia."[7] In the cross sections the outline of the "capillary tubules" or spicules approaches a circle only when the outer dark laminated ring is included. The core, the filling of the spicule, is generally irregular in outline, with ragged edges. Sections cut parallel to the spicular axis show that the generally straight spicules have minutely wavering edges but average the same diameter throughout. Occasionally an individual lamina crosses a spicule but with no effect on its diameter or direction.

A few spicules bifurcate, some more than once. This verifies Shulga-Nesterenko's observation that "toward the periphery the capillaries may divide repeatedly" (1941, p. 36).

The diameter of a spicule is fairly constant from its base through the whole length and does not increase appreciably even below the point of bifurcation. The tubules are nearly perpendicular to zooecial branches and to the laminated tissue, which they traverse. The external diameter of the spicules ranges from 1–1½ μ to 12 μ, seldom reaching 15 to 20 μ.

The halo, not part of the "tubules," should be excluded when measuring spicule diameter. Moreover, our observations indicate that the spicules may possess very thin walls which are faintly indicated. These are much thinner than the dark halo,

[7] This remark seems to imply that the acanthopore produced its "primary wall," but probably not the "secondary deposits," which are not parallel to it.

and about as thin as the surrounding laminae. In some spicules this faint wall (?) measures 0.8 to 0.9 μ. In larger spicules the wall measures circa one-eighth the external diameter; but in the smallest ones, circa 1 μ in diameter, the wall measures up to circa one-third the diameter.

The basal or initial part of the spicules is the most difficult to study, but the knowledge of it is essential to their biologic explanation.

We have not observed direct connection of the lumen of the "capillary tubules" with the "capillary canals," that is, with the inside of the ribs in the colonial plexus. Under the most favorable conditions of observation—thinnest possible slide, good preservation of material, and orientation of the axis of the spicules parallel to the slide—the lower parts appear to rise perpendicularly from a short, prostrate base, whose extent is obscure, but whose thickness is about the same as the diameter of the spicule. Although many spicules start from the flanks of the ribs of the plexus, others rise far away from it from various levels or laminae of the laminated sclerenchyma.

POSSIBILITY OF ALGAL NATURE OF SOME STRUCTURES IN THE WALL OF FENESTRATA

From 1944 through 1947 consultations were held orally and through letters with leading American algologists, particularly Dr. Gilbert M. Smith of Stanford University and Dr. George F. Papenfuss of the University of California. These colleagues suggested that if the phytomorphic tissue in the Fenestrata belongs to algae at all, it is likely related to the living Red Algae. Following this hint Elias concentrated on comparative investigation of living and fossil Red Algae, though not neglecting others. The structure of the encrusting tissue in some thin sections of Fenestrata, notably in the Permian representatives of *Thamniscus*, seemed like the vegetative tissue of some coralline algae. Furthermore, the discovery of parallel rows of oval bodies in the basal plate of this bryozoan, which in size, shape, and general management resembles the conceptacles in living and fossil *Archaeolithothamnium* could be regarded an evidence for some relationship of the encrusting phytomorph to Red Algae. While investigating the various appendages to Fenestrata on material from American localities, particularly in the morphologically complex umbrellalike *Palaeocoryne*, Papenfuss noted that their branches bore a striking external resemblance to the specialized barbed branches of the living Red Alga *Asparagopsis armata* (*see* Elias, 1946, p. 285, Pl. 2, fig. 1). However, as the study progressed, it became clear that sections of ordinary thickness, 20 or more microns, do not allow a sufficiently clear picture of the minute and well-preserved spicules because of the overlap of these structures.

After very thin sections were prepared, previous observations were revised. This resulted in discarding the previously concluded relationship between the fossil *Palaeocoryne* and the living *Asparagopsis*. However, some new evidence favors the theory of algal nature of the spicules, while the pores and pseudopores in living bryozoans are now excluded from comparison with them.

Some minute filamentous algae are capable of finding permanent shelter in living bryozoans. Reinke (1889) described and illustrated such habitual association of

Epicladia flustrae Reinke on cheilostomatous bryozoan *Flustra foliacea*, which inhabits deep waters near the eastern shores of the Baltic Sea. The branching filaments of the green alga range from 5 to 10 μ in diameter and crowd in bunches inside ovicellate (?) hollows in *Flustra*. A similar green alga habitually covers the surface of the ordinary aquarium snail, and a similar alga grows on the shell of the snapping turtle. Hence certain simple marine Paleozoic algae possibly grew on the surface of Fenestrata. The problem remained, however, how such an alga could become calcified and entrapped within the calcified laminated sclerenchyma. The distinct drag of the laminated sclerenchyma around the spicules seems to indicate that they grew before the layered sclerenchymatous accretions, which buried their basal parts while their apices continued to grow outward. This is what should have been if the spicules were originally filamentous algae. The remaining difficulty in this interpretation was the apparent absence of any published data on algae that had their basal parts solidly calcified while their apical parts continued to grow.

Good specimens of *Pleurocladia lacustris* A. Brown from near Berlin, Germany, examined at the University of Nebraska Herbarium, exemplify such calcification among the living algae. Slides of this material (and also of the additional specimens supplied by Dr. Waern from Lake Erken, Sweden) show clearly a solid basal calcification of more than half the length of all the filaments, while their uncalcified apical parts remain tender and bright green. This alga grows on the submerged portion of stems of small hydrophytic angiosperms, encrusting their surfaces near the water level. The stems remain uncalcified, and only the basal parts of the algal filaments and the intervals between them are solidly filled with glasslike calcite (determined by mineralogist Dr. C. M. Riley). In a botanical publication this alga was reported to have its calcification external "between the upright threads," but we believe that it was probably assumed so, because this is the customary method of calcification in many other algae. Notwithstanding its green color, *Pleurocladia lacustris* is classified with brown algae. It is generally postulated that its adaptation to fresh water from marine habitat is comparatively recent. The diameter of the filaments in *Pleurocladia*, 6–13 microns, and the transparency of the calcification are comparable to those in the "spicules" of the Fenestrata.

These data give substantial biologic support to the interpretation that the "spicules" are calcified filamentous algae.

Johnson described from the Permian (probably the Word or post-Word) of Apache Mountains, West Texas, *Solenopora texana*, a supposed Red Alga, forming "nodular or hemispherical masses, others encrusting bryozoan shreds and other foreign material" (1951, p. 23). Bigby reports that this same alga "forms the entire minutely cellular reverse side" of *Acanthocladia guadalupensis* Girty; the two organisms "consistently occur together in many thin sections of Permian limestone from Texas and New Mexico" (1956, p. 82). In our judgment Johnson's illustrations (1951, Pl. 6, figs. 4, 5, especially fig. 4) show cross sections of bryozoan branches, probably of *Acanthocladia guadalupensis*; the filamentous alga makes regular crust, thicker on the reverse than on the obverse of the bryozoan. The densely spaced filaments replace almost all of the laminated tissue, as indicated by faint concentric banding across the algal filaments. Girty's thin section of *Acanthocladia guadalupensis* from the Delaware

Mountain formation of Guadalupe Point, West Texas (1908, Pl. 22, figs. 10, 10a) shows the same nearly complete displacement of the laminated tissue by what he called "radiating and transverse tubules" (explanation to figs. 10, 10a). Johnson states that there are "no cross partitions visible" in the filaments of *Solenopora texana* (1951, p. 23)—an important point of similarity to the spicules or filaments in *Thamniscus pinnatus* Condra from the Big Blue Series of Nebraska; their diameters are also similar. In genus *Solenopora* the filaments are crossed by partitions; hence *S. texana* does not seem to belong to *Solenopora* but is nearer to *Ortonella*, and perhaps represents a new genus of Paleozoic algae, which occurred earlier in the Paleozoic as isolated filaments in laminated tissue of Fenestrata and in some Permian species replacing it, where it assumed densely packed growth form.

VI. ZOARIAL FEATURES AND ECOLOGIC CONSIDERATIONS

APPENDAGES TO *FENESTELLA*

Discussion of the structure and nature of the appendages that develop on *Fenestella* and other Fenestrata will be presented in a separate paper. The curious and complex appendages that develop only on *Fenestella*, named *Palaeocoryne* by Duncan and Jenkins (1869), belong exclusively to the upper Mississippian forms of England and America (Condra and Elias, 1941, p. 44–45; Elias, 1946, p. 285); the simple, smooth to striated, barbed, cylindrical to variously bifurcating appendages are developed on forms that range from Devonian to the end of Permian. They are occasionally illustrated in various papers on Fenestrata, but rarely mentioned or discussed in the text. Ulrich casually mentions, but does not illustrate, that in *Fenestella tenax* "at the base and along the free lateral margins there are those peculiar[8] barbed spine-like appendages" (1890, p. 546), and this seems to be the only reference in America to the barbed appendages on *Fenestella* prior to our paper of 1944. They were described and discussed by English zoologists and paleontologists in a series of papers published between 1859 and 1879, particularly by Young and Young (1874). Vine (1879) suggested that these appendages possibly functioned as a special sort of vegetative reproduction.

Understanding of the nature of the colonial plexus has an important bearing on the explanation of the nature of the appendages because they have an axial core with a stellar outline similar to that of the plexus. This may indicate that the cores of the appendages may also belong to the plexus, and Elias attempted to find a direct connection with it.

However, repeated sectioning of the basal parts of the appendages failed to establish any direct connection between the core of *Palaeocoryne* and the colonial plexus. The core seems to terminate within its base, never extending to the plexus of the branches to which it is attached.

Duncan and Jenkins (1869) believed that the hydra of a tubularian hydroid lived in the central cavity of *Palaeocoryne*, but Young and Young (1874) observe that the axis in *Palaeocoryne* is solid and could not be a seat of an animal. The core can occasionally weather out and thus appear as a central cavity, but their conclusion that this could not possibly be a living quarter for hydra or similar animal is supported by the fact that a weathered core would have no opening at the distal end where *Palaeocoryne* branches into several spreading terminal arms. This investigation indicates that these appendages have a closed inner system that occupies the axis of the short stem and branches into the arms, which spread out from it.

Russian authors call the nonbarbed appendages radicles or radicle outgrowths and pay little attention to them. Shulga-Nesterenko (1941, p. 27–28) remarks that "radicle outgrowths develop upon nodes of the nonporiferous surface of the zoarium, particularly near its base, and serve its attachment to the substratum. . . . These

[8] The expression "those peculiar . . . " does not seem to refer to previous or subsequent descriptions or discussions.

outgrowths are generally incidental" and of no systematic value. "Their inner build and microstructure are the same as in carinal outgrowths," that is, the spines. Fredericks (1914) and Bolkhovitinova (1915) discuss briefly the origin and purpose of "radicle outgrowths," but only Likharev (1926) attempted a comprehensive review of the literature and a study of their structure. He was inclined to accept King's explanation (1850) that these outgrowths served attachment and also "guarded against approaches toward it by other bryozoan colonies and other organisms" (Likharev, 1926, p. 1019). Although he doubts that the outgrowths connect opposite sides of a cup or cylindrical zoarium, discussed by Fredericks (1914), we have found similar bracing columns in some American zoaria (Condra and Elias, 1945, p. 120, Pl. 13, fig. 103; *see* discussion of *Fenestella cylindrica*).

The "radicle outgrowths" on the Permian species of Russian *Fenestella* grow perpendicular to the obverse or as prolongations of branches; even in the latter such outgrowths bend toward the obverse (Likharev, 1926, p. 1021; Pl. 14, fig. 3). However, nearly all similar outgrowths in American *Fenestella* rise perpendicular to the reverse; the exceptional pillars that grow perpendicular on the obverse are not only striated, as the outgrowths on the Russian *Fenestella*, but also are armed with inverted barbs. No barbed outgrowths have been described or illustrated from Russia, and none were found by us on specimens of *Fenestella* collected in Russia by Condra in 1937.

Bolkhovitinova (1915) describes and illustrates thick, solid, striated radicles on *Fenestella novlinsky* from the upper Carboniferous (Uralian) at Novlinskaia village on Pakhra River, Moscow district. They are attached to the reverse, which faces outside a basketlike zoarium, like those in American *Fenestella*.

Cumings seems to be the only American who published an opinion on the utility of the various appendages in Fenestrata, remarking that the Salem limestone forms, "when perfect, as at Bedford, abound in strong brace roots, anchoring spines, and all the paraphernalia indicative of agitation of the water" (1906, p. 1200).

The development of barbed and nonbarbed appendages in many species of *Fenestella* is recorded in this paper, but their anatomy is not described in detail because the species from the Glass Mountains are silicified. The simple barbed appendages (Pl. 6, fig. 10; Pl. 17, figs. 4, 10) are attached to a few species of *Fenestella* from many horizons of the upper Mississippian, Pennsylvanian, and Permian of the Mid-Continent and the Rocky Mountains. Fragments of the barbed appendages are occasionally found in samples from wells drilled in rocks of these ages.

ZOARIAL GROWTH FORMS

Complete zoaria are seldom found because of their fragility, only a few genera being reinforced by crusts and supports (*Archimedes*, *Lyropora*, and others) or by superstructures (*Hemitrypa*, *Unitrypa*, and others). Yet by repeated collecting it is possible to obtain sufficiently large zoaria of nearly all kinds of bryozoans.

In the early stages the growth form of any zoarium is primarily, even exclusively, controlled by its inherited ontogeny. Thus, in *Fenestella* and related genera the initial growth form tends to be a more or less symmetrical inverted cone, as a consequence of the manner of budding upward and outward from a circle of zooecia around the initial cell (*see* Cumings, 1904). In the subsequent stages of development factors other than ontogeny play an increasingly effective role in shaping the zoarial growth form. There are abundant minute, cuplike initial zoaria in the collections at the Nebraska Geological Survey, but few large symmetrical inverted cones, cups, or funnels of full-grown zoaria. This fact seems to indicate preponderance of lopsided adult growth forms from an initially symmetrical cup; this may be caused by growth in a current, greater abundance of food on one side, interference from other growing zoaria, or other external causes. Evidently a slight advantage in growth on one side is apt to result in a gradually emphasized lopsided growth of a zoarium, as faster-growing zoarial branches spread laterally by repeated bifurcation and interfere with the growth of neighboring, slower-growing branches. Perhaps still greater influence on lopsided growth is the ability of the more numerous polypides on the longer branches to suck more water charged with food, leaving less available to the fewer polypides on the slower-growing branches.

It seems reasonable to conclude that funnel-shaped adult zoaria are most primitive, and may be designated as zoarial group I.

In definition of *Fenestella* attempts were made to include mode of occurrence of zooecial apertures in a funnel-shaped zoarium, whether on its outer or inner surfaces (Cumings, 1904, p. 66). Cumings claims that "the zooecia of *Fenestella* always lie on the outer surface of the cone," and where funnel-shaped zoaria of *Fenestella* have apertures on the inner side, they are believed to result from turning inside out because of reversal of curvature at an early growth. According to this author the apertures in *Polypora* are "always on the inner surface of the cone" (p. 72).

However, we find about as many inner as outer dispositions of zooecial apertures in the zoarial cones of *Fenestella* and in the zoaria of *Polypora* and *Hemitrypa.*

When the initial radially symmetrical growth about a disc is restricted to a single point and direction, bilaterally symmetrical zoaria are produced, which may be classified as group II. They are usually more or less foliate, and commonly regularly or irregularly curved. These growth forms are most common among the Permian zoaria examined, and, therefore, need particular attention. The direction and bifurcation of branches and the spacing of dissepiments have a more or less definite relationship to the position they occupy in foliate zoaria and also in the compound zoaria that are apparently derived from foliate ones. In many bilaterally symmetrical growth forms there is marked tendency for the branches to curve to the left or to the right on left and right side respectively.

The following principal growth forms can be recognized in foliate group II:

(1) Fan-shaped. Semicircular, regularly expanding, with branches straight, regularly radiating from a point in an initial disc.

(2) Leaflike. Longer than wide, with straight and subparallel branches in middle part, curving outward in lateral parts.

(3) Mushroomlike. With a narrower leaflike proximal part that spreads distally into a mushroomlike expansion. Branches straight and subparallel in proximal part, gradually curving to the left and right in distal part.

Foliate zoaria that are complicated by curving, plication, and fusion, may be classified as group III, where the following zoaria may be listed:

(4) Spirally curved or coiled zoarium without central axis (*F. archimediformis* n. sp.). When a zoarium is spirally coiled and its shaft is encrusted the growth form is referred to genus *Archimedes*.

(5) Conically curved foliate form. Lateral edges are fused to make a funnel, with or without opening at its base.[9]

(6) Cylindrically curved foliate form. Lateral edges are fused to make an elongated basket with a circular to oval cross section. The basket tends to be closed in distal part by fusing of distal edges.[9] This type tends to develop bifurcation of the whole cylindrical form: *Fenestella cylindrica* n. sp., and *Bicorbis arizonica* (Condra and Elias).

(7) Intense plication of zoarium parallel to its main axis results in a shrublike form, which may be complicated by lateral outgrowths (*Fenestella plicata* n. sp.).

(8) A large fan-shaped growth form may be divided into several large festoons, each bilaterally symmetrical and coalescing along its lateral edges with neighboring festoons, as *F. stocktonensis* var. *magnolobata*, n. var.

(9) Two (or more?) bilaterally symmetrical growth forms of the same type may grow parallel or subparallel one above the other, with both zooecial apertures on the same side, as *F. parviuscula* var. *libellus*.

(10) Two bilaterally symmetrical zoaria may grow back to back and be fused along the margins into a flattened bag, as *F.* (*Loculiporina*) *muscus*, n. sp.

GROWTH FORMS IN RELATION TO ENVIRONMENTS

Because no close relative of *Fenestella* is known among living Bryozoa, its ecologic relationships can be only broadly conceived through consideration of its association with other organisms and comparison with living bryozoans that have similar growth forms. The latter is based on an assumption that similar growth forms result among unrelated Bryozoa in the same physical environments. This is not an entirely safe premise but has some collaborative value when combined with such evidence as association with other marine organisms.

Elias concluded (1937a) that early Permian (Big Blue) bryozoans lived in association with brachiopods and horn corals on the bottom of shallow seas 60–160 feet deep; below these depths lived mostly fusulines, a few thinshelled brachiopods, and calcareous algae. The Fenestrata of the Permian in the Glass Mountains lived in about the same association, and separate from fusulines. In only a few rocks do bryozoans occur with fusulines. In view of its rarity such association may be considered abnormal or incidental, probably indicating border depths common to bryozoan and fusulinid associations.

On account of the wave action it seems unlikely that the fragile calcareous *Fenestella* could endure a depth as shallow as the zone of tides or slightly deeper. Stach (1935; 1936), who studied the ecology of Bryozoa off the shores of Australia, observed that *Fenestella*-like fenestrate zoaria of *Petralia undata* Livingstone live attached by a "filamentous union of numerous radicles to the sandy bottom in fairly deep water affected by currents," (not stating how deep, but undoubtedly meaning the deeper part of the sublithoral zone). Other fenestrate forms characterized by more rigid

[9] In growth forms 5 and 6 fusion of the lateral edges is clearly recognized by angular contact of the branches on both sides of the suture line of fusion.

zoaria, such as Reteporidae, "heavily calcified and secondarily strengthened by successive layers of avicularia developed on the basal" live in regions where wave action and currents are strong (Stach, 1936, p. 62). Stach places the large bilaminate fenestrate *Adeona* in the same ecological group with Reteporidae, though its rigidity is due to heavy secondary calcification of the frontal wall. This is the type most prolific in sublittoral region. Stach generally considers (1936, p. 646) that the "zoarial variation" of Cheilostomata living off the shores of Australia is "a purely mechanical effect due to the varying force of the movements of sea water as waves and currents in different habitats." The principle is exemplified by recent *Caleschara denticulata* (MacGillivray), which occurs in the form of "flattened, bilaminate, foliaceous zoaria in shallow water, but at greater depths it assumes a slender erect bilaminate condition, which can only be correlated with its immunity from wave and strong current action."

Vaughan and Wells (1943, p. 60–62, Fig. 24) describe and illustrate similar effects of water movements on the growth form of some fragile reef corals: *Porites porites* (Pallas), *Diplosolen clivosa* (Ellis and Solander), and others. They observed that only those corals that have strong attachment and massive, encrusting, or palmate growth form can live near the surface on the exposed seaward side of the reef where "the surf is strong and storm waves break." The corals with strong skeletons also extend into quiet waters, while corals with fragile skeletons occur exclusively "in shallow quiet waters of lagoons or outside lagoons in depths between 33 and 40 meters" (100 to 140 feet). The two kinds commonly are found "along the sides of channels through which water flows into and out of lagoons."

These observations by Stach (1935; 1936) and by Vaughan and Wells (1943), made on sessil colonial organisms unrelated to fenestrate Bryozoa that live in a similar off-shore environments in shallow semitropical seas, are in agreement as to the effectiveness of water disturbances, waves, and currents on growth forms. Because about the same physical conditions existed in late-Paleozoic seas where Fenestrata grew, their growth forms must have been similarly controlled. Thus it seems that only encrusting fistuliporoid forms where not associated with fenestrate and delicate ramose forms can be considered evidence of littoral or shallow sublittoral zones, while delicate ramose and fenestrate forms must have lived at a depth beyond the direct effect of waves and strong currents, below 80–100 feet.

The combined evidence indicates that most Fenestrata probably inhabited quiet waters or lived at depths from 80 to 160 feet in waters with moderately strong currents.

RELATION OF APPENDAGES TO GROWTH FORMS

Many examples show that crusts and appendages on the reverse of a zoarium have little effect on the character of zoarial growth form, although apparently they add to its rigidity, durability, and anchorage. The crusts are either more or less evenly distributed over a zoarium, as in *Fenestella compactilis* (Pl. 12, fig. 1), *F. kingi* n. sp. (Pl. 3, fig. 6), *F. parviscula* var. *libellus* n. var. (Pl. 22, figs. 4, 6), or are variously located—for instance, arranged along selective adjacent dissepiments and across or diagonally over the branches that they connect as, in *Fenestella stocktonensis* var. *magnolobata* n. var. (Pl. 7, fig. 4). Pillars are connected with zoarium by a spreading to palmate basal part, the margins of which thin out quickly. An upright may ascend from one short rootlike pedestal prostrate on a zoarial branch (Pl. 13, fig. 4), but in most the base is divided into several short rootlets that spread out palmately (Pl. 18, figs. 6, 7) and connect it to the reverse of the underlying branches and dissepiments. Uprights may be scattered, rising individually at any part of the zoarium (*F. stocktonensis* var. *magnolobata*), but usually concentrate in groups, commonly near the base of a zoarium (*F. binodata* var. *leonardensis*, Pl. 11, fig. 2; *F. compactilis*, Pl. 12, figs. 1, 6), or in an irregular row (*F. binodata* var. *wordensis*, Pl. 11, fig. 7; *F. clinospina* Pl. 13, figs. 1, 5). Localized encrustations may be extremely thick and may be accompanied by numerous crowded ascending pillars (*F. parviscula* var. *libellus*, Pl. 22).

The effect of the uprights on zoaria, from the reverse of which they usually rise is nil, and there is no evidence that individual zooecia from the back of which they ascend differ from others in the zoarium. Some excess crust at the base of pillars tends to seal adjacent fenestrules and even encroach upon the obverse of branches, but only a few zooecial apertures nearest to uprights become fully sealed. Most pillars are straight and perpendicular to the surface of attachment, even when they are distally curved. However, where they grow near an edge of a zoarium, their orientation is no longer perpendicular to its surface but is generally in its plane, or at an acute angle to it (*F. rogersi*, n. sp., Pl. 4, figs. 9, 11).

The tendency to grow straight and perpendicular to the surface of attachment is common to all pillars and, therefore, seems important to the explanation of their nature.

Only a few pillars found were growing from the obverse of a zoarium. On one form observed a dozen barbed pillars rise from the bottom of a funnel-shaped zoarium, its obverse faces inward (*F. cornuta*, Pl. 17, figs. 4, 9). The bases of these pillars are subperpendicular to the obverse (Pl. 17, fig. 9, left), but their distal parts assume varied orientation achieved partly by curving. It appears that they were forced to do so because of crowding and in order not to interfere with each other's growth. The acuminate tips of most are free, but a few close to the distal part of the zoarium are connected to it by thin links or proliferations. Such are the tips in the only pillar in the group that has two lateral branches (Pl. 17, fig. 10), as if for the purpose of such attachment.

A series of short perpendicular pillars connect the reverse of the upper-floor expanse and the obverse of the lower-floor expanse in *F. parviuscula* var. *libellus* n. var. (Pl. 22, figs. 3, 5). Among the thick and smoothly surfaced pillars of the group, two are much thinner and armed with reverted hooks. In contrast with the perpendicular orientation of others these pillars are oriented diagonally in their distal part, although their bases apparently are nearly perpendicular to the reverse of the upper-floor expanse (Pl. 22, fig. 5). The acuminate tip of one slender pillar is attached to the obverse of the opposite lower-floor by a slender link or proliferation, while a similarly acuminated tip of another remains free and protrudes through its fenestrules (Pl. 22, fig. 6).

In a similar prolific development of pillars connecting upper- and lower-floor expanses in *F. archimediformis* (Pl. 19, figs. 5–9) there is no sharp distinction between the thinner and thicker pillars that rise from the reverse of the upper-floor expanse;

some of these pillars have irregularly spaced branches while others branch only near the apex into several subequal slender branchlings just in front of the delicate contact with the obverse of the first-floor expanse (Pl. 19, figs. 8, 9). A few random reverted hooks occur near the tips on some pillars.

There seems to be some relationship between prolific development of encrusting tissue on the obverse of a zoarium and coiling of the zoarial expanse, which results in more than one parallel floor. Besides the well-known spiral coiling of *Archimedes* there is a similar spiral coiling in *Fenestella archimediformis* n. sp., but it lacks development of the screwlike shaft in the axis of coiling. Coiling may also result in a single funnel, such as *F. cornuta*, n. sp. In the holotype of *F. archimediformis* (Pl. 18, figs. 1–3) there is only a slightly thicker crust, and several pillars rise along the edges of the central opening, where, if it were an *Archimedes*, a screw-shaped shaft should have formed.

The marginal development of the encrusting tissue on the obverse could be responsible for budding of adjacent polypides along a spiral surface instead of a plane; however, perhaps the encrusting tissue tended to grow particularly intense where the zoarium coiled spirally. Condra and Elias (1944) suggested that in *Archimedes* coiling is caused by zoarial growth in a whirlpool created by the divergence of the ordinary current that brings food to the zoarium; by concerted action of polypides, the current divergence is caused by localized algal growth along lateral edges of the growing zoarium.

Ordinarily, the appendages, here called pillars, on *Fenestella* and related Paleozoic genera are explained as structures developed by the zoaria for anchoring and for better resistance to waves and currents. Although there is hardly any doubt that encrustations do strengthen zoaria and that at least some pillars are attached to the substratum, serving as a brace against destructive physical forces, it does not follow that these structures were developed by bryozoan colonies alone. It seems that their development can be reasonably considered only in the light of adaptation to environment perfected through natural selection. Observation of distribution of encrustations, pillars, and other external structures on zoaria does not suggest purposefulness. They develop haphazardly, and their service in anchorage and reinforcement is apparently accomplished in irregular hit or miss manner. For instance, they are usually absent where a zoarium seems particularly weak and commonly develop densely where no reinforcement seems needed, or where need is far less than that provided by the appendages developed (*see F. parviuscula* var. *libellus*, and *F. cornuta*). If the pillars were organisms *per se* attached to these Bryozoa or if their growth was induced by symbiotic algae, their casual development would be easily explained while their help in anchorage and reinforcement would be as effective as if it were developed by the bryozoans.

It appears that crusts and appendages are important to the coherence of the reef-building bryozoan growth forms.

FENESTRATA AS REEF BUILDERS

Bryozoan reefs are known to occur from Silurian (possibly Ordovician) to late Tertiary age, but no recent bryozoan reefs are known.

Russian scientists recently found that the massive knolls or "shikhany" in the west central Urals were built principally by fenestrate and ramose Bryozoa, which provide the fundamental intricate framework to which other adnate organisms are attached and within which debris settles.

Massive reefs are common in the Leonard, Word, and Capitan, but the scarcity of identifiable fossils prohibits a direct conclusion as to degree of responsibility of the individual builders. However, the possibility that bryozoans played an important role must be considered, especially in view of the fact that they build the framework in Russian oil-producing massive mound reefs. Abundant and well-preserved bryozoans were obtained from some limestones in the Wolfcamp, the Leonard, and the Word, and many of their growth forms are unbroken and build an intricate framework (Pl. 23, fig. 12) similar to that in the massive reefs of Russia. Encrustations and appendages also occur in American and Russian Carboniferous and Permian reef-building bryozoans.

MINUTE ALGAE IN THE REEF-BUILDING FENESTRATA

The role which algae play in the origin and durability of modern coral reefs is an additional, though indirect, argument for the presence of some kind of algae in those bryozoans which built Paleozoic reefs. Mere presence of sclerenchymatous calcareous encrustation observed in Adeonae, Reteporidae, Horneridae, and similar massive living Cheilostomata and Cyclostomata does not result in their building of gregarious reeflike concentrations. Their small disconnected colonies live on the sea floor and spread as mat-like veneer only in some shallow banks—for instance in the "secca's" (banks) of the Bay of Naples (Walther, 1910). Silén (1944, p. 454) claims that colonies of living bryozoans never contact and connect. Colonies of Fenestrata do connect and thus apparently produce coherence needed for reef building. If the Fenestrata were self encrusting their ability to build reefs should not exceed that of similarly encrusted living bryozoans. Therefore, it seems probable that some algae were instrumental in the reef building. The presence of Zooxanthellae or similar minute unicellular algae is conceivable because Zooxanthellae are known to inhabit zooecia of some living marine Bryozoa (Oltmanns, 1923, p. 511). Habitual invasion of Fenestrata by the same or similar algae could have been beneficial and enhanced their colonial habit, as it is believed to do for the modern reef-building colonial corals. Because of the small size and the softness of the unicellular algae, one could hardly expect to find traces of their remains in the fossil Bryozoa (they have not been observed in the fossil reef corals), and only their effect on the vigor, extensive branching, and possibly greater calcification would be observed. This is all that is observed. Furthermore, such algae could have stimulated the growth of localized encrustations and appendages, such as the encrustation around the shaft of coiling in *Archimedes*, the lateral branches in *Lyropora*, and the pillars in these and other genera of Fenestrata. Zooxanthellae or similar small symbiotic algae could easily enter zooecia. Borg and other naturalists found amoebocytes floating in albuminous fluid of the zooecial chambers, caelomic cavity, and pseudopores of various living Cyclostomata (Borg, 1926, p. 228–229, 252; Pl. 2, fig. 10); it seems possible that the same openings, could also be invaded by symbiotic algae.

VII. TAXONOMIC CONSIDERATIONS

PROXIMAL OR EARLY AND DISTAL OR LATE VERSUS YOUNG AND OLD STAGES OF GROWTH

Customarily, the concepts of (1) the order in development of parts of the zoarium and (2) age of its parts (young, mature, senile) are taken to be synonymous. Hence, an early or proximal stage of a zoarium is spoken of as old, and the distal or later stages as young. However, some specimens of fossil Bryozoa represent early stages of zoaria that did not develop to maturity; therefore, these zoaria could and should be spoken of as young, although they represent an early stage of a normal, complete zoarium.

In the living calcareous Bryozoa the calcification progresses with age. Zooecial walls are chitinous at first, but almost immediately primary calcification begins. Then follows secondary calcification, resulting in an additional thickness of wall and in some external ornamentation of the zooecia and the zoarium. The progress of calcification with age should be applicable to the calcareous Paleozoic Bryozoa; yet the zoaria of most, if not all, show no appreciable difference in thickness from the initial to the most distal parts. In some zoaria the basal part attached to substratum appears more massive than the zoarial expanse above. However, in Fenestrata this thickening is largely the result of fusing of the crowded initial zoarial branches. Although Cumings (1904, p. 59) states that the senile stage in Bryozoa is marked "frequently by profuse deposits of secondary sclerenchyma, as well as by other more or less extensive modifications affecting the basal portion of the zoarium", he describes and illustrates considerable development of this sclerenchyma in the early stages of zoaria that never developed into adult colonies (1904, Figs. 47–54; 71–77). Our comparison of numerous initial parts of *Thamniscus* from the lower Permian of Nebraska with variously developed adult stages showed no difference in the thickness of the branches. The gradual thickening of the calcified skeleton in some living Bryozoa has influenced recognition of similarly thickened zoaria of fenestellids as supposedly old or even senile. However, Vine and Simpson observe that the extraordinarily thick and camouflaged or deformed fossil zoaria and their basal parts are in fact partly overgrown by other organisms. Even if some additional encrustation has developed over the basal part in some zoaria, in others it occurs, on the contrary, on latest or distal parts. Such encrustation of distal parts of *Fenestella* is connected with the development of a spiral growth form, *Archimedes* (Condra and Elias, 1944). The parts of *Fenestella* on which *Archimedes* developed may become somewhat encrusted, apparently simultaneously with the development of the *Archimedes* screw (Condra and Elias, 1944, Pl. 10, fig. 2); ordinarily such bases are slightly encrusted or not encrusted (Condra and Elias, 1944, Pl. 5, fig. 3).

The majority of fossil Bryozoa are represented by mature or old zoaria, but it seems preferable to call their basal parts proximal or early, but not necessarily old, and the distal parts late, but not necessarily young.

The terms early or proximal and late or distal are used here for the parts of zoaria described.

STAGES IN THE DEVELOPMENT OF ZOARIA AND THEIR RECOGNITION IN ZOARIAL FRAGMENTS

Where the zoarium is complete or nearly so it is not difficult to recognize its growth stages from earliest to latest. However, it is difficult to assign to the stages the fragments which are most commonly collected. Most species of *Fenestella* named in the last 60 years are known from fragments, commonly from a single fragment. However, the concept of a species is well substantiated only when its complete growth form is known or satisfactorily restored from fragments. While knowledge of most species is not at this advanced stage, the complete and nearly complete zoaria show how their stages differ structurally and aid in the correct placement of fragments of incompletely known zoaria. Because certain features of a zoarium of *Fenestella* and related genera change more or less regularly with growth, it is important to correlate these changes with the stages of normal growth to facilitate the identification where only fragments of zoaria are available.

The stages of the colonial growth in *Fenestella* and related genera are (Fig. 5a–d):

(1) Phylastic[10] or embryonic, represented by primary zooecium or protecium.

(2) Nepiastic or earliest, represented by a primary disc and its folds developed from protecium (ancestrula), a circle or rosette of zooecia around it, and short, initial branches radiating from the circle.

Ulrich's genus "*Sphragiopora*" is the nepiastic stage of a fenestrate zoarium that Cumings (1904, footnote to p. 72) considers probably *Polypora*.

(3) Neanastic or early, represented by a lower or proximal part of a fan- or cone-shaped growth form—In this stage the divergence of the branches is pronounced; they bifurcate very frequently, so that only one or two dissepiments form between successive bifurcations, and every other or every third fenestrule is triangular instead of rectangular in outline.

(4) Ephebastic or late (full grown), represented by the largest part of an average zoarium—In this part the branches diverge slightly and bifurcate at greater intervals, allowing the development of many dissepiments between the points of bifurcation. However, pronounced lateral curving of groups of branches on both sides of the zoarium, which occurs at this stage, is accompanied by localized more closely spaced bifurcations.

(5) Gerontastic or latest, represented by the most distal part of an average zoarium—In this part the branches are commonly subparallel to parallel, and bifurcate extremely seldom, or not at all. Less vigorous growth is indicated by abrupt termination of some branches, above which the neighboring branches converge and continue to grow, and at nearly the same distance to each other as in the mature part of the zoarium; or are spaced narrower than there.

The approximate zoarial position of most fragments can be determined by these features, although some irregular growths occur. For instance, some rows of lateral branches bud spontaneously from a normal branch at a moderate to wide angle to the initial branch (Pl. 11, fig. 10; Pl. 18, fig. 5; Pl. 20, fig. 2). Such abrupt departure of a series of lateral branches is usually accompanied by a change in spacing of

---

[10] This and the following ontogenetic terms were introduced for the stages of zoarial growth by Cumings (1904).

dissepiments; this adds to the difficulty of recognizing species on the evidence of dissepimental spacing, which in most species is fairly constant. It seems reasonable to regard such local changes of spacing anomalous—an extreme case of a similar abrupt change in orientation of branches accompanied by increased frequency of bifurcation, occurring usually in the lateral parts of foliate zoaria. In the greater, middle part of the mature stage of this zoarial type branches are parallel and bifurcate at long intervals; on both sides of the middle part the branches curve outward intensely and bifurcate at short intervals. Zoaria of this type are particularly common among the late-Mississippian and early-Pennsylvanian species of *Fenestella* (*see* Condra and Elias, 1944, Pls. 13, 21, 35), and the foliate type of zoarium, although modified in form, persists into early and possibly even late Permian (Pl. 3, fig. 1; Pl. 9, fig. 6; Pl. 15, fig. 5).

VIII. TAXONOMY OF FENESTELLIDAE

GENERAL PRINCIPLES

In the historic development of the taxonomy of Fenestellidae and other Bryozoa various views have been expressed on the relative importance of zooecial versus zoarial characters. Prior to the extensive use of the microscope by paleontologists, the bryozoan classification was based on megascopic zoarial features; with the advance of microscopic study the fundamental importance of the microstructure of the zooecium became evident. Subsequently, advanced knowledge of the ontogenetic development of zoaria brought about the recognition of the importance of ontogeny in the major taxonomic subdivisions of Bryozoa. The structure of ovicells has been prominent in the taxonomy of living Bryozoa, but, because the development of ovicells in Fenestellidae is rare and because they are frequently only partially (bases only preserved) they have not been used in classification. Cumings (1904) attempted to use ontogenetic development for differentiation between *Fenestalla* and *Polypora* and some related genera, but it has not been generally accepted. The identification of these and other genera of Fenestellidae is still based primarily on the morphologic characters of branches in their full-grown zoaria.

Living Reteporae, not closely related to *Fenestella*, were originally established (as a broad genus *Retepora*) on account of their reticulate zoarial growth form, similar to that in *Fenestella* and related genera. However, as in Fenestellidae, the Reteporae as now recognized include not only the species that have the branches connected by the regularly developed dissepimentlike trabeculae, but also the species that have their branches connected through anastomosis, like the fossil *Phyllopora*, and others have branches free, like the fossil genera *Diploporaria* and *Thamniscus*. The difference in the manner in which the branches are connected is not given generic or subgeneric significance in living Reteporae and is used in the recognition of species; but in Fenestellidae such differences are used in generic differentiation. Other internal zooecial characters, such as the shape of chamber and the presence or absence of lower hemiseptum, are also used in recognition of species in *Fenestella* and related genera.

After detailed comparative study of the ontogeny of zoaria of some living and fossil bryozoa Cumings concludes (1904, p. 66) that "the only reliable criterion of a species is the entire zoarium." A rational taxonomic differentiation between these forms should be based on balanced study of both zooecial and zoarial features.

TAXONOMIC SIGNIFICANCE OF WALL STRUCTURE

While the study of the wall structure in the species of *Fenestella* and other genera is important, it has not been considered essential in taxonomic recognition of species. It seems that the Russian authors hold the opposite view, but we find that we are able to recognize species defined by Russians in American material without taking into consideration the finest details of wall structure. Wherever possible, however, they were taken into account.

An obstacle to the use of details of wall structure in the comparison of Russian

Permian Fenestellidae with the Fenestellidae from the Permian of the Glass Mountains is the silicification of the latter, which partly destroyed the original delicate structures and superposed inorganic details. However, other American specimens are calcareous and have their delicate structure wholly preserved. These are comparable in this respect to Russian fenestellids (Pl. 9, fig. 4).

Another obstacle to the comparison of Russian and American (Glass Mountains) material is the fact that while Shulga-Nesterenko and Trizna describe the Bryozoa exclusively, or almost exclusively, from thin sections prepared from cores of deep wells (where the fossils are not affected by weathering), we study and describe them chiefly and, in some cases, exclusively from material collected at the surface, where occasionally the details are affected by secondary silicification and/or weathering. In some material differential weathering of calcareous and silicified fossils clearly reveals their microstructure, the finer internal details standing out in bold relief (*see* Condra and Elias, 1944, Pl. 11, figs. 4–7).

The species of *Fenestella* here described are commonly illustrated not by thin sections, but by enlarged photographs of external views of the zoaria that show as much detail of the internal structure as is exposed by differential weathering. Thus they provide as much information as possible under these circumstances for comparison with the similar details described and illustrated from thin sections by Russian authors, including the shape of zooecial chamber, which has been proved (particularly by Russian authors) to be of primary importance in the recognition of species of *Fenestella.*

DIFFERENTIATION OF SPECIES IN *FENESTELLA*

Currently the features on which species of *Fenestella* are usually recognized are those that can be observed even in the small fragments. In view of the fact that usually only fragments of zoaria are available for study this practice is quite natural. However, many species of *Fenestella* named in the early paleontological studies were established on complete or nearly complete zoaria. Studies of microstructure of *Fenestella* and other fossil Bryozoa gradually developed and became standardized since the end of the last century. The species of *Fenestella* named earlier generally were based on megascopic characters of the zoaria and incomplete small morphological and anatomical details. Besides, often these microscopic features were described only in a general qualitative manner, or, where given their dimensions were not as accurate as now practiced. Remeasurement of the diagnostic features on the types of such species is necessary in order to bring their description to the present level of accuracy in paleontologic taxonomy. Restudy and remeasurement has been done on many well-known species from North America, Russia, Australia, and to less extent on some from other parts of the world. Revision of many species, particularly from England and western European countries, is still pending. Nekhoroshev (1926b; 1929; 1930) made a good start in this direction but did not illustrate the types and topotypes which he studied or restudied, and the early illustrations of some species of *Fenestella* and other genera are still the only ones published. Some diagnostic features can be measured on them, but, because these illustrations are commonly generalized sketches and the magnification if indicated is approximate, the value of such measurements for taxonomy is uncertain. They are useful only where corroborated by measurements given in the original descriptive text, or can be otherwise verified.

Revision of some of the British Paleozoic bryozoans has been undertaken by Elias on material lent by the University and the Kelvingrove Museum at Glasgow, Scotland. The first paper is devoted to the revision of *F. subantiqua* and related species from the Wenlock Silurian (Elias, 1956).

The method of recognition of species of fossil Bryozoa by illustration and mensuration of their finer morphological and anatomical details was developed chiefly in America, particularly by Ulrich, whose monograph on Paleozoic Bryozoa (1890) is a paleontological classic and a starting point for all modern works on these fossils. The methods employed by Ulrich have been followed and expanded by workers in the United States and other countries, particularly in Russia where fossil Bryozoa are now extensively and persistently used in detailed stratigraphic studies of surface and subsurface late-Paleozoic rocks.

Although Ulrich's concept of species and genera of Paleozoic Bryozoa is far superior biologically and practically (for recognition of taxonomic units on most material) to that held by the earlier students (Phillips, Lonsdale, D'Orbigny, Schlotheim, Goldfuss, Stuckenberg, McCoy, King, Hall, Simpson, and others), some of his concepts need revision and improvement. Although Ulrich did more than any of his contemporaries to show the importance of microstructure of the fossil bryozoa for their natural classification, he did not illustrate the inner structure of many species of *Fenestella* that he established. Because of this, for many years after the publication of Ulrich's monograph some American paleontologists continued to recognize these species and describe new ones on external mega- and microstructure without sectioning the fossils. Though this procedure is sufficient for recognition of many species of *Fenestella,* Russian paleontologists proved that a few forms similar externally differ internally, principally in shape and details of the zooecial chamber. Because the shape and other features of the zooecial chamber proved constant for species, and for natural groups of species of *Fenestella,* and because certain changes of the zooecial chamber have evolutionary significance, as pointed out by Nekhoroshev, the study of internal structure of species of *Fenestella* is now considered indispensable for differentiation and identification. Thus all species in which the character of the zooecial chamber has not been established must be studied in this respect and their taxonomy revised. Some species of *Fenestella* from the Mississippian of America were restudied and revised by Condra and Elias (1944), and some Pennsylvanian and Permian species of America are here being revised.

VARIABILITY OF MESHWORK

The superb sketches of bryozoan fragments published by Ulrich show accurately all the external details necessary for identification of species, but they do not reveal possible variability within complete zoaria. It is evident from his description and illustrations that he assumed that the characters of branches, dissepiments, and zooecia, particularly their number per given space, remain constant, or nearly constant, throughout a zoarium. Ulrich did distinguish between "younger" and "older," or "immature" and "mature" parts of a zoarium, but these were defined by the degree of development of encrusting tissue (the older part being more encrusted) and not by changes in disposition or spacing of the elements in its meshwork. Ulrich undoubtedly studied many larger fragments and even complete or nearly complete zoaria of some species and apparently became convinced of the constancy of the meshwork within a zoarium of a species. Our quantitative studies of variability of meshwork within some complete or nearly complete zoaria of *Fenestella* indicate that, although only slight and irregular variability exists in most species, considerable variability in others affects proximal and distal parts of a zoarium in about equal degree. In other species definite regular change in the spacing of branches and dissepiments more or less correlates with their position in a zoarium. In *Fenestella serratula* from the Warsaw (Condra and Elias, 1944, p. 73, Table 2) the coarse or more diffuse meshwork of its initial part grades to denser meshwork in a more distal (middle) part; in a still more distal part it is again as coarse as at its initial part. In *F. tenax* from the Chester (Condra and Elias, 1944, p. 100, Table 21), the fine meshwork of the initial part coarsens in its distal part. Where spacing of zooecia and dissepiments becomes closer, as in *F. tenax* (Condra and Elias, 1944, Table 21), the number of zooecia per fenestrule remains the same throughout the zoarium. But where the spacing of zooecia per given length remains more or less constant throughout the zoarium while fenestrules change from shorter to longer there are more zooecia in longer fenestrules. Regular change from shorter to longer fenestrules in the direction from initial to distal parts in a small zoarium of *Fenestella compressa* var. *elongata* is shown on a photograph by Cumings (1906, Pl. 38, fig. 2).

A different kind of variability in length of fenestrules, and corresponding variability in number of zooecia per fenestrule is here described for the zoaria of *Fenestella geminanoda*, *F. binodata*, and related late-Pennsylvanian and Permian forms; in them there is intermittent disposition of shorter and longer fenestrules throughout a zoarium, and, depending on length, the fenestrules contain one to exactly two, three, or four zooecia on each side.

Variability of meshwork in some species of *Fenestella* has been recognized by Ulrich, Shrubsole, Condra, Nekhoroshev, Nikiforova, and Shulga-Nesterenko, but only a few attempts were made to express it quantitatively (Nekhoroshev, 1926a, p. 790–794, 799; Nikiforova, 1938, p. 83–84; Condra and Elias, 1944). The variability of meshwork must be taken into account in the differentiation and recognition of species and, in order to make use of it in taxonomy, it must be expressed quantitatively. Only by the establishment of the character and degree of variability within a meshwork of a complete or nearly complete zoaria can the concepts of species, especially those established on small fragments, be advantageously revised and improved.

Because the thin section method used here in the study and differentiation of species is about as practiced by Nekhoroshev and his associates, we are in general agreement with the Russians on the concept of species of late-Paleozoic *Fenestella*. Ulrich, who was criticized as a species maker, actually introduced fewer species than is now found necessary to recognize. We do not agree with McFarland (1942) that the species of *Fenestella* described by Ulrich (1890) from the Chester should be lumped into five species, as we find significant differences in their internal structure (Condra and Elias, 1944).

SPACING OF BRANCHES AND DISSEPIMENTS

In considering variability of meshwork in species of *Fenestella* it is essential to differentiate between the nature of (1) the variability in the spacing of branches and (2) variability in the spacing of fenestrules. Unless the difference in these variabilities is recognized, it will be impossible to reconcile Shulga-Nesterenko's opinion (1941) that the spacing of branches in Permian species of *Fenestella* is more nearly stable than the spacing of fenestrules with our opinion that the spacing of branches is most variable. Apparently, the reason for these contradictory conclusions lies in the difference of understanding of the nature of this variability. There are some major irregular changes in length of fenestrules within a zoarium in some species of *Fenestella*, but some major changes are orderly and are characteristic of the species. Generally there is less orderliness in variability and major changes of spacing of branches in a zoarium. In a normally developing zoarium the branches are disposed in a plane or in a more or less regularly curved surface, a cone or cylinder. The branches grow within the confines of such geometric surfaces in a radiating manner, particularly at the initial part of a zoarium. The regularity of spacing of the branches is maintained by sporadic bifurcation. It appears that bifurcation can take place at any point in any of the branches, and there seems to be no reason why a branch bifurcates at a certain place and the other does not bifurcate. In some species the branches, which are destined to bifurcate, manifest their intention to do so, (figuratively speaking) by the gradual increase of the width, as they approach the point of bifurcation. In some species this increase in width is accompanied by the introduction of a third row of zooecia for a short and variable distance below the bifurcation; this phenomenon is of some diagnostic value in characteristics of species. However, in some an increase in width of branches and the introduction of a third row of zooecia do not result in subsequent bifurcation, and a branch returns to normal conditions (with two zooecial rows) directly above a short run with an abnormal 3-row conditions, as if it "changed its mind" about originally intended bifurcation (See *Fenestella veneris*, Nikiforova, 1938a, p. 85 fig. 48).

In many zoaria the points of bifurcation are scattered in such manner that spacing of branches remains about the same throughout its meshwork, but in some zoaria of the same species several branches bifurcate at the same or about the same distance from its initial part, resulting in nearly doubling the number of branches just beyond such bifurcation. The branches and the fenestrules between narrow as their number per given width is thus increased. However, in the distal parts of some zoaria, where branches are nearly parallel, there is a similar crowding of branches accompanied by narrowing which is not a result of excessive bifurcation. Hence, spacing of branches, although characteristic of a species, may be abnormal and deceptive when observed only on a few small zoarial fragments.

PRINCIPAL DIAGNOSTIC CHARACTERS

Spacing of dissepiments in a zoarium, which determines the length of fenestrules, especially when combined with spacing of zooecia in relation to dissepiments, is usually the most diagnostic character in the differentiation of species in *Fenestella*. The number of zooecial apertures per fenestrule is easily observable and is the principle feature which characterizes the coarseness of meshwork and thus places a species in one of the major groups within the genus. Relationship between the two characters can be expressed by stating that there are so many (2, 2½) zooecial apertures per fenestrule. The average number of zooecia per fenestrule can be calculated from a formula now customarily given for each species, in which the number of branches, fenestrules, zooecia, and carinal nodes per given space (10 and 5 mm) are entered.[11]

The number of zooecia per fenestrule is obtained by dividing the number of zooecia by the number of fenestrules per equal space. However, the figures in the formula do not always indicate whether the position of an aperture is stabilized in relation to a dissepiment and never indicate possible occurrence of shorter and longer fenestrules. Also these figures do not indicate whether the carinal nodes are simple or complex, and disposed in one or two rows. These characters are important in differentiation of species. In some species apertures are located on the bases of dissepiments, while in others these bases are free from apertures and the apertures are disposed symmetrically on both sides of a dissepimental base. Information on inner structure should be supplemented by a description of outline of the zooecial chamber at its different levels and by a statement as to whether hemisepta are developed: the lower hemiseptum is highly diagnostic as it occurs only in a few species. Of somewhat less diagnostic importance is the degree of diffusion of its meshwork; it can be expressed by stating whether the branches are wider or narrower than the fenestrules and by giving the width of dissepiments.

In most species apertures are circular and are separated by about the distance of their diameter. Their size is commonly proportional to the size of the zooecial chamber, but in a few species they are unusually small in comparison with the chamber and are spaced more than their diameter apart. Outline and ornamentation of apertures, where preserved, are diagnostic. Bifurcation of branches is typically symmetrical; however, in a few exceptions (*see* Pl. 11, figs. 3, 10, 11, 12) there is a marked unilateral branching, rare in Fenestellidae and generally characteristic of *Septopora* and other genera of Acanthocladiidae.

SUBGENERA OF *FENESTELLA*

From time to time some groups of species were removed from *Fenestella* and segregated into new genera. Thus *Semicoscinium* Prout, *Fenestrapora* Hall, *Isotrypa* Hall, *Loculipora* Hall, *Unitrypa* Hall, *Hemitrypa* Hall, and other genera were established, primarily on the evidence of various developments of the carina and its expansion into superstructure parallel to and above a meshwork more or less typical of *Fenestella*. In addition, most of these genera are characterized by modification of dissepiments into wide and short anastomotic connections between the branches. Somewhat similar groups of Permian species are here regarded as subgenera of *Fenestella*, and their polyphyletic nature is apparent.

[11] The numerical data on the new Permian species of *Fenestella* from Peru have not been given in conventional formulae by Newell, Chronic, and Roberts (1949; 1953). However, because Chronic tabulated his statistical measurements made on fragments of zoaria selected at random ("ten zoarial fragments have been selected without conscious bias . . . from each conspecific sample"), the numerical data for the formulae pertaining to his species have been calculated and are here entered for comparative purposes in the tables of the groups of species in the chapter on Systematic Description.

Thus new subgenus *Loculiporina* is here introduced in systematic description; and subgenera *Cervella* Chronic and *Minilia* Crockford are reviewed.

SUBGENUS *CERVELLA* (CHRONIC)

Chronic (*in* Newell, Chronic, and Roberts 1949) erected genus *Cervella* for the Permian species of *Fenestella* in which the apices of the carinal spines are extended laterally into repeatedly forking branches. Chronic's point of view is reminiscent of Simpson's attempt at grouping the species of *Fenestella* "upon the character of the carina," but the species whose carinal nodes have expanded summit, typified by the Devonian *Fenestella stellata* Hall, have not been separated by Simpson from the species having ordinary carinal nodes (Simpson's group β, 1897, p. 500–501; Pl. 2). The Permian species with expanded summits of their carinal nodes are not considered by us generically different from other species of *Fenestella*. Thus, when observing lunate lateral barlike expansions of the carinal nodes in the fenestellid meshwork of *Archimedes moorei* and *A. lunatus* from the Pitkin limestone of Arkansas (Condra and Elias, 1944, Tables 24, 26), we accepted these meshworks as mere variations in *Fenestella rectangularis* and *F. serratula*. Likewise, we intended to treat the similarly ornamented *Fenestella cornuta* n. sp. and *F. crusiformis* n. sp. as variations of *F. spinulosa* Condra and *F. nikiforovae* Shulga. This follows the well-established practice of taxonomic differentiation of fenestellids, but in view of some differences in the spacing of the elements in their meshwork, which seem correlated to stratigraphic position, they are entered in this taxonomic record as species, which conforms to Chronic's recognition of the closely related Permian forms as species.

The expanded summits of the carinal nodes are not developed over all parts of the zoaria, noted by Chronic and observed by us. Hence fragments of these zoaria that have no expansions, could not be assignable to the respective species of *Cervella* except through possible matching of other characters of the meshwork. Furthermore, it seems clear that the expansion of the summits of the nodes occurred in more than one phyletic lineage in Permian time, and even in Mississippian and Devonian times. Hence *Cervella* would have to be accepted as a polyphyletic genus, just as subgenus *Loculiporina*, which is introduced in this paper. Unless a thorough re-evaluation of taxonomic significance of developments of carina in *Fenestella* and related genera is undertaken, it seems that at the present *Cervella* may be provisionally accepted as a polyphyletic subgenus of *Fenestella*.

SUBGENUS *MINILIA* (CROCKFORD, EM. ELIAS AND CONDRA)

Miss Crockford (1944) introduced a new generic name *Minilia* for species of *Fenestella* with a double row of zigzagging nodes on the carina. She put in this taxonomic unit all species with a double row of nodes that were listed in a group "with double row of spines on carina" by Elias (1937b). However, for the generotype she selected her own species from the Permian of Australia: *Minilia duplaris* Crockford. Her generic diagnosis of *Minilia* is as follows (1944, p. 172): "Fenestrellinae in which the branches show two rows of alternating zooecia, one on each side of a slight median carina; nodes small, in two rows on the carina, placed so that one node is lateral to each zooecial aperture; zooecia sub-triangular; structure of the reverse surface as in

Fenestrellina." She lists in the genus the following species (p. 173): *F. geminanoda* Moore, *F. bispinulata* Moore, *F. binodata* Condra, *F. conradi* var. *compactilis* Condra, *F. bituberculata* Crockford, *F. perelegans* Waagen and Pichl (not Meek), *F. jabiensis* Waagen and Pichl (not Fredericks), *Minilia duplaris* Crockford, and *M. princeps* Crockford.

On the basis of her diagnosis of *Minilia* this genus differs from *Fenestella* (*Fenestrellina* Crockford), for which she also gives a diagnosis of her own, by three characters: (1) nodes arranged in two rows instead of one row as in *Fenestella*; (2) each of these nodes is lateral to each zooecial aparture; and (3) zooecial chamber is triangular instead of more variable shape as in *Fenestella*. However, she includes in the genus one of her species, *F. bituberculata*, in which according to her own sketch and description (1941, fig. 213, p. 507) "the spacing of nodes is very irregular." Thus the occurrence of nodes laterally to each aperture is not a constant generic character. Also triangularity of the zooecial chamber is not a constant character in the genus. Crockford observed it only on the genotype, and Waagen and Pichl (1885, Pl. 87, fig. 2b) show it in *F. jabiensis*. Many other species listed in the genus have differently shaped zooecial chamber; in fact, among the species with a double row of nodes described from Russia and America, zooecial chamber shows as much divergence in shape as that in the known species of *Fenestella* with a single row of nodes.

The difference remaining, therefore, is the presence of a double row of carinal nodes, compared with a single row of carinal nodes in most species of *Fenestella*, that distinguishes the genus *Minilia* from *Fenestella*. This distinction does not seem of sufficient value for erection of a genus separate from *Fenestella*, and it would be impossible to distinguish *Minilia* from *Fenestella* where the carinal nodes, commonly delicate, are not preserved. Furthermore, in some well-preserved zoaria the nodes are originally unequal in size, even to complete nondevelopment in parts of a zoarium. Also, according to Shulga-Nesterenko (1941, p. 49–51), in one of several varieties of *Fenestella virgosa* that normally has two rows of nodes there is only one row of nodes (var. *sparsituberculata*), and another variety has none (var. *atuberculata*). It seems therefore more logical to consider *Minilia* a subgenus of *Fenestella*, and in this sense the name may be usefully applied to those species that possess a double row of carinal nodes. The presence of a double row of carinal nodes is used here as one of the several principal features in segregation of species of genus *Fenestella* into groups, and the species with double rows of nodes are placed in groups VI, VII, VIII, and IX.

REJECTION OF GENUS *FENESTEPORA* FREDERICKS

This genus was introduced by Fredericks (1913) for Fenestellidae that have, besides two lateral rows of zooecia, an additional central row supposedly located upon a carina. *Fenestella jabiensis* Waagen and Pichl was first in the list of three species of *Fenestepora*. Bassler (1935, p. 111; 1953, p. 121) lists *Fenestepora* among the accepted genera of Bryozoa and indicates "*F. jabiensis* Frederiks, 1915, Russia" as the genero-type.

Likharev investigated the case of *Fenestepora* and makes the following comment (1926, p. 1012–1013):

"Presence of nodes upon a carina in some representatives of genus *Fenestella* was made a basis for segregation of a special genus (*Fenestrellina* d'Orbigny) by some authors, but the idea did not get general recognition (Hall, who at first admitted generic independence of *Fenestrellina*, later changed his opinion); G. Fredericks, who apparently was not aware of the history of the problem, suggested in 1913 a new subgeneric name *Fenestepora* for similar forms. In doing so apparently he based the suggestion on the circumstances that many authors described the said tubercles upon a carina (which Ulrich considers acanthoporae), as if they were zooecia. However, Fredericks seemingly did not see any difference between them and true zooecia, and, as a result, made erroneous conclusions about genetic relationships between various representatives of *Fenestellidae* (Fredericks, 1915, p. 47)".[12]

In a further investigation of the problem Miss Crockford concludes as follows, (1944, p. 173, footnote):

"In 1915 Fredericks (p. 47–48) described a new sub-genus of *Fenestella*, *Fenestepora*, with three species, *Fenestepora jabiensis* (Waagen and Pichl), *Fenestepora foraminosa* (Eichwald), and *Fenestepora retiformis* (Schlotheim). The species considered by Fredericks to be identical with *Fenestella jabiensis* Waagen and Pichl is a different form; *Fenestepora* is considered to be a distinct genus, and *Fenestepora jabiensis* Fredericks (not Waagen and Pichl) has been chosen as genotype by Bassler (1935).

"*Fenestepora* Fredericks is distinguished from *Fenestrellina* d'Orbigny by the presence of a row of small cellules (as distinct from nodes) on the carina of each branch."

We agree with Likharev that the genus *Fenestepora* was not based on the occurrence of a third, central row of zooecia on a carina of the fenestellids, but rather on a misconception of the nature of the carinal nodes created by the resemblance of depressions upon carina, left by broken or weathered-out nodes, to zooecial apertures. We also agree with Bassler and Crockford that *Fenestella jabiensis* Waagen and Pichl is not the same species as that which Fredericks identified with it on Russian material. Thus *Fenestepora* is rejected as a generic or subgeneric taxonomic unit. We agree with the placing of *F. jabiensis* Waagen and Pichl in subgenus *Minilia* Crockford, but not Fredericks' form from Russia, which he misidentified with this Indian species.

TENTATIVE DIVISION OF *FENESTELLA* INTO SMALLER GROUPS

Besides the formally introduced taxonomic subdivisions of *Fenestella*, considered here of subgeneric rank, further tentative segregation of its more than 400 species seems desirable.

It appears that the first attempt at such grouping of the species of *Fenestella sensu stricto* was made by Simpson (1895, p. 500) who divided *Fenestella* into seven groups "upon the character of the carina." This attitude was indeed consistent with Hall's separation of the numerous subgenera or genera from comprehensive *Fenestella* on the basis of the excessive development of the carina. Contrary to general acceptance of most taxonomic units originated by Hall, Simpson's suggestion for more detailed grouping of species of *Fenestella* on same basis, as initiated by Hall, has not been generally followed.

In 1937 Elias made an attempt to group Pennsylvanian and Permian species of *Fenestella* on a different basis, and for this purpose he selected as the most diagnostic features the number of zooecia per fenestrule and the number of rows of carinal nodes. Thus he established four provisional groups, indicated characteristic or typical species for each, and expressed belief in close biologic relationship between the members in each group.

Shulga-Nesterenko (1941, p. 44) and Trizna (1939, p. 103–111), apparently independently and without a review of Simpson or Elias' attempts, suggested a somewhat

[12] *Fenestrellina* misspelled as *Fenestellina* in Lichaver's discussion.

similar grouping for Permian species of *Fernestella*, which they call complexes, each characterized by a particular species, and considered them as provisionally established "phylogenetic rows" (Shulga-Nesterenko); however, Shulga-Nesterenko used, in part somewhat different morphological and anatomical features in the differentiation of the groups than those employed by Elias. Thus, she placed together in the same group (her no. 1) species with one and with two rows of carinal nodes, which are placed in different groups by Elias, and even in different genera (here accepted as subgenera) by Crockford (1944).

In 1949a and 1951 Shulga-Nesterenko further arranged the Carboniferous and Permian species of *Fenestella* (and *Polypora*) into 10 "phyletic branches" (lineages). The first 5 generally correspond to her "complexes" (1941) and to the groups here recognized: I, II, III, IV, and IX. She thinks (1949a, p. 297) that *F. veneris* phyletic branch perhaps developed from *F. tenax* Ulrich, but this would imply phyletic increase of zooecia from 2–2¼ to 3–4 per fenestrule, the change occurring between species *F. kaschirensis* and *F. podolskensis*. *F. kashirensis* (1949a, Pl. 3, fig. 7, holotype; 1951, Pl. 13, figs. 2, 4) may be easily admitted in the group of *F. tenax* Ulrich in which the number of zooecia per fenestrule is 2–2¼, and not 3 as entered in Shulga-Nesterenko's table 1949a, p. 298; but *F. podolskyensis* is sharply distinguished from both *F. tenax* and *F. kashirensis* by the differentiation of its fenestrules into shorter and longer, with 2 and 3 zooecia per fenestrule respectively, as seen in the right side of plate 13, figure 3 (Shulga-Nesterenko, 1951). Nearest this unusually sharp inequality of fenestrules is that in our group VIII of *Fenestella* (*Minilia*) *binodata* Condra, but in the species of this group carinal nodes are arranged in two rows instead of one row as in *F. podolskiensis*.

However, Shulga-Nesterenko found that two-row arrangement of carinal nodes evolved from one-row arrangement in the branch of *F. virgosa*, phyletically diverging from the ancestral nodes-in-one-row stock of *F. tschechurensis* Shulga from the Tschernyshinskii stage of the Lower Carboniferous (1949a, p. 297; 1951, p. 26), the change from one to two rows of nodes occurring between *F. luzhkensis*[13] from the Steshevskii stage of the "Middle Carboniferous" or C_2, and *F. praevirgosa* from the Gjelskii stage of the "Upper Carboniferous" or C_3. This conclusion gives indirect support to the idea of possible derivation of *F.* (*M.*) *binodata* Condra from Russian *F. podolskensis* Shulga, and indicates polyphyletic nature of nodes-in-two-row arrangement, hence of subgenus *Minilia*.

Use by Shulga-Nesterenko and her colleagues of names of various other American species necessitates further comments as follows:

Shulga-Nesterenko says (1951, p. 84) that the Asiatic form referred by Nikiforova in 1933 to *F. serratula* Ulrich has been subsequently differentiated in her manuscript as *F. serratula* var. *asiatica*. However, Shulga-Nesterenko's description and illustrations of *F. asiatica* (elevated by her to specific rank) are based on the material collected from Tarusskii horizon of Serpukhov stage of the Upper Tournaisian in European Russia, and Nikiforova's Asiatic material named var. *asiatica* remains without illustration. Judging by Shulga-Nesterenko's photograph (1951, Pl. 16, fig. 5) her var. *asiatica* is as close to *F. cumingsi* as Nekhoroshev's *F. serratula* (1926c, Pl. 20, fig. 2).

[13] Originally spelled (1949a, Table 1, facing p. 306) *F. lujkensis*, but at that time the species was *nomen nudum*.

All three forms have nearly the same meshwork formula, and the outline of zooecial chamber is pentagonal to subtriangular. Only the encrustation of the reverse of the branches in European specimen (Shulga-Nesterenko, 1951, fig. 33-A) is much thicker than in *F. cumingsi*; but judging by even thicker encrustation in the type of *F. compactilis* Condra, as compared with the other specimens of same species, the thickness of secondary sclerenchymatous encrustation in Fenestrata varies greatly within a species and has no taxonomic value.

Hence *Fenestella asiatica* (1951) should be considered junior synonym of *Fenestella cumingsi* Condra and Elias (1944), and the whole synonymy of *F. cumingsi* may be written thus:

Fenestella cumingsi Condra and Elias

1890. *Fenestella serratula*, "Chester examples." ULRICH, p. 544–545 (no illustrations given) (Not *F. serratula* Condra and Elias from the Chester, 1944, p. 73–75, Pl. 21, figs. 4, 5).
1926. *Fenestella serratula*, NEKHOROSHEV, Bull. Com. Géol., vol. 43, p. 1247–1248, Pl. 19, figs. 3, 4; Pl. 20, fig. 2
1933. *Fenestella serratula*, NIKIFOROVA, Trans. United Geol. and Prosp. Service of USSR, fasc. 207, p. 15. No illustration published, but considered identical with the above mentioned form by Nekhoroshev.
1951. *Fenestella serratula*, SHULGA-NESTERENKO, Trudy Paleont. Inst., tom 32, p. 82, Pl. 16, fig. 1
1951. "*Fenestella asiatica*, Nikiforova in lit." in SHULGA-NESTERENKO, p. 85–86, Fig. 33; Pl. 16, fig. 5

Somewhat wider spacing of the dissepiments and much wider spacing of carinal nodes in *F. asiatica* Shulga as compared with the other forms placed in this synonymy could justify retention of *asiatica* as advanced Waagen's mutation or transient of *F. cumingsi* (her *F. serratula* Pl. 16, fig. 1, from position in C_1 lower than her "*F. asiatica*"). However, slightly coarser meshwork of *asiatica* could be mere variation of the meshwork within the same zoarium, see variability of meshwork in *Fenestella cumingsi* Condra and Elias, 1944 p. 103, Table 23. Because Shulga-Nesterenko's published type of *F. asiatica* comes from Europe and it is not certain that Nikiforova's Asiatic material to which she applied manuscript name *asiatica* is identical with it (Nikiforova does not mention carinal nodes), it may be that Shulga-Nesterenko's name *asiatica*, will have to be applied to the European material only.

The somewhat tentatively differentiated (by Shulga-Nesterenko 1951, p. 92) Lower Carboniferous group of *Fenestella tulensis-F. karakubensis* includes *F. multispinosa* Ulrich repeatedly identified on Russian material; but here American *F. multispinosa* is placed in group III of *F. veneris*.

The species, as recognized on Russian material, is placed in Shulga-Nesterenko's new group *Fenestella praelimbata* Shulga-*F. vischerensis* Nikiforova. However, the form described by Shulga-Nesterenko as *F. limbata* (1951, p. 79–80, Pl. 15, fig. 4) is said to have a small node in the middle of the dissepiments, and the carina is low; Neither Foerste nor Ulrich (comments to Foerste's manuscript, *in* Foerste, 1887, p. 87) noticed nodose character of dissepiments, and Ulrich notes that the carina "is more prominent and distinct" than in *F. mimica* Ulrich of Illinois. Hence doubt may expressed as to identity with *F. limbata* of the form from Russia.

The species described by Shulga-Nesterenko as *Fenestella* cf. *regalis* Ulrich (1951, p. 112, Pl. 22, fig. 3) is much closer to British *F. arthritica* Phillips, as per its revision by Whidborne and its examination by Elias on the Scottish specimens from Hunterian

Museum of Glasgow University. Shulga-Nesterenko's species has from 4 to 5 zooecia per fenestrule, just as in *F. arthritica*, and only slightly fewer fenestrules (7 to 8); the fenestrules are subequal in length. The fenestrules in Ulrich's species are irregular in shape and length, and the species thus belongs to *Fenestrellina* d'Orbigny and not to *Fenestella* Lonsdale.

The further grouping of Permian and Pennsylvanian species of *Fenestella* here attempted is based on various diagnostic characteristics, some previously used by Elias and some by Shulga-Nesterenko. Shulga-Nesterenko proposed 7 provisional groups, but did not attempt their definition. Furthermore, she left most of the species described by her outside the admittedly provisional groups. We now attempt to place all Permian species here described, with many known previously from the Pennsylvanian, into 13 groups and give characteristics and range for each. This grouping expresses not only understanding of the phyletic relationships between the species, but also serves as a key in their practical recognition, thus taking the place of the various previously proposed artificial keys, the usefulness of which, however, is not denied.

The principal characters used in the differentiation of the proposed groups areas follows:

(1) Degree of coarseness of zoarial meshwork, particularly as expressed by the number of zooecia per fenestrule.

(2) Relationship of zooecial apertures to dissepiments, wherever it is stabilized.

(3) Structure of zooecial chamber, particularly the outline of its lower or basal part.

(4) Development of carinal nodes: in one or two rows.

(5) Coexistence of longer and shorter fenestrules, and manner in which they are disposed within a meshwork.

(6) Zoarial growth form, if more or less stabilized.

The 13 groups of *Fenestella*, here recognized may be conveniently classified in 3 sections, as follows:

A. groups with long fenestrules: 3½ to 5 zooecia per fenestrule and a single row of nodes;

B. groups with double row of nodes and long and short fenestrules, in some species intermittently regularly combined; and

C. groups with short fenestrules: 2 to 3½ zooecia per fenstrule, and a single row of nodes.

Besides the recognized 13 groups, representatives of which are known in Permian and Pennsylvania of America, additional groups could be established with equal propriety for the remaining species known from Russian Permian and from the Pennsylvanian, Mississippian, and still older rocks of America, Russia, and the rest of the world. But it would be somewhat premature to do this before a comprehensive revision of these forms is undertaken.

Group XIII, which has no representative species in the Permian of West Texas, is entered here to emphasize the fact that a number of fenestellid species have poorly developed or no carina. This is an important evidence in view of Shulga-Nesterenko's erroneous belief that the meshwork in *Archimedes* differs from that in *Fenestella* by the absence or poor development of carina.

To group XIII belongs *F. gratiosa* Moore and the related *F. nodograciosa* Chronic, neither belonging to *F. mimica* group, Chronic's opinion (Newell, Chronic, and Roberts, 1953, p. 112) notwithstanding.

KEY TO PENNSYLVANIAN-PERMIAN SECTIONS AND GROUPS OF *FENESTELLA*

A. Single row of nodes; long fenestrules:
- 3½ to 5 zooecia per fenestrule:
  - I. Chamber oblique oval....group *F. foraminosa*
  - II. Chamber pentagonal triangular....group *F. basloensis*
- 3 to 4 zooecia per fenestrule:
  - III. Chamber oblique oval....group *F. veneris*
- 2¼ to 3½ zooecia per fenestrule:
  - IV. Chamber rectangular pentagonal....group *F. lahuseni*
  - V. Chamber pentagonal triangular....group *F. retiformis*

B. With double row of zig-zagging nodes (subgenus *Minilia*):
- Apertures in relation to dissepiments unstabilized:
  - VI. From three to five zooecia per fenestrule....group *F. virgosa*
- Apertures stabilized, all bases of dissepiments being occupied by apertures:
  - VII. Variously intermittent long and short fenestrules: containing even number, 4, 3, and 2 zooecia per fenestrule....group *F. binodata*
- Short fenestrules with even number 2 zooecia per fenestrule throughout:
  - VIII. Branches narrower than fenestrules; chamber oblique oval......group *F. compactilis*
  - IX. Branches wider than fenestrules; chamber triangular at base to rhombic above group *F. plummerae*

C. Single row of nodes; short fenestrules:
- Apertures in relation to dissepiments unstabilized:
  - X. Cylindrical zoarium....group *F. cylindrica*
  - XI. Fan-shaped zoarium....group *F. mimica*
- Apertures stabilized, all bases of dissepiments occupied by apertures:
  - XII. Well-developed carina....group *F. spinulosa*
  - XIII. Poorly developed carina....group *F. elevatipora*[14]

LIST OF GROUPS OF *FENESTELLA* AND OF THEIR SPECIES

I. *Fenestella foraminosa* Eichwald (group 1, Shulga-Nesterenko, 1941)
F. foraminosa Eichwald and its varieties, *F. polyporoides* Condra, *F. kansasensis* Rogers, *F. varifenestrata* n. sp., *F. gaptankensis* n. sp., *F. austini* n. sp., and *F. petschorica* Shulga.

II. *Fenestella basloensis* Bassler (group 3, Shulga-Nesterenko, 1941)
F. basloensis Bassler and its varieties described by Shulga-Nesterenko, *F. licharevi* Shulga *F. quinquecella* Crockford, *F. schucherti* n. sp., probably also *F. bifida* Eichwald and *F. donaica* Lebedev, var. *major* Nikiforova (but not *F. donaica* Lebedev or its other varieties).

III. *Fenestella veneris* Fisher
F. veneris Fisher; *F. multispinosa* Ulrich, *F. multispinosa* var. *chesterensis* Condra and Elias, *F. stocktonensis* Condra and Elias, *F. hexagonalis* Rogers, *F. rossica* Shulga, and *F. (Loculiporina) pavonia* n. sp.

IV. *Fenestella lahuseni* Stuckenberg (group 5, Shulga-Nesterenko, 1941)
F. lahuseni Stuckenberg and varieties, *F. stuckenbergi* Nikiforova and varieties, and *F. kingi* n. sp.

V. *Fenestella retiformis* Schlotheim
F. retiformis Schlotheim, *F. retiformis* var. *tenuis* Trizna, *F. nodulosa* (Phillips), *F. nalivkini* n. sp., *F. strukovi* Trizna, *F. strukovi* var. *vidrioensis* n. var., *F. strukovi* var. *tenuiformis* n. var, *F. ornata* Shulga, *F. ornata* var. *propinqua* Shulga, *F. picchuensis* Chronic, *F. inornata* n. sp., and *F. pseudovirgosa* Nikiforova

[14] No species of this group is here described or reviewed.

VI. *Fenestella* (*Minilia*) *virgosa* Eichwald (group 6, Shulga-Nesterenko, 1941)
F. virgosa Eichwald, *F. virgosa* var. *sterlitamakensis* Nikiforova, *F. permiana* Stuckenberg, *F. virgosa* var. *minus* Shulga, *F. kukaensis* Bassler, *F. bituberculata* Crockford, and *F. amplia* Crockford

VII. *Fenestella* (*Minilia*) *binodata* Condra
F. binodata Condra and its varieties and *F. geminanoda* Moore.

VIII. *Fenestella* (*Minilia*) *compactilis* Condra
F. bispinulata Moore, *F. compactilis* Condra, *F. compactilis*, var. *plattsmouthensis* n. var., and *F. infranodosa* n. sp.

IX. *Fenestella* (*Minilia*) *plummerae* Moore (parts of Shulga-Nesterenko's group 4 and group 2)
F. plummerae Moore, *F. rhomboidea* Nikiforova, F. *rhomboidea* var. *podtscheremensis* Shulga, *F. clinospina* n. sp., *F. quadratopora* Shulga, *F. duplaris* Crockford, and *F. princeps* Crockford.

X. *Fenestella cylindrica* n. sp. (*Fenestella* with ramose zoarial basket)

XI. *Fenestella mimica* Ulrich
F. mimica Ulrich, *F. tenax* Ulrich, *F. permica* Shulga, *F. plicata* n. sp., and *F.* (*Loculiporina*) *muscus* n. sp.

XII. *Fenestella spinulosa* Condra
F. spinulosa Condra, *F. archimediformis* n. sp., *F. pectinis* Moore, *F. parviuscula* Bassler, *F. aspratilis* Bassler, *F. nikiforovae* Shulga, *F. pulcherrima* Shulga, *F. tschernovi* Shulga, and *F. shulgae,* n. sp.

XIII. *Fenestella elevatipora* Ulrich (none in the Permian of West Texas)
F. wortheni Ulrich, *F. elevatipora* Ulrich, *F. servillensis* Ulrich, *F. moorei* Sayre, and *F. gratiosa* Moore.

IX. SYSTEMATIC DESCRIPTION

Group I, **Fenestella foraminosa** Eichwald

F. foraminosa Eichwald and its varieties: **F. polyporoides** Condra, **F. kansasensis** Rogers, **F. gaptankensis** n. sp., **F. austini** n. sp., **F. petschorica,** and **varifenestrata** n. sp.

1941. Complex *Fenestella foraminosa* Eichwald, SHULGA-NESTERENKO, Paleont. U.S.S.R. v. 5, pt. 5, fasc. 1, p. 44 (*F. foraminosa* and its varieties)

This group comprises species with zoarial growth nearly flat or slightly curved, apparently fan-shaped (only fragments are known). Species have 3.5–5 zooecia per fenestrule; spacing of zooecia in relation to dissepiments not generally stabilized. Carina angular in cross section, made by junction of two more or less flat lateral slopes, and slight swelling or expansion at crest of carina. Carina ornamented by large nodes two to three times farther apart than adjacent zooecia, with small and densely spaced pimples in a single line on crest of carina between large nodes. Branches slightly to pronouncedly flexuous or zigzag; their interior divided by central vertical wall, nearly straight above, becoming flexuous below; lateral walls come out in featherlike fashion, inclined forward. Interior is divided into zooecia whose outline in horizontal and tangential sections is subpentagonal to more or less elliptical, with forwardly inclined long axis of ellipses and flexuous central line.

This group is most closely related to group *F. basloensis* Bassler: has same number of zooecia per fenestrule ($3\frac{1}{2}$–5), but fundamentally different type zooecial chamber and more nodes. Its chamber has pentagonal outline at higher level, changing to rounded triangular and even trapezoidal near base, as zooecia of two opposite rows interwedge deeply. The carina in the *F. basloensis* group is narrow but well developed, and bears subequally developed spines, ranging from equal number to half the number of zooecia in one row. *F. quinquecella* Crockford from the Upper Marine Series (classified as Permian) of Australia seems to belong to the *F. foraminosa* group rather than to the *F. basloensis* group, but the shape of its zooecial chamber is not known and the number of nodes not counted. *Fenestella kansasensis* var. *multituberculata* Shulga belongs to this group and not related to *F. kansasensis.*

Shulga-Nesterenko believes that *F. foraminosa* stock is a "biologic entity, that consists of mutations and varieties, which developed with some regularity in the course of a considerable stretch of time: Carboniferous-Permian" (Shulga-Nesterenko, 1941, p. 61). In Table 3 the known species of the group and their meshworks are listed in general stratigraphic order of occurrence, but except the undoubted earliest form *F. kansasensis* and the undoubted latest form *F. foraminosa* var. *grandissima,* all forms of the group indicate considerable variability of meshwork rather than a clear-cut evolutionary trend from finer to coarser mesh. The evolution of the group in the late Pennsylvanian (Virgil; Orenburgian) and the early Permian (Wolfcamp-Leonard; Sakmarian-Artinskian) was complicated perhaps by some ecologic influences on phenotypes that account for variability of meshwork formulae. In spite of this, and allowing for inexact age determination and correlation within the upper Pennsylvanian-lower Permian strata, it appears that in late Pennsylvanian *F. kansasensis* of the Missouri Series branched out into four stocks: one typified by *F. polyporoides* with nearly the same number of zooecia (17 per 5 mm) as the parent form; the second, typified by *F. foraminosa* with the number of zooecia reduced to 13–15 per 5 mm; the third typified by *F. austini*; and the fourth typified by *F. grandis* with 13–14 zooecia per 5 mm. *F. polyporoides* and *F. foraminosa* stocks are apparently more conservative than the other two, as they show only slight reduction of number of fenestrules and of zooecia in Permian representatives. From *F. gaptankensis,* which has occasional shorter fenestrules, apparently developed *F. varifenestrata* of the Upper Leonard with its intermittent longer and shorter fenestrules, reminiscent of similar phenomenon in the group *F. binodata*. *F. foraminosa* stock probably gave rise to a rapidly evolving *F. grandis*-*F. grandissima* evolutionary series, in which "specialization went on in the direction of increasing size of meshwork, and increasing

[15] The error is not in identification but in the use of a preoccupied, by Eichwald, name for a new species from the Devonian of Michigan.

TABLE 3.—*Species of the* Fenestella foraminosa *group*

Species	Principal measurements				Age and location
	Branches in 10 mm	Fenestrules in 10 mm	Zooecia in 5 mm	Nodes in 5 mm	
F. foraminosa var. *grandissima* Shulga	6.5–7	3.5	12.5	....	Usinskaia P_1^2, Urals, Russia.
F. foraminosa var. *grandis* Shulga	8.5	5–6	13–14	6	P_1^{1a} to P_1^2, Urals, Russia.
F. petschorica Shulga, (Elias and Condra)	11–12	7	16	?	Upper Leonard Series, West Texas.
F. petschorica Shulga	10–12	6.5–7	16–17.5	4	Artinskian P_1^{1a}, Urals, Russia.
F. varifenestrata n. sp.	12	10	16	7–8	Upper Leonard Series, West Texas
F. foraminosa Eichwald, (Nikiforova)	10–12	6.5–8	13–14	5.5	Upper or Lower Artinskian, Urals, Russia.
F. foraminosa Eichwald, (Elias and Condra)	8–9	7	15	3–4	Artinskian shale, Urals, Russia.
F. austini n. sp.	10.5–11	5.5–6	14	8	Wolfcamp Series, West Texas.
F. polyporoides Condra	11–13	7–8.5	17	5–6	Big Blue Series, Nebraska.
F. gaptankensis n. sp.	12	6.5–7	15–17	6–7	*Uddenites* zone, West Texas.
F. kansasensis Rogers	16	9	18	9–10	Missouri Series and Shawnee Series, Kansas.
F. kansasensis Rogers, (Condra)	16	9	17–18	6–10	Missouri Series and Virgil Series, Kansas.

width of branches and dissepiments" (Shulga-Nesterenko, 1941, p. 64). The growth in width of branches and dissepiments and in the expansion of the whole meshwork seems to be correlated with the considerable development and balanced distribution of dense encrustation over the zoarium. In contrast apparently the same kind of encrustation in American forms, such as *F. rogersi* and possibly *F. gaptankensis*, is localized on parts of the zoarium (Pl. 4, fig. 9–12). In these forms the dissepiments and the branches are narrow and the zooecial apertures unusually small, as if the zooecia were undernourished, and the encrusting tissue concentrates into localized spots from which arise stout pillars. No such appendages are reported on the Russian forms described by Nikiforova and Shulga-Nesterenko.

Fenestella foraminosa Eichwald

1860. *Fenestella foraminosa* EICHWALD, Lethaea Rossica, p. 363, Pl. 22, figs. 7a, b
1895. *Fenestella foraminosa* STUCKENBERG, Mém. Com. Géol., St. Petersburg, v. 10, fasc. 3, p. 145–146 (summary in German), Pl. 21, fig. 8
1938. *Fenestella foraminosa* NIKIFOROVA, Paleontology of U.S.S.R. v. 4, pt. 5, fasc. 1, p. 34, 73–75, 229–230 (summary in English), Figs. 33–35, Pl. 13
1939. *Fenestella foraminosa* SHULGA-NESTERENKO, Atlas of index fossil faunas of U.S.S.R., v. 6, p. 68, Pl. XI, fig. 2
1941. *Fenestella foraminosa* SHULGA-NESTERENKO, Paleontology of U.S.S.R. v. 5, pt. 5, fasc. 1, p. 13, 59–61, Figs. 12–14; Pl. 5, figs. 2, 3; Pl. 6, fig. 1; Table 1, opp. p. 52
not 1932. *Fenestella foraminosa* DEISS, Contrib. Mus. Paleont., Univ. Mich., v. 3, no. 13, p. 245 pl. 3, figs. 3, 4 (renamed *F. deissi*, Elias, 1950).

Types: Holotype in the museum of State University of Leningrad, specimen XXXIV/17; it was redescribed from two prepared thin sections by Nikiforova (1938, p. 73–74, Fig. 33). Topotypes from Stuckenberg's collection Nos. 877–878/305, in Central Geological Museum, Leningrad, provided an ample material for her redescription. Age of holotype C_3^S or C_3^i; now considered of Artinskian age.

Discussion: In redescribing the species Nikiforova (1938, p. 75) pointed out that it is nearest to *Fenestella polyporoides* Condra from Nebraska, the two species differing essentially only in the number of zooecia: 17–18 per 5 mm in America form and 13–14 in Russian form. Representatives of both American and Russian comprehensive species apparently are present in the Permian of Texas, while in the corresponding Big Blue Series of Nebraska only *F. polyporoides* is known.

Shulga-Nesterenko (1941, p. 59–64; 1936, p. 274–276) described not only *F. foraminosa* but also several varieties of this species from the lower (P_1^1 Inga and Sarga horizons) and higher (P_1^2 or Usinsk beds) Permian beds of the Urals and northeastern European Russia. *F. foraminosa* var. *pechorica* from P_1^{1a} is similar to American *F. polyporoides* with 16 to 17.5 zooecia per 5 mm, and seemingly differs from the American species only in its thick encrustation, which increases the width of the dissepiments and results in shorter, oval to nearly circular fenestrules. The American species has narrow, elongate rectangular fenestrules. Other forms described by Shulga-Nesterenko are *F. foraminosa* var. *grandis* from P_1^{1a} to P_1^2 and *F. foraminosa* var. *grandissima* from P_1^2, showing progressive evolutionary increase in coarseness of the meshwork, with the number of fenestrules decreasing correspondingly, 5–6, and later to 3–5 per 10 mm.

Fenestella polyporoides Condra

1902. *Fenestella polyporoides* CONDRA, Am. Geologist, v. 30, no. 6, p. 347, Pl. 22, figs. 6, 7
1903. *Fenestella polyporoides* CONDRA, Nebr. Geol. Survey, v. 2, pt. 1, p. 65–66, Pl. 10, figs. 8–10

Types: Types collected from Neva limestone at Roca, Nebraska, all medium-sized fragments of zoaria with the reverse exposed. For the holotype we now select specimen Nebr. 6–12–5–01; the other of the two types mentioned by Condra (1903, p. 66) is apparently lost. Specimens were also collected and identified by Condra (1903) from upper Shawnee beds of upper Pennsylvanian at Plattsmouth and Nehawka, Nebraska.

Description: Zooecial chamber much like that in *F. foraminosa*, with zigzag central line dividing two rows of elliptical chambers.

Thin calcareous veneer of sclerenchyma covers zoarium, but in most specimens slight weathering easily exposes grooved surface of the reverse; further weathering frequently exposes zooecial chambers. Moderately prominent carinal nodes distantly spaced; in most places very small pimples occupy intervals between them, and in many cover crests of ridges on the reverse of branches.

Meshwork formula: 11–13/7.5–8.5//17/5–6, remeasured on the type and topotypes from Neva limestone, 1 mile north of Roca, Nebraska.

Discussion: The species resembles *Polypora* by occasional addition of a third row of zooecia for a short distance below bifurcation, but was confidently placed in *Fenestella* by Condra (1903, p. 65). Its close resemblance to *Fenestella kansasensis* Rogers and *F. foraminosa* Eichwald, including the occasional development of the additional zooecial row for short distance below bifurcations, substantiates classification of *F. polyporoides* in genus *Fenestella* and in the group *F. foraminosa*.

Fenestella gaptankensis n. sp.

(Plate 4, figure 12)

Holotype: Nebr. Geol. Survey no. 501, Univ. Texas coll. T-88, *Uddenites* zone, Gaptank Series, Pennsylvanian, at Wolf Camp, Glass Mountains, Texas.

Description: Nearly flat fragment of fan-shaped zoarium, 17 mm long and 10 mm wide, having wider fenestrules in proximal than in distal parts, a result of nearly simultaneous bifurcation of several adjacent branches in proximal part. In spite of more crowded spacing distad, fenestrules remain about as wide as branches throughout fragment, with only slight tendency to become narrower. Branches bifurcate abruptly; no additional row of zooecia is added just below bifurcations, though branches widen slightly toward them. As branches widen, lateral slopes of the obverse become less steep, and zooecial apertures protruding through them assume more nearly horizontal, upward-facing position. Normally lateral sides are very steep, and zooecial apertures inclined to steep angle correspondingly. Carina made by junction of two lateral slopes, only slightly swelled at its crest, carries prominent nodes opposite dissepiments. Crest between nodes covered by small pimples, mostly destroyed by weathering. Dissepiments only half as wide as branches, much depressed on obverse. Fenestrules very narrow, about 3 times longer than wide. However, just above some points of bifurcation, dissepiments connecting two forking branches are spaced at about half normal distance, so there are only two zooecia on each side of shorter fenestrules. Elsewhere four to five zooecia in a fenestrule, spacing of zooecia in relation to dissepiments not stabilized. Branches generally straight, some slightly undulating, making adjacent fenestrules look slightly hexagonal, though much elongated.

Apertures, though poorly preserved, are circular, with solid peristomes; distance from peristome to peristome about equals their diameter. Zooecial chamber difficult to observe, but seemingly its shape is as should be for species in the *F. foraminosa* group. Reverse of zoarium largely unknown; specimen solidly fused by siliceous cement with coarse-grained sandstone. Finer details of ornamentation not well preserved, except dissepiments are clearly striate.

Meshwork formula: 12–17/6–7//15–17/6–7.

Discussion: The form is nearer to *F. polyporoides* than to *F. foraminosa* in the number of zooecia, while in the number of fenestrules it is intermediate between them. Crowding of branches in the distal part of the described specimen is somewhat unusual for a species in a group of *F. foraminosa,* but it seems rather an incidental result of simultaneous bifurcation of two neighboring branches. The crowding is accompanied by considerable thinning of the branches. The number of fenestrules and zooecia in *F. petschorica* Shulga-Nesterenko is practically identical to those in *F. gaptankensis,* but the Russian form has much wider dissepiments and correspondingly shorter, elliptical to almost circular fenestrules. Apparently this difference is due to the considerable development of the encrusting tissue in the Russian form, and *F. gaptankensis* could be considered identical with *F. petschorica* minus the crust.

Fenestella austini n. sp.

(Plate 4, figures 9–11)

Types: Several fragments obtained by dissolution in hydrochloric acid of limestone specimen from Wolfcamp Series, probably collected at Wolf Camp, Glass Mountains, Texas; largest fragment selected as holotype, Nebr. Geol. Survey No. 502. Named after Doctor Austin F. Rogers of Stanford University.

Description: Judging by large number of fragments with lateral curvature of branches to right and left complete zoarium has leaf- or mushroomlike growth form, probably 2 or 3 cm long and wide. Branches average narrower than fenestrules; dissepiments depressed, range from a third to nearly as wide as branches. Branches straight to zigzag, turning at points of bifurcation, and in few branches also at points of departure of dissepiments. Usually neighboring branches assume zigzagging where bifurcating one after another within short space. This results in subhexagonal fenestrules; elsewhere they are elongate subrectangular.

Zooecial apertures subcircular, small, about twice their diameter apart, two rows separated by wide, nearly flat carina, upon which develop numerous fine spines and a few stronger, tall, slightly forwardly inclined. Zooecial apertures usually protrude into fenestrules. From one to three zooecia usually added below points of bifurcation, making a third row.

The reverse of branches coarsely grooved, but locally overgrown by thin crust. From locally developed thicker crust arise perpendicular pillars, some with reverted barbs (Nebr. Geol. Survey 502a; Pl. 4, fig. 11). Outline of zooecial chamber subpentagonal, as seen through semitransparent crust covering the reverse.

Meshwork formula: 10.5–11/5.5–6//14–8, with 4 to 5.5 apertures per fenestrule.

Discussion: The species is apparently closely related to *F. foraminosa* and its varieties from the lower Permian of Russia. In common with these Russian forms are its general relationship of the spacing of zooecia to dissepiments, outline of zooecial chamber, scarce and strong nodes, and sporadic zigzagging of branches, with corresponding local change of rectangular to hexagonal outline of fenestrules. However, *F. austini* differs from the Russian forms by its insignificant carina, narrower branches and dissepiments, much smaller apertures, and their protrusion into the fenestrules; also by the form and distribution of the encrusting tissue. In the Russian forms the crust is thicker and apparently more or less evenly distributed over the reverse, adding much width to the dissepiments. In *F. austini* the crust develops on the reverse sporadically, and from it usually arise the pillars. *F. subvirgosa* Shulga from Tastuba horizon, Permian of Russia (1952, p. 32–33; Pl. 3, fig. 3), has almost the same meshwork (11/6//14–15) but differs in having wide carina with two rows of nodes.

Fenestella petschorica Shulga

(Plate 5, figures 1, 2)

1936. *Fenestella foraminosa* var. *petschoricus* Shulga-Nesterenko, Trudy, Poliarnaia Komissia. Akad. Nauk. Leningrad, p. 274–275; Pl. 3, fig. 1; Pl. 6, fig. 3; Figs. 10, 11
1941. *Fenestella foraminosa* var. *petschorica* Shulga-Nesterenko, Paleont. U.S.S.R., v. 5, pt. 5, fasc. 1, p. 13, 61–62; Pl. 6, figs. 2, 3; Figs. 15, 16

Types: Holotype in Moscovskii Pedagogicheskii Institut, no. 526, from Permian P_1^1, exposure No. 6, right, at Edjid-Kirta, Pechora River, Russia.

Single specimen from Leonard Series, plesiotype Nebr. Geol. Survey No. 503, was etched out at Peabody Museum, Yale University, from material collected by Dr. C. O. Dunbar from Leonard Series (probably upper part) at Word Ranch, Glass Mountains, Texas, and numbered 5443-6.

Description: Shulga-Nesterenko describes zoarium as regular meshwork, having wavy wide branches and wide dissepiments; zooecial chamber pentagonal to rectangular, lateral interzooecial walls inclined; apertures round; low carina carries a few large and many small beadlike tubercles; "capillary tubes fine; between them starlike tubercles, as seen in thin sections."

Meshwork formula: 10–12/6.5–7//16–17.5/5.5.

Single specimen from Texas is basal part of zoarium, with slightly wavy branches connected by extraordinarily wide dissepiments, averaging twice as wide as branches, and about as wide as fenestrules are long. Basal part heavily encrusted so that it forms a single thick basal pillar connected to substratum by a flangelike base. Obverse is considerably weathered, so that carina is completely gone and zooecial chambers exposed.

Meshwork formula: 11–12/7//15/?.

Discussion: The specimen is very close to the original *F. petschorica* from Russia, and seems to differ only by the slightly smaller number of zooecia per given space. But in this respect it is quite like the well-preserved Russian *F. petschorica*, as identified by us from the collection made by Condra in the Artinskian shale at Simsk Industrial Plants, Russia.

Fenestella varifenestrata n. sp.

(Plate 10, figures 1–4)

Type: Only one fragment obtained by etching of specimen from locality 119, upper part of Leonard Series, at Clay Slide, Glass Mountains, Texas. Type Nebr. Geol. Survey No. 504.

Description: Judging by rapid divergence of branches fragment belongs to proximal part of full-grown stage of fan-shaped zoarium. If closely related to *Fenestella modesta* Ulrich (1890, p. 55, Pl. 52, figs. 33a, 33b), which seems very probable, complete zoarium of *F. varifenestrata* was small. Most striking feature of species is considerable variability of fenestrules, hence specific name *varifenestrata*. Length of fenestrules varies almost in proportion 1 to 2 and shape is also variable, from ordinary oval to appreciably elongated, to rounded hexagonal and to wider than long. Slightly zigzagging branches, with wide angular diversion just above points of frequent bifurcation, combined with general diffuse meshwork and some irregularity in spacing of dissepiments are responsible for variability of fenestrules. Branches average only half as wide as fenestrules, dissepiments about as wide as branches. Occasionally dissepiments become wider than branches, but even so possess neither carina nor zooecial apertures. Carina narrow, sharp, and weak in comparison with stout, long, and distantly spaced nodes, which it connects. Apertures also rather distantly spaced, nearly twice their diameter apart. Dissepiments faintly striated, slightly depressed on obverse and reverse. Both branches and dissepiments encrusted on the reverse, the surface of encrustation coarsely granular. Outline of zooecial chamber unknown.

Meshwork formula: 12/10//16/7–8, with 2½–5½ zooecia per fenestrule.

Discussion: Similarity of the described form to *Fenestella modesta* Ulrich is striking, particularly the diffuse character of meshwork, rapid diversion of branches and their frequent bifurcation, and essentially same kind of variability of fenestrules. But the fenestrules in *F. modesta* are more nearly angular, obviously because of negligible amount or absence of encrusting tissue, which is thick in *F. varifenestrata*. It differs from the latter also by slightly smaller number of zooecia per fenestrule, from 2½ to 4½, and by much coarser meshwork. Meshwork formula in *F. modesta*: 17–20/12–14//20–21.

The new species is placed in the group of *Fenestella foraminosa* rather than *F. basloensis* or *F. veneris* because of its manner of bifurcation and the tendency of branches to zigzag, but the taxonomic assignment is somewhat arbitrary owing to lack of information on shape of zooecial chamber either in *F. varifenestrata* or in *F. modesta*, its apparent predecessor.

Group II, **Fenestella basloensis** Bassler

F. basloensis Bassler and its varieties described by Shulga and by Trizna, and **F. b.** var. **shaktauensis** n. var., **F. specifica** Shulga, **F. licharevi** Shulga, **F. quinquecella** Crockford, **F. schucherti** n. sp.; probably also **F. bifida** Eichwald and **F. donaica** Lebedev, var. **major** described by Nikiforova.

1941. Complex *Fenestella basloensis* SHULGA-NESTERENKO, Paleontology U.S.S.R., v. 5, pt. 5, fasc. 1, p. 44

Shulga-Nesterenko segregated this group with reservation that "some of these forms may belong perhaps to another, as yet unestablished phylogenetic group" (1941, p. 44).

TABLE 4.—*Species of* Fenestella basloensis *group*

Species	Principal measurements				Age and location
	Branches in 10 mm	Fenestrules in 10 mm	Zooecia in 5 mm	Nodes in 5 mm	
F. schucherti n. sp.	10	8	13–14	abt. 12–13	Word, West Texas
F. basloensis Bassler	14	8	16	12	Basleo, Timor
F. basloensis Shulga	13–14	7–9	16–17	11–16	P_1^1 and P_1^2 Urals, Russia
F. basloensis var. *shaktauensis* n. var.	11–12	7–9	15–16	9.5	P_1^1 Urals, Russia
F. quinquecella Crockford	14–15	7–8	abt. 16	7–16	Upper Marine Series, N. S. Wales
F. basloensis var. *lata* Shulga	10–5–11	8	16.5–17	7–8	P_1^1, Urals, Russia
F. basloensis var. *magna* Shulga	12–13	5.5–7	14.5–15.5	abt. 10	P_1^1, Urals, Russia
F. basloensis var. *speciosa* Shulga	12	7–8.75	14–15	7–8	P_1^1, Urals, Russia
F. basloensis var. *limatula* Trizna	16–18	9	14–15	12	P_1^1, Urals, Russia
F. specifica Shulga	12–13	7.5	13–14	6–7	P_1^1, Urals, Russia
F. licharevi Shulga	10.5–11.5	5.75–7	16–17	15	P_1^1, Urals, Russia
F. bifida Eichwald, (Nikiforova)	10–14	10–11	16–17	9 (?)	C_3^8 or C_3^1, Urals, Russia
F. donaica var. *major* Nikiforova	14–16	9–10	17–18	11	C_2^2, Donetz Basin, Russia

Group characterized by elongated fenestrules, with 3½–5 zooecia per fenestrule and sharply pentagonal to triangular and interwedging trapezoidal shape of zooecial chamber, and thus clearly differentiated from externally similar group of *Fenestella foraminosa*. Other distinctions are arrangement of spines in single row and spiniferous peristomes.

The group in its original scope (Shulga-Nesterenko, 1941), including the Australian species *F. quinquecella*, is exclusively early and medial Permian in age. However, it seems that Russian species *F. donaica* (Lebedev) var. *major* Nikiforova from lower horizon of Middle Carboniferous (Moscovian) of Donetz Basin and also *F. bifida* Eichwald from Upper Carboniferous (C_3^S or C_3^t) or Urals are its Russian Carboniferous predecessors from which the Permian forms of the group have descended.

Fenestella basloensis var. **shaktauensis** n. var.

(Plate 4, figure 2; Plate 6, figures 1–3)

1952. *Fenestella lata* SHULGA-NESTERENKO, (Sterlitamak horizon), Trudy Paleont. Inst. U.S.S.R., t. 37, p. 42, fig. 20; Pl. 5, fig. 1.

not 1941. *Fenestella basloensis* var. *lata* SHULGA-NESTERENKO, Paleont. U.S.S.R., v. 5, pt. 5, Permian, p. 106; Pl. 21, fig. 2.

Types: One fairly large and possibly nearly complete zoarium is designated holotype. Unfortunately, only its reverse is exposed, but two thin sections from proximal part reveal shape of zooecial chamber and character of the obverse. Holotype Nebr. Geol. Survey No. 505; paratype no. 505a. The specimens were collected by Condra from Shak-Tau massive limestone, probably reef, of Lower Permian age, U. S. S. R.

Description: Holotype 40 mm high, 45 mm wide; complete zoarium probably about 45 mm high, 80 mm wide, fan-shaped, radially plicated; branches generally straight, arching at lateral lower margins of fan to right and left (probably left side broken off), correspondingly. Branches average as wide as to slightly less than fenestrules. Dissepiments about as wide as branches, slightly depressed on the obverse and the reverse. Fenestrules elongate rectangular with rounded corners to elliptical in outline. Chamber sharply triangular at base and middle level, with zigzag central line changing from angular to sinusoid toward upper level of branch where zooecial chamber becomes elliptical in outline, then grades into circular aperture above distal part of ellipsis. Upper and lower hemisepta absent. Carina strong, with clearly visible central canal, carries conspicuous nodes in single row spaced at wider intervals than zooecia. Normally 4, but occasionally 3 and 5 zooecia per fenestrule; central line of dissepiments symmetrical between two nearest zooecial apertures. Occasionally third row of zooecia is added to normal two rows for short distance along branch, as observed also on *F. basloensis* by Shulga-Nesterenko (1941, p. 104, fig. 64).

Meshwork formula: 11–12/7–9//15–16/ about 10. Number of fenestrules per 10 mm is 8 in middle part of zoarium and from 7 to 9, in lateral parts.

Discussion: Shulga-Nesterenko identified var. *lata* Shulga (1941) as full-fledged species *F. lata* from borehole 13/21 of Kuzminovskii massive oil field in western Urals (1952, p. 42), but admitted that the latter has 15–16 zooecia per 5 mm instead of 16–17 in the type of var. *lata* from Tra-Tau (1941), and also wider spacing of branches. The meshwork formula of var. *shaktauensis* is the same as in "*F. lata*" from Kuzminovskii borehole, and is almost the same as given by Bassler for *F. basloensis* of the Basloe beds in the Permian of Timor, and the variety here described differs from it only in smaller number of nodes per 5 mm and wider spacing of branches; neither difference is taxonomically important. Of more importance is the shape of zooecial chamber in its upper part (Bassler, 1929, Pl. 16, fig. 8), which differs from that in variety *shaktauensis*, though apparently the outline of lower part of zooecial chamber is the same (triangular). Another difference may be the frequent occurrence of 5 zooecia per fenestrule in the form from Timor, as observed on the same thin section and on Pl. 16, fig. 5, while in the description (Bassler, 1929, p. 74) 4 zooecia are mentioned "for" each fenestrule. The form from Russia, which Shulga-Nesterenko identfied with *F. basloensis* (1941, p. 102), and the varieties of same also described by her (1941, p. 105–109) and by Trizna (1939, p. 108), are not as close to variety *shaktauensis* as Bassler's type. The new variety *shaktauensis* is named after Shak-Tau mountain, where it was collected.

The illustrated holotype is apparently the largest fragment of zoarium of *F. basloensis* described.

Fenestella schucherti n. sp.

(Plate 5, figures 3–6)

Types: Two silicified fragments obtained by etching brownish platy shaly limestone of Altuda member, Vidrio formation, basal Capitan, locality no. 50 in Del Norte Range south of James Ranch, Glass Mountains, Texas (R. E. King, 1930, p. 134; P. B. King, 1930, p. 70). Fragment representing early or proximal part of flat fan-shaped zoarium is selected as holotype, Nebr. Geol. Survey No. 506. Paratype represents slightly more distal part of same, Nebr. Geol. Survey no. 506a.

Description: Poorly preserved, nonsilicified fragments available indicate fan-shaped flat zoarium up to 5 or 6 cm wide and 3 or 4 cm long, with constant meshwork throughout. Prevalence of stabilized position of apertures at base of dissepiments is typical with 3 zooecia per fenestrule; shorter fenestrules with 2 or 2½ zooecia per fenestrule scattered among ordinary fenestrules; occasionally, just above bifurcation, some are slightly longer, with 3½–4 zooecia. Silicification of zoarium accompanied by profuse crystallization of magnetite in form of small octahedrons, dispersed at and near surface throughout zoarium.

Branches average slightly narrower than fenestrules; dissepiments half as wide as branches, depressed on the obverse and the reverse. Fenestrules usually elongate rectangular. Remnants of partly silicified secondary crust around some fenestrules indicate suboval outline when crust was intact and before specimen was etched out of the rock. Bifurcation is frequent in proximal part of the holotype, with two branches diverging abruptly and symmetrically above points of bifurcation. Carina prominent, raised considerably above apertures, carrying one row of low spines (not always preserved), slightly inclined distad, and as many as there are zooecia in a row. Outlines of zooecial chamber not easily observable as thin walls nearly destroyed in process of silicification. Where somewhat preserved, they cross branches at an angle, indicating triangular to interwedging type of zooecial chamber.

Reverse covered by uniform secondary crust over grooved surface of branches, characterized by profuse development of nodes, more prominent than carinal nodes of the obverse, arranged in one or more frequently two rows, some nodes slightly inclined distad.

Stumps of numerous columnar uprights rise upon the reverse, concentrating toward initial part of zoarium. To the obverse is attached a group of cups of an organism imitating *Aulopora*, apparently parasitic upon *Fenestella*, with different stages of growth represented: the youngest starts distinctly not from a zooecium but from a dissepiment; its base nearly filling fenestrule. Similar cuplike forms have been etched from the limestones of the Wolfcamp Series, and collected from the Upper Pennsylvanian in Nebraska; attached parasitically to obverse, commonly of *Polypora*, and less commonly of *Fenestella*; seldom to obverse of other fenestrate bryozoans. They seem to belong to a fungoid alga, to be described in separate paper.

Meshwork formula: 13–14/9.5–10//15–16/14–16.

Discussion: Disposition of carinal nodes in one row, evidence of triangularity of zooecial chamber, and some additional peculiarities place *F. schucherti* in the group of *F. basloensis*; it seems nearest to this species and its numerous varieties described from the Permian of Russia by Shulga-Nesterenko. It differs from the original *F. basloensis* of Timor by commonly having only 3 zooecia per fenestrule, while the latter has 4 or more. It differs from this species and all its numerous varieties by larger number of fenestrules per given space. The nearest to it in this respect is *F. basloensis* var. *compacta* Shulga, with 9–9½ fenestrules per 5 mm, but the latter variety differs from *F. schucherti* by a larger number of zooecia per space and per fenestrule, only half as many carinal nodes, much wider dissepiments, and more nearly pentagonal than triangular outline of the zooecial chamber.

An additional similarity of the new species to the varieties of *F. basloensis* from Russia (but not to its type from Timor) is profuse development of nodes on the reverse. *F. basloensis* from Timor has neither nodes nor secondary crust on the reverse, which possesses an ordinary grooved sculpture typical for the primary skeleton of *Fenestella*.

Group III, **Fenestella veneris** Fisher

F. veneris Fisher, **F. multispinosa** Ulrich, **F. pustulosa** Moore, **F. multispinosa** var. **chesterensis** Condra and Elias, **F. stocktonensis** Condra and Elias, **F. hexagonalis** Rogers, **F. rossica** Shulga, **F. (Loculiporina) pavonia** n. sp.

1944. Phyletic group *Fenestella multispinosa—F. stocktonensis* CONDRA AND ELIAS, 1944, p. 163

Group characterized by very large foliate and occasionally variously irregularly curved zoaria, whose narrow fenestrules have in average 3 to nearly 4 zooecia. Locally groups of fenestrules tend to be hexagonal. Outline of chamber characteristically pentagonal, but with lateral zooecial walls inclined forward to middle wall; in some species outline nearly elliptical, with long axes of ellipses distally inclined.

Group resembles that of *Fenestella foraminosa*: have same shape of chamber, about as many zooecia per fenestrule (from 3½ to 5 in *F. foraminosa* group), and general lack of stabilization of position of zooecia in relation to dissepiments. However, meshwork of *F. veneris* group much finer than in *F. foraminosa,* differing also by tendency toward much larger growth form.

The earliest species of the group is *F. veneris,* which is perhaps the most common *Fenestella* in the upper part of the Lower Carboniferous (Visean), middle Carboniferous (Moscovian), and lower part of Upper Carboniferous of Russia. *F. multispinosa* Ulrich of Warsaw, *F. multispinosa* var. *chesterensis* Condra and Elias of Chester, and *F. stocktonensis* Condra and Elias of the Oquirrh fm. (upper Des Moines) differ from *F. veneris* by more nearly universal tendency toward development of hexagonal fenestrules. The American *F. hexagonalis* Rogers from the upper Pennsylvanian (Topeka limestone, Topeka, Kansas) is rare, and was described from small fragments. It differs from *F. veneris* by the more conspicuous nodes on the obverse, presence of small and numerous nodes along the center of branches on the reverse, and the local development of nearly perfect hexagonal fenestrules.

In the Upper Carboniferous of Russia the group is represented by *F. rossica* Shulga (*F. exigua* var. *rossica,* Shulga-Nesterenko, 1936, p. 280). In Glass Mountains of western Texas the group is represented by *F. stocktonensis* var. *magnolobata* from the Wolfcamp, and *Fenestella* (*Loculiporina*) *pavonia* n. sp. from the Word.

The evolution of the group did not result in great change of the meshwork: the tendency toward coarser meshwork with advance of geological age was almost imperceptible. This change seemingly was more effective in the course of time from Warsaw to Des Moines (Condra and Elias, 1944, p. 110–112, 162–163). The Mississippian-Pennsylvanian—(Des Moines) forms are characterized by

TABLE 5.—*Species of* Fenestella veneris *group*

Species	Principal measurements				Age and location
	Branches in 10 mm	Fenestrules in 10 mm	Zooecia in 5 mm	Nodes in 5 mm	
F. (*Loculiporina*) *pavonia* n. sp.	15–19	11	19–20	.....	Word, West Texas
F. rossica Shulga	19–20	11–13	17–20	17–20	Upper Carboniferous, Russia
F. stocktonensis var. *magnolobata* n. var.	18–23	13–15	20–23	16–23	Wolfcamp, West Texas
F. hexagonalis Rogers	19	12	17	abt. 17	Shawnee, Kansas
F. stocktonensis Condra and Elias	20–22	12–14	20–21	15.5–16	Des Moines, Utah
F. veneris Fisher	16–22	13–14 (to 16)	20–23	10–12	C_3^0, Russia
F. multispinosa var. *chesterensis* Condra and Elias	15–20	13–15	abt. 21		Chester, Illinois
F. multispinosa Ulrich	20–21	14–15	21	abt. 23	Warsaw, Illinois

carinate dissepiments and considerable width of branches, which average nearly twice as wide as fenestrules. In the late Pennsylvanian and early Permian forms, such as Russian *F. veneris* and *F. rossica* and American *F. hexagonalis* and *F. stocktonensis* var. *magnolobata*, the dissepiments are not carinate and are narrower than in the forms from the Mississippian and the Des Moines, while the branches also are much narrower than in the latter forms, as they average as wide as fenestrules or narrower. The latest representative of the group, *F.* (*Loculiporina*) *pavonia* n. sp. from the Word, has the coarsest meshwork in comparison with all other forms of the group, and also possesses a complex superstructure; its dissepiments became again carinate, as they were in the earlier forms of the group.

Fenestella stocktonensis var. **magnolobata** n. var.

(Plate 6, figure 10; Plate 7, figures 1–4, Plate 18, figure 7)

1944. *Fenestella stocktonensis* CONDRA AND ELIAS, Geol. Soc. America, Special Paper 53, p. 162–163, Pl. 35, fig. 5; Pl. 36, figs. 1, 2

Types: Holotype U. S. Geol. Survey no. 5204-10, from Oquirrh formation, Des Moines Series, mountain side about 1 mile southwest of Stockton, Utah. Holotype of described variety Nebr. Geol. Survey No. 507, No. 93-14 of King and King coll., from Wolfcamp Series, locality 93, section 24, bed 9, and float from the next few higher beds on the side of the arroyo northeast of Wolf Camp (R. E. King, 1930, p. 134; P. B. King, 1930, p. 54–55).

Description: Several specimens of the variety collected; largest 2 cm long and 7 cm wide, apparently representing three lobes of a single large zoarium; largest, on the right side, curved into nearly complete cylinder; obverse facing outward. Each complete lobe apparently at least 5 cm x 5 cm, foliate, curved outward. Branches generally straight, in some places regularly undulating to produce elongate hexagonal fenestrules. Occasionally branches bifurcate abruptly, with only slight widening of branch just before bifurcation, and no additional row of zooecia added (addition of third row of zooecia before bifurcation common in related contemporaneous Russian form, *Fenestella veneris*). Bifurcating branches gradually diverge in plane of meshwork; at left and right margins branches arch gently to left and right respectively. Where two neighboring lobes of an expanse fuse, marginal branches, which arch in opposite direction, meet at acute angle (Pl. 7, figs. 1, 3). Branches average slightly narrower than fenestrules; dissepiments narrower than branches, but where branches undulate dissepiments nearly as wide as branches. Fenestrules rounded-rectangular to rounded hexagonal and elongate oval. Average of 3 to slightly more than 3 zooecia per fenestrule, seldom 2½ per fenestrule. Disposition of zooecia in relation to dissepiments stabilized. Carina made by joining of two lateral slopes of the obverse of branches; slight swelling marking crest upon which weak nodes make single row. Apertures round to oval, to slightly pyriform, about own diameter apart or slightly more distant. Dissepiments slightly depressed on obverse, nearly flush with branches on reverse, where both branches and dissepiments thinly encrusted in such manner that it emphasizes the difference between straight and undulating branches, which run parallel and next to each other. Typical, sharply longitudinally grooved surface of the reverse of branches clearly seen through thin edges of semitransparent encrustation. Shape of zooecial chamber difficult to observe because of destruction of thin inner walls, but seems subpentagonal or oval, with featherlike disposition on both sides of slightly undulating central wall.

From the reverse arise thick upright pillars, striated and bearing rows of reverted barbs, starting about 6 or 7 mm above pillar bases.

Meshwork formula: 18–23/13–15//20–23/16–23.

Discussion: The variety differs from *F. stocktonensis* of the Oquirrh (upper Des Moines) in Utah by the absence of carinae on dissepiments, and much narrower branches and dissepiments than in the original Des Moines form.

Fenestella (**Loculiporina**) **pavonia** n. sp.

(Plate 6, figures 4–9)

Holotype: Nebr. Geol. Survey No. 508; from King and King localities 46 and 46.7, section 8, basal Word, Glass Mountains, Texas.

Description: Larger of two specimens selected for holotype, represents proximal part (though without initial portion) of nearly flat, rapidly expanding growth form. Differs from similar foliate and rapidly expanding growth forms so typical of many species of *Fenestella* by straight course of all radiating branches, in other foliate forms lateral branches arch distinctly to right and left. Uniformly developed superstructure above whole preserved part of zoarium imitates underlying poriferous meshwork just as in *Fenestella (Loculiporina) muscus* n. sp. Smaller paratype represents initial part of zoarium, absent in holotype.

The obverse of the poriferous meshwork was observed by breaking off superstructure, an operation not easily accomplished without damage to zoarium, because wall-like carina connecting with superstructure is solid and strong, though locally perforated by subcircular holes, one or two per fenestrule. Branches of poriferous meshwork vary considerably in width, variability controlled by manner of radiation of branches not accompanied by lateral curving. Branches bifurcate frequently, increasing width slightly and gradually toward points of bifurcation. Bifurcations abrupt, two daughter branches above bifurcation only about half as wide as parent branch below point of bifurcation. Two thin daughter branches maintain width for distance of many fenestrules without appreciable change but eventually show slight gradual increase in width. Dissepiments vary little, average as wide as narrowest branches; are depressed on the reverse. Fenestrules generally rectangular and narrow, average slightly wider than branches; widest just below points of bifurcation and narrowest just above. Character of bifurcation more nearly like *Septopora* than *Fenestella*; daughter branches disposed not symmetrically but one in line with parent branch below (though only half as wide) while other turns abruptly sideways but subsequently parallels the other. This type of branching is imitated by the branches in superstructure above, with even greater emphasis on offset position of lateral daughter branch.

Zooecial apertures circular, not protruding into fenestrules, less than own diameter apart, with thick peristomes seldom preserved. Zooecia average about 3½ per fenestrule, with disposition in relation to dissepiments not stabilized. Frequently exactly 3 or 4 zooecia between dissepiments, none opposite the latter. Surface of branches between apertures slightly shagreened, with even, about 45-degree slopes, on either side of carina. Dissepiments extend upward into low and narrow crests, with node in center; or crests continue as thin walls with pairs of symmetrical circular perforations. All walls that rise from carinae and dissepiments are made of two laminae, with very thin slit between. Slits expand upward into system of canals inside crests of these walls; crests build heavy meshwork of superstructure, which generally imitates underlying poriferous meshwork, but differs from it in having rougher, irregularly tuberculate surface. "Dissepiments" of superstructure usually about as wide as its "branches", both similarly sculptured and equally elevated.

The reverse of poriferous meshwork apparently evenly encrusted, roughly and irregularly tuberculate, tuberculation possibly caused by mineral granulation during silicification rather than representing original zoarial sculpture. At some places crust covers rough longitudinal grooves on the reverse of branches.

Shape of zooecial chamber seldom discernible; its thin walls mostly not silicified, but destroyed at silicification. Where destruction was incomplete some evidence indicates slightly undulating central wall and nearly pentagonal chambers with lateral walls inclined distad, or nearly elliptical with same distal inclination.

Initial part of zoarium (Pl. 6, fig. 8) starts as very open cone, obverse facing inward, but almost at once is transformed into slightly curved foliate expanse, all radiating branches remaining straight, showing no right or left curving of shorter lateral branches. The reverse of branches locally perforated by what looks like auxillary pores (Pl. 6, fig. 9). However, these holes are result of differential weathering of basal walls under zooecial chambers.

Superstructure developed over initial part nowhere different from that over more distal part of the holotype.

Meshwork formula: 15–9/11//19–20, average about 3½ zooecia per fenestrule. Near initial point formula is (in paratype) 12–15//12–14//18–20, with about 3 zooecia per fenestrule. Thus, fenestrules are generally shorter in proximal part, while spacing of zooecia remains practically unchanged.

Discussion: The peculiar superstructure combined with the type of meshwork and the nearly flat growth form, with straight, radiating branches, make this form strikingly different from all previously known fenestrate Bryozoa. Its superstructure is the same type as *Fenestella muscus* n. sp., and both are classified here in the new subgenus *Loculiporina*. The closest related previously described forms are some Devonian species, particularly the forms classified in genus *Loculipora* Hall, which develop somewhat similar regular meshlike superstructures (*see* discussion of new subgenus *Loculiporina*).

Group IV, **Fenestella lahuseni** Stuckenberg

F. lahuseni Stuckenberg and varities; **F. stuckenbergi** Nikiforova and varieties; **F. kingi** n. sp.

1941. Complex *Fenestella lahuseni* Stuckenberg SHULGA-NESTERENKO, Paleontology U.S.S.R. v. 5, pt. 5, fasc. 1, p. 44

Group is characterized by rectangular to slightly pentagonal zooecial chamber; number of zooecia per fenestrule is 2¼–3½, disposition of which in relation to dissepiments not stabilized; wide dissepiments may be ornamented by node or carina; nonprotrusion of zooecial apertures inside fenestrules; thick encrustation on the reverse.

Most important character of group is rectangularity of zooecial chamber, which is generally more common in earlier fenestellas (observation of Nekhoroshev) and also among the Permian species with coarser meshwork than in this group. This character differentiates group from externally similar groups of *Fenestella mimica*, *Fenestella retiformis*, and group X of *Fenestella* which has ramose zoarial basket; in all of these zooecial chamber is pentagonal.

Russian species of group belong to higher horizons of Carboniferous (*F. stuckenbergi*) and to lower Permian (*F. lahuseni* and its varieties), while the American species here described belongs to the Word, or middle Permian, of Texas.

Fenestella kingi n. sp.

(Plate 7, figures 5–7)

Holotype: Nebr. Geol. Survey no. 509, collected by R. E. King in 1928, locality 53, lower part of Word, section 11, beds 1 and 2 ("between fusulina bed and *h*", as written on the label), 1½ miles southwest of Sullivan Peak (R. E. King, 1930, p. 134; P. B. King, 1930, p. 135).

Description: Single specimen 8 by 5 mm fragment of saddlelike curved expanse, thickly encrusted on reverse, from which arise numerous supporting pillars. Coarse silicification destroyed finer details, but principal features on which specific identification is customarily based are preserved. Branches straight, slightly diverging, occasionally bifurcating, with addition of third zooecial row below points of bifurcation for distance less than one fenestrule. Branches with prominent, sharp-edged carina and prominent carinal nodes, 2 to slightly more per fenestrule. Dissepiments, frequently carinate, average as wide as branches, about level with them on obverse. Zooecial apertures circular, not well preserved, about own diameter apart, 2–2½ per fenestrule, position in relation to dissepiments not stabilized. Zooecial chamber nearly rectangular, with slightly zigzagging central wall separating 2 zooecial rows, making chambers look slightly pentagonal. Encrustation on the reverse as thick as primary zoarial skeleton (*see* Pl. 4, fig. 5), encrusted branches and dissepiments flush on the reverse. Lumina of fenestrules generally not reduced by encrustation, which concentrates on reverse, and so fenestrules remain elliptical and wide; even where upright, thick pillars, which arise from reverse, cover underlying fenestrules, which remain unsealed.

Meshwork formula: 20/15//17/ about 17.

Discussion: In general character of meshwork and its measurements the species is very near *Fenestella retiformis* described by Shulga-Nesterenko from the Permian of Russia (1936, p. 271; 1941, p. 77), but differs in its rectangular shape of zooecial chamber. Among the species of the *F. lahuseni* group, to which *F. kingi* belongs, it is nearest to *F. stuckenbergi* Nikiforova, from which it differs in smaller number of zooecia per given space, which results in slightly smaller number of zooecia per fenestrule; the number of fenestrules per same space in the two species is about the same (15 to 16 in *F. stuckenbergi*). Other differences are the greater prominence of carina, very large nodes, and carinate dissepiments in *F. kingi* compared with the moderate carina, small nodes, and noncarinate dissepiments in *F. stuckenbergi*. *F. infraseptata* Shulga from Burtzevka horizon, Permian of Russia

(1952, p. 33, fig. 12; Pl. 3, fig. 2) has almost the same meshwork (16–18/15//16) as *F. kingi*, but its zooecial chamber is rectangular and divided by hemiseptum into subequal halves, and it has thinner carina with small, twice as many nodes as in *F. kingi.*

Group V, **Fenestella retiformis** Schlotheim

F. retiformis (Schlotheim), **F. retiformis** var. **tenuis** Trizna, **F. strukovi** Trizna, **F. s.** var. **vidrioensis** n. var., **F. s.** var. **tenuiformis** n. var., **F. ornata** Shulga, **F. nalivkini** n. sp., **F. ornata** var. **propinqua** Trizna, **F. tenuiseptata** Shulga, **F. picchuensis** Chronic, **F. inornata** n. sp., **F. pseudovirgosa Nikiforova.**

Group characterized by unstabilized disposition of zooecia in relation to dissepiments, with slightly more than 2 to about 3 zooecia per fenestrule. Zooecial chamber distinctly pentagonal to triangular, with short transverse walls inclined slightly forward; branches carinate, with single row of nodes.

Fenestella strukovi Trizna

1939. *Fenestella basloensis* var. *strukovi* TRIZNA, Trans. Geol. Oil Inst., ser. A, fasc. 115, p. 107–108 Pl. 2, fig. 6

Types: Variety *strukovi*, here elevated to rank of species, established on material from exposure 13 of Kazarmenny Kamen (rock bluff) in Ash-Vavilovo district of west central Urals, in a zone of *Ascopora nodosa* var. *sterlitamakensis*, or Jurezan horizon of upper Carboniferous (as correlated by Nikiforova and Tolstikhina).

Description: From brief description and single illustration of a thin section of form by Trizna the following diagnosis is compiled: meshwork regular; branches average as wide as fenestrules; dissepiments about half as wide as branches; fenestrules oval; outline of chamber triangular to nearly pentagonal with short lateral walls; carina prominent with slightly elongated nodes arranged in one row; reverse encrusted with capillaries scattered and concentrated in spots, with some nodes.

Meshwork formula: 16–17/12 to 13//15–16/15–16.

Discussion: Trizna considers the form a variety of *F. basloensis*, and says it is nearest to *F. basloensis* var. *pedisequa* Novik (apparently a manuscript name, as literature reference not given), the latter having fewer branches (14) and fenestrules (11–12). Because the concept of the species *F. basloensis* and its varieties is here limited to forms with 3½–5 zooecia per fenestrule, Trizna's form is elevated to specific rank and removed from the *F. basloensis* group.

TABLE 6.—*Species of* Fenestella retiformis *group*

Species	Principal measurements				Age and location
	Branches 10 in mm	Fenestrules in 10 mm	Zooecia in 5 mm	Nodes in 5 mm	
F. inornata n. sp.	19–20	17–17.5	23	. . .	Altuda, West Texas
F. strukovi var. *vidrioensis* n. var.	14–19	12	15	15	Vidrio, West Texas
F. strukovi var. *tenuiformis* n. var.	16–19	12	14.5–15.5	9	Word, West Texas
F. retiformis Schloth, (Licharev)	18–20	14	abt. 13	14–15	Upper Permian, Russia
F. retiformis Schloth., (Korn)	18–19	14–15	19	19	Zechstein, Germany
F. nalivkini n. sp.	21–25	21–24	25–27	25–27	Lower Permian, Russia
F. ornata Shulga	14–16	13–14	18	?	Lower Permian (P_1^1), Russia
F. ornata var. *propinqua* Trizna	13	10–12	16–17	6–7	Lower Permian (P_1^{1a} or P_1^{1b})
F. tenuiseptata Shulga	15–16	14–15	19–20	18–19	Lower Permian (P_1^1), Russia
F. strukovi Trizna	16–17	12–13	14–16	15–16	Upper Carbonif., Russia

Fenestella strukovi var. **vidrioensis** n. var.

(Plate 8, figures 1–3)

Types: Fragmentary holotype and paratype obtained by dissolution of limestone specimen from locality 50–1, Altuda member of the Vidrio, which is basal Capitan from northeast part of Del Norte Range, south of James Ranch, Glass Mountains, Texas. (R. E. King, 1930, p. 134). Holotype Nebr. Geol. Survey no. 510; paratype no. 510a.

Description: The two fragments may seem to represent two species, differing in thickness and spacing of branches. However, in view of identity of all other features the two are referred to same species, difference in thickness and spacing of branches due to positions of fragments in zoarium: paratype from more distal, and holotype from more proximal part. Paratype shows divergence and frequent bifurcation of stout branches, while in holotype subparallel branches lack bifurcations. Zoarium apparently flat and fairly large (a few centimeters across); fan-shaped growth form has straight branches spaced wider (14 per 10 mm) in proximal part and closer (19 per 10 mm) in distal part. Branches as wide as fenestrules; dissepiments about half as wide as branches; outline of fenestrules oval to elongate and rounded rectangular. Zooecial apertures round; position in relation to dissepiment unstablized, from 2¼ to 2¾ per fenestrule. Carina fairly strong with single row of nodes, about as many as zooecia. Outline of chamber apparently more triangular than pentagonal; difficult to observe because of coarse silicification of the fossil. Reverse moderately encrusted with dense tissue; structural details apparently destroyed by silicification.

Meshwork formula: In proximal part of zoarium, 14/12//15/15; in distal part, 19/12//15/15.

Discussion: The distal fragment (holotype) is much like the original of *F. strukovi*, the difference being only in slightly denser spacing of the branches in the specimen from Vidrio, this is caused by a closer spacing of three middle branches, while spacing of the other branches is exactly like that in *F. strukovi* from Russia. The spacing of zooecia and nodes is slightly more diffuse in this form, which is the reason for its differentiation as a new variety. It is stratigraphically much higher than the Russian form, and the slight change toward diffuse spacing may be a slow evolutionary advance of a generally conservative stock.

Fenestella strukovi var. **tenuiformis** n. var.

(Plate 8, figures 4–6)

Types: Two fragments: holotype Nebr. Geol. Survey no. 511 paratype no. 511a obtained by dissolution of specimen from locality 192, "Fourth limestone," Word group, north of junction of Road and Gilliland canyons, section 17 R. E. King, 1930, p. 136, no. 192; P. B. King, 1930, section 17, probably bed 8 of Word.

Description: Two fragments represent slightly more proximal and more distal parts of flat, fan-shaped growth form, differing from each other in the same way as the two fragments of *F. strukovi* var. *vidrioensis*. More proximal fragment has 16 branches per 10 mm, with frequent bifurcation and marked divergence. Only one bifurcation within the fragment in more distal fragment; branches subparallel, 18 to 19 branches per 10 mm.

Branches average narrower than fenestrules; dissepiments half as wide as branches; fenestrules oval to rounded rectangular, zooecial apertures projecting into fenestrules. Where preserved, zooecial apertures perfectly circular and small, 1½–2 times their diameter apart; position in relation to dissepiments not stabilized. Carina fairly prominent, with large nodes spaced more distantly than zooecia. Internal structure poorly preserved, but with indication of triangular outline of zooecial chamber.

Meshwork formula: Proximal part: 16/12//14.5–15.59. Distal part: 18–19/12//14.5–15.5/9.

Discussion: Variety *tenuiformis* differs from *F. strukovi* of Russia and its variety *vidrioensis* here described by having narrower branches, more diffuse meshwork, more distantly spaced and larger carinal nodes, and slightly smaller zooecial apertures spaced farther apart. The number of zooecia per 5 mm is the same as in variety *vidrioensis*, in which respect both upper Permian forms from Texas differ similarily from Russian form from near the top of the Carboniferous.

Fenestella nalivkini n. sp.

(Plate 8, figures 7–9)

Types: Largest fragment among several collected by Condra selected as holotype; thin sections prepared from two smaller fragments; types designated Nebr. Geol. Survey nos. 512, holotype; and 512a and 511b (thin sections).

Collection of Bryozoa including *F. nalivkini* consists of small fragments of crumbly yellowish gray shale with well-preserved bryozoans; collected from exposures of Lower Permian (Artinskian) rocks at Sims Industrial Plants, Russia.

Description: Fragments apparently from moderately large, fan-shaped, irregularly undulating zoarium. In holotype and other fragments branches diverge slowly and occasionally bifurcate, thus indicating their position within ephebastic or late (full-grown) stage of zoarium. Branches somewhat wider than fenestrules; dissepiments about half as wide as branches and nearly flush with them on reverse and obverse; fenestrules elongate rectangular to elliptical.

Position of zooecial apertures in relation to dissepiments unstabilized; average is slightly more than 2 zooecia per fenestrule. Nodes low, in single row along low carina. Zooecial chamber more triangular than pentagonal, with pronounced interwedging of successive chambers. Moderately thick encrustation on reverse of branches and dissepiments.

Meshwork formula: 21–25/21–24//25–27/abt. 25–27.

Discussion: The three fragments described by Nikiforova (1938a, p. 97–98, Pl. 18, figs. 6–8) as *Fenestella* sp. (no. 5) and previously referred by Stuckenberg (1895, p. 141–142) to *F. retiformis* are seemingly closely related to *F. nalivkini*, but have somewhat coarser meshwork (20–22/17–21//20–22). There is hardly any doubt that both belong to the group *F. retiformis* and probably are ancestral to the upper Permian *F. retiformis* for which Likharev established the following meshwork: 18–20/14//abt. 18/14–15 (on the material from limestone pebbles in Pleistocene glacial till of Vologodsk region of the U.S.S.R.) Nikiforova suggested (1938a, p. 98) the restriction of the name *F. retiformis* to the Permian forms. We feel that the name applies to the Upper Permian form with the coarse meshwork, as indicated from Likharev's measurements and by Korn illustrations (1930, p. 354, Pl. 1, figs. 1–4), on which the following meshwork formula was measured: 18–19/14–15//19/19. Comparison of the photographs by Likharev and Korn with the sketches by King (1849, Pl. 2, figs. 8–19), all representing *F. retiformis* from the Upper Permian, indicates variability of the spacing of zooecia in relation to fenestrules as follows: from slightly more than 2 to 3 or slightly more than 3 per fenestrule. Larger number of zooecia per fenestrule and coarser zoarium seem to be generally correlated with the evolution of *F. retiformis* group from early to late Permian.

Likharev described and illustrated apical extension of spines in the upper Permian *F. retiformis*, which results in a regular superstructure similar to that in *Unitrypa* or *Hemitrypa* (Likharev, 1926, p. 1016, Pl. 14, figs. 5, 7), but the clearly localized development of the superstructure within a zoarium caused him to regard it of no taxonomic significance, generic or specific. It is merely a result of unexplained local intense precipitation of calcium carbonate. By analogy with the two new species described here as *Fenestella* (*Loculiporina*) *pavonia* and *F.* (*L.*) *muscus* the form with the locally developed superstructure described by Likharev could be referred to the subgenus *Loculiporina*, a polyphyletic evolutionary stage in genus *Fenestella*.

Fenestella inornata n. sp.

(Plate 10, figures 5, 6)

Types: Several fragments obtained by etching from platy brownish shaly limestone, Altuda member, Vidrio formation or basal Capitan, locality 50 in Del Norte Range, south of James Ranch, Glass Mountains, Texas (R. E. King, 1930, p. 134; P. B. King, 1930, p. 70). All belong to full-grown zoarium; largest fragment selected as holotype Nebr. Geol. Survey No. 513.

Description: Fragments probably all from single zoarium, indicate nearly flat fan, at least 2 or 3 cm wide and long. Branches as wide or slightly wider than fenestrules; dissepiments less than half as wide as branches, depressed on obverse and reverse; fenestrules narrow elliptical. Length of fenestrules irregularly variable, variability depending on difference in number of zooecia, from 2 to 3 per fenestrule (seldom less than 2); position of apertures in relation to dissepiments wholly variable (unstabilized); nodeless carina narrow, rising slightly above apertures. Outline of zooecial chamber generally not preserved, but rarely preserved internal molds indicate their featherlike arrangement, with pentagonal base, which changes upward to elliptical outline. Thin secondary crust on reverse does not obscure grooved surface of primary skeleton.

Meshwork formula: 19–20/17–17.5//23/none.

Discussion: The species is rather featureless and conservative for its stratigraphic position in the highest bryozoan-bearing Permian of Texas. Externally it resembles some early Pennsylvanian or Mississippian forms, such as *F. rarinodosa*, but its zooecial chamber is characteristically advanced Permian. The species is placed in group V because of its unstabilized, variable position of apertures in relation to dissepiments, its type of zooecial chamber, and the number of zooecia per fenestrule from 2 to nearly 3. Perhaps its most characteristic feature is the absence of any trace of nodes either upon moderately well-developed carina or on the reverse. The meshwork formula is fairly constant for all fragments examined, and is somewhat different from those previously published for the late Paleozoic species of *Fenestella*.

Fenestela picchuensis Chronic (Newell, Chronic and Roberts 1953, p. 115) from the Copacabana group (Lower Permian) of Peru is much like *F. inornata*, but its prominent carina carries distinct elongated nodes and its dissepiments are spaced somewhat wider. Chronic's topotype of *F. picchuensis* (Pl. 22, fig. 5b) is more nearly like *F. inornata* than holotype (Pl. 22, fig. 4). The apertures in the latter are distinctly enlarged where occupying the bases of the dissepiments, so that such dissepiments become almost wholly occupied by the apertures, a feature not mentioned in the description of the species.

Group VI, **Fenestella (Minilia) virgosa** Eichwald

F. virgosa Eichwald, **F. v.** var. **sterlitamakensis** Nikiforova, **F. v.** var. **minus** Shulga, **F. virgosa** var. **atuberculata** Shulga, **F. virgosa** var. **dubia**, n. var., **F. permiana** Stuckenberg, **F. kukaensis** Bassler, **F. bituberculata** Crockford, and **F. amplia** Crockford.

1941. Complex *Fenestella virgosa* SHULGA-NESTERENKO, Paleontology U.S.S.R. v. 5, pt. 5, fasc. 1, p. 44

Group characterized by spacing of 3 to 5 zooecia per fenestrule, with position of zooecial apertures in relation to dissepiments tending toward stabilization. Zooecial chambers elongate oval, in feather like arrangement; carina well developed, but development of nodes variable, in contrast with stability of this feature in other groups. In *F. virgosa* and some of its varieties two rows of nodes; in its variety *sparsituberculata* Shulga the few nodes arranged in one row; in its variety *atuberculata* Shulga carina has no nodes. In spite of variability of development and arrangement of carinal nodes, classification of varieties under single name *virgosa* by Shulga-Nesterenko appears correct. Sole representative (classified as its new variety) of group in Permian of West Texas practically without nodes on prominent carina, and only broad elevations at points opposite some dissepiments, much like Russian species and its varieties.

Group thus segregated includes species of late Carboniferous (C_3) and of Permian in Russia, Timor, Australia, and Texas. Comparison of forms in respective stratigraphic positions seems to indicate some tendency toward a coarser zoarium in later forms; for instance, the spacing of zooecia is widest in *F. bituberculata* of Australia. There is also a tendency toward stricter regularity in relationship between apertures and dissepiments, strictest attained in *F. kukaensis* from Amarassi of Timor.

Fenestella virgosa Eichwald

1860. *Fenestella virgosa* EICHWALD, Lethaea Rossica, p. 358, Pl. 23 fig. 9b. (not fig. 9a)
1938. *Fenestella virgosa* NIKIFOROVA, Paleontology of U.S.S.R., v. 4 pt. 5, fasc. 1, p. 35–36, 66–68, 227, summary in English Figs, 24–25; Pl. 11, figs. 2–5

Type: Holotype by Nikiforova's subsequent designation in the museum University of Leningrad, specimen no. XXXIV/22, N. Saraninski foundries; C_3^s or C_3^i; now considered Artinskian; redescribed from prepared thin section (1938a, p. 67–68, Pl. 11, fig. 4).

Discussion: Nikiforova found that the two specimens originally referred by Eichwald to his *F. virgosa* have different inner structure, although externally similar in appearance and in dimensions of meshwork. Hence she retains only one of them and makes it holotype of *F. virgosa:* that illustrated by Eichwald on Plate 23, figure 9a, republished on her Plate 11, figure 5. The other specimen, illustrated by Eichwald (Pl. 23, fig. 9b) was also sectioned by Nikiforova (1938, Fig. 27, p. 69) and is designated holotype of her new species *Fenestella pseudovirgosa*. It differs from *Fenestella virgosa* by triangular-shaped, occasionally interwedging zooecial chambers. It belongs in group V, *Fenestella retiformis*.

Several varieties of *F. virgosa* were established by Nikiforova and Shulga-Nesterenko and one is now added from the Wolfcamp of Texas.

Fenestella virgosa, var. **dubia,** n. var.

(Plate 8, figures 10, 11)

Holotype: Nebr. Geol. Survey No. 514; from C. Schuchert coll. no. 3829, Peabody Museum, Yale; R. E. King's locality 93 (-S), section 24, bed 9 (King, 1930, p. 55), Wolfcamp Series, northeast of Wolf Camp, Texas.

Description: Specimen somewhat weathered; 25 by 20 mm; fragment from distal part of slightly convex (on the obverse) zoarium, with subparallel, only slightly divergent branches, indicating position of fragment in distal part of a zoarium. Strong carina on crest of junction of steeply inclined slopes on obverse of branches. No distinct nodes, but locally developed broad elevations at points opposite some dissepiments. Bifurcation abrupt, with no additional zooecial row. Branches straight, with only slight and incidental tendency to zigzag. Occasionally develops additional dissepiments between those disposed at regular intervals; abnormal development occurring also just above apparently accidental termination of a branch; longer dissepiments above termination connecting two neighboring branches.

Meshwork formula: 15/9–10//16/8, with 3–3.5 zooecia per fenestrule.

Discussion: In the spacing of fenestrules and zooecia this variety is very close to *F. virgosa* var. *minus* Shulga from P_1^1 of Russia, but the latter has numerous nodes arranged in two rows. The Russian variety *sparsituberculata* is somewhat like var. *dubia* having few nodes; differs in much broader spacing of fenestrules and zooecia.

Group VII, **Fenestella (Minilia) binodata** Condra

F. binodata Condra, and its varieties; **F. geminanoda** Moore

Group characterized by double row of carinal spines, and by peculiar irregular spacing of dissepiments resulting in intermittent shorter and longer fenestrules, with stabilized dimensions, and localization of apertures at base of dissepiments. Among all species of *Fenestella* with 2 to 4 zooecia per fenestrule, this is the only group that has this kind of intermittent change in size of stabilized fenestrules. Zooecial chambers elongate oval, and disposed in featherlike fashion. In this latter respect as well as in the disposition of nodes in two rows, *F. binodata* group is like *F. compactilis* group and *F. virgosa* group. *F. compactilis* group differs from *F. binodata* group: by having 2 zooecia per fenestrule, stabilized to nearly stabilized; every other aperture at base of dissepiment. *F. virgosa* group has 3 to 4 (occasionally 5) zooecia per fenestrule, while occurrence of 2 zooecia per fenestrule is rare.

Earliest known form of group *F. geminanoda* (Pl. 11, fig. 8) from lower part of Stanton limestone (east of Bonner Springs, Kansas), with stabilized arrangement of 2 apertures per short fenestrule; less frequently 3 apertures per longer fenestrule; and rarely 1 aperture per very short fenestrule. Long fenestrules with 3 apertures occur sporadically in any part of zoarium among 2-aperture ones, singly or up to 5 long fenestrules in succession. Position of apertures at base of dissepiments well stabilized in all these fenestrules. *F. geminanoda* from Cass limestone of South Bend, Nebraska, much like same from basal Stanton, except 3-aperture fenestrules predominate over 2-aperture ones. *F. geminanoda* from Adams Branch limestone of Texas shows apparent departure from stability, by occasional absence of apertures at base of dissepiments and by development (though rare) of 4-zooecial fenestrules—tendencies apparently indicating mutability toward *F. binodata* of upper Shawnee.

In younger rocks of the Big Blue and the Wolfcamp new variety *F. binodata* var. *wolfcampensis*

TABLE 7.—*Species and varieties of* Fenestella binodata *group*

Species	Principal measurements				Age and location
	Branches in 10 mm	Fenestrules in 10 mm	Zooecia in 5 mm	Nodes in 5 mm	
F. binodata var. *wordensis* n. var.	14–20	10.5	16	32	Word, West Texas
F. binodata var. *leonardensis* n. var.	15–20	12–13.5	17–20	34–40	Upper Leonard, West Texas
(proximal and distal parts)	15	13–14.5	17.5–18	35–36	
F. binodata var. *wolfcampensis*, n. var.	20	11.5–13	17–18	34–36	Wolfcamp, West Texas
proximal (above) and distal (below) parts	13–15	11–12	17–18	34–36	
F. binodata Condra	13–16	11.5–13	17–20	34–40	Upper Shawnee, Nebraska
F. geminanoda Moore	25	15–17.5	17.5	35	Upper Shawnee, Nebraska
F. geminanoda Moore	19	14–19	19	38	Upper Missouri, Kansas, Nebraska

apparently direct descendant of *F. binodata*; its meshwork formula practically same; but relationship between apertures and dissepiments becomes again stabilized, much like in *F. geminanoda*. Stabilization retained in higher levels of Leonard Series, where further evolutionary progress results in *F. binodosa* var. *leonardensis* with still greater stabilization of some elements and 3 zooecia per fenestrule becoming a rule throughout zoarium. In stratigraphically higher *F. binodata* var. *wordensis* shorter fenestrules with 1 or 2 zooecia per fenestrule occur only sporadically among stabilized 3-zooecial fenstrules, and spacing of fenestrules and zooecia becomes broader than in earlier forms. Count of fenestrules per 10 mm (standardized for species of *Fenestella*) has little meaning for the species just discussed, because of the peculiar intermittent combination of longer and shorter fenestrules within their zoaria; thus, the figures for fenestrules in Table 7 do not express the trend of evolution as just described.

Fenestella binodata Condra

1902. *Fenestella binodata* CONDRA, Am. Geol. v. 30, p. 350–351
1903. *Fenestella binodata* CONDRA, Nebr. Geol. Survey Bull., v. p. 66–67, 110–111, Pl. 10, figs. 12, 13

Types: Holotype Nebr. Geol. Survey 32-16-7-00, from upper Shawnee at Weeping Water, Nebr., designated by Condra (1903, p. 67). Plesiotypes by Condra from rocks of same age exposed at Nehawka (no. 5–19–7–99), Nebraska.

Description: Holotype, 5 by 5 mm, fragment of apparently proximal part of nearly flat zoarium, with frequently bifurcating and rapidly diverging straight branches; only one additional aperture added at points of bifurcation; two branches above bifurcation only slightly narrower than parent branch below. Number of zooecia per fenestrule from 2 to 3½, corresponding to two sizes of fenestrule; no stabilization of position of apertures in relation to dissepiments. Disposition of shorter fenestrules among the longer ones as follows: 2 or, less frequently, 3 long fenestrules in succession followed by 1 short fenestrule along branch.

Dissepiments from a half to two-thirds width of branches; flat, striate, flush with apertures on obverse, and flush with branches on the reverse. Zooecial chambers elongate oval at base to beanlike at slightly higher level; arranged in featherlike fashion.

Meshwork formula: 16/11.5–13//17–18/34–36, remeasured on the holotype. In plesiotypes from Nehawka 13–14/11.5//20/40.

Discussion: The species differs from its apparent predecessor *F. geminanoda* from the upper Missouri Series at South Bend, Nebraska, by coarser meshwork and departure from strict stabilization of apertures in relation to dissepiments, even though the occurrence of shorter fenestrules among the longer ones—1 short fenestrule after 2, rarely 3, long ones—is similar in the two species.

Fenestella binodata var. **wolfcampensis** n. var.

(Plate 9, figure 1)

Types: From numerous fragments obtained by dissolution of limestone specimens from Wolfcamp Series; largest fragment selected for holotype; Lower Wolfcamp, location no. 93, section 24, bed 9, and float from next few higher beds on side of arroyo northeast of Wolf Camp, Texas (R. E. King, 1930, p. 134; P. B. King, 1930, p. 54–55). Nebr. Geol. Survey No. 515.

Description: Holotype, 10 x 15 mm, proximal part of full-grown, slightly undulating, fan-shaped zoarium; most other numerous fragments represent more distal parts. They differ mostly in spacing and degree of divergence of branches, more distantly spaced, more divergent, and, in average, more frequently bifurcating in holotype. Complete zoarium probably about 20–25 mm high and 30–40 mm wide fan, with branches generally straight, but gently curving within meshwork to right and left at corresponding sides; also similarly curving at places along whole periphery of fan. Branches average as wide as fenestrules, dissepiments half or slightly more than half as wide as branches; fenestrules subrectangular to nearly oval in outline. Zooecial apertures not projecting into fenestrules in proximal part of zoarial fan, but do in its distal parts; apparently correlated with variability of width of branches and carina: the narrower a branch and wider a carina, the more projecting are apertures, being pushed by carina to sides. Carina strong, with two rows of elongated spines, which curve to right and left intermittently (similar to Pl. 9 fig. 8). However, these spines are poorly developed on holotype, possibly worn out. Form of zooecial chamber observed locally because of peculiar preservation. A fine film of silica lines walls of chambers (*see* Pl. 9, fig. 1). Chamber approaches pentagonal outline at base, changing to oval at higher levels, curving right and left. Central canal in carina tends to sink between two rows of chambers, making a straight line between them. Position of zooecial apertures tends to stabilize to an aperture at base of each dissepiment. Commonly number of zooecia per fenestrule 3, but few scattered fenestrules have 4, and a few have 2 zooecia per fenestrule. Fenestrules with 4 zooecia more common in proximal than in distal part of zoarium; fenestrules with 2 zooecia more frequent in distal part. Short 2-zooecia fenestrules occur frequently in pairs, 2 short fenestrules in succession. Moderate development of crust on the reverse, locally thinning to almost nothing, so that grooved surface of reverse of branches can be seen.

Meshwork formula: Holotype, 13–15/11–12//17–18/34–36; paratypes, representing more distal parts of zoarial fan, 20/11.5–13//17–18/34–36.

Discussion: Variety *wolfcampensis* resembles *F. compactilis* in outer appearance, stabilization of apertures on bases of dissepiments, sculpture, growth form, and structure of zooecial chamber; but differs in predominance of fenestrules with 3 zooecia per fenestrule, while in *F. compactilis* 2-zooecial fenestrules predominate overwhelmingly.

Variety *wolfcampensis* of the lower Permian differs from its progenitor *F. binodata* of upper Pennsylvanian only by the greater degree of stabilization of the zooecial apertures in relation to the dissepiments: in most of the latter there are 3 to 3½ zooecia per fenestrule, and frequently the base of one dissepiment is not occupied by an aperture.

Fenestella binodata var. **leonardensis** n. var.

(Figure 16; Plate 9, figures 2–9; Plate 10, figures 7–10; Plate 11, figures 1–4)

Types: Several fragments, representing different parts of zoarium, obtained by dissolution of brown limestone from middle and upper parts of Leonard Series. Specimen from proximal part of zoarium selected holotype because of excellency of preservation. Specimen came from middle Leonard, locality 123, bed 14 of section 17 (R. E. King, 1930, p. 135; P. B. King, 1930, p. 140). Holotype, Nebr. Geol. Survey No. 516. Others came from Upper Leonard, below and west of Clay Slide, Texas (R. E. King, 1930, p. 135).

Description: Proximal parts of full-grown stage of apparently fan-shaped, undulating zoarium have much wider spacing of branches, only half as wide as fenestrules, as compared with those from more distal parts. In fragments from most distal part branches as wide as fenestrules, gently curving in proximal parts, probably to right and left on corresponding sides of zoarial fan; dissepiments straight to distally arched, varying much in width, from a fourth to two-thirds the width of branch, not due to development of encrustation. Both thinner and thicker dissepiments with well-preserved grooved surface. The reverse of branches, also groved; U-shaped grooves divided by narrow ridges (*see* Pl. 9, fig. 5) with serrate crests.

Fenestrules subrectangular; complicated by protrusion of zooecial apertures along sides; apertures smaller than usual for *Fenestella*, with nodose peristomes and distance between edges of successive peristomes two to three times their diameter; nodes or spines in two rows, sitting upon moderately developed smoothly rounded carina. Where well developed, long spines curve intermittently to the right and left. Short and long fenestrules, with 2 and 3 zooecia per fenestrule respectively, mostly 3, a zooecial aperture at base of each dissepiment. In distal part all fenestrules narrow, with 3 zooecia per fenestrule, and every third aperture at base of dissepiment. Reverse, thinly covered by crust, carries locally developed prominent round nodes variously disposed along branches: at places in one row, at others in two rows (in Upper Leonard example), or not developed at all. Outline of zooecial chamber unknown.

Meshwork formula: Proximal part of zoarium 15/13–14.5//17.5–18//35–36; distal part 15–20/12–13.5//17–20/34–40.

Discussion: Variety *leonardensis* differs from *wolfcampensis* by the complete or nearly complete disappearance of very long 4-zooecial fenestrules, and also of short 2-zooecial fenestrules in the distal part of a full-grown stage of zoarium, but short fenestrules remain fairly common among the 3-zooecia fenestrules in the proximal part of a zoarium. Diffuse meshwork and narrowness of branches in the proximal part of zoarium may be another distinctive character of the variety.

Fenestella binodata var. **wordensis** n. var.

(Plate 11, figures 5–7)

Types: Several fragments obtained by dissolution of limestone from locality 192, "Fourth limestone)) (from bottom up) of Word group, section 17, north of junction of Road and Gilliland canyons (R. E. King, 1930, p. 136; P. B., King, 1930, p. 139). The least encrusted fragment is selected holotype Nebraska Geol. Survey No. 517; representing distal part of fan-shaped zoarium.

Description: Fragments apparently from various parts of fan-shaped zoarium. Only long fenestrules with stabilized 3 zooecia per fenestrule observable, but one small fragment has both 3-zooecial and 2-zooecial fenestrules. Holotype has one fenestrule with only 1 zooecium per fenestrule. Bases of depressed dissepiments invariably occupied by zooecial apertures. Branches as narrow as down to half as wide as fenestrules; dissepiments narrower than branches; fenestrules elongate subrectangular, with more or less distinct protrusion of apertures along sides; carina narrow and prominent, with two closely set rows of nodes, inclined intermittently to right and left, where developed into sufficiently long spines; the reverse moderately encrusted, branches smooth or seldom adorned with nodes, rather small, sharply conical, inclined slightly forward. Locally encrustation thick, envelops both the reverse and the obverse of branches and dissepiments. Variously inclined thinner and thicker cylindrical pillars arise from the reverse.

Meshwork formula: 14–20/10.5//16/32; closest spacing of branches observed where branches bifurcate most frequently.

Discussion: Variety *wordensis* differs from the stratigraphically lower representatives of *F. binodata* by having coarser meshwork and only very few short fenestrules (with 2 zooecia and 1 zooecia per fenestrule), which seemingly appear sporadically and without particular regularity among the standardized, long, 3-zooecial fenestrules. In the part of the zoarium of var. *wordensis*, where branches diverge more rapidly and are frequently bifurcating, the spacing of branches becomes closer.

Group VIII, **Fenestella (Minilia) compactilis** Condra

F. bispinulata Moore, **F. compactilis** Condra, **F. c.** var. **plattsmouthensis** n. var., **F. infranodosa** n. sp.

Not the "Complex" of **Fenestella conradi-compactilis** Condra, Shulga-Nesterenko, 1941, Paleontology U.S.S.R., v. 5, pt. 5, fasc. 1, p. 44. These species, except for **F. compactilis,** belong to group **Fenestella plummerae.**

Group characterized by stabilized occurrence of 2 zooecia per fenestrule, with every other zooecial aperture at base of dissepiment. Branches usually narrower than fenestrules. Carinal nodes arranged

TABLE 8.—*Species of* Fenestella compactilis *group*

Species	Principal measurements				Age
	Branches in 10 mm	Fenes-trules in 10 mm	Zooecia in 5 mm	Nodes in 5 mm	
F. infranodosa n. sp.	20	18	18	30–36	Upper Leonard, West Texas
F. compactilis var. *plattsmouthensis* n. var.	20	18–19	18–19	36	
F. compactilis Condra (E. and C.)	18–19	18–20	18–20	36–38	Basal Cass, Douglas group, Nebraska
F. bispinulata Moore (E. and C.)	18–20	18–20	18–20.5	36–42	Ranger limestone, Canyon group, Texas

in two rows, one node for each zooecium; zooecial chamber subpentagonal at base; two short sides of pentagon inclined forward, changing to parallelogram at higher level, and then to bean-shaped; arranged in feather-like fashion at top just under zooecial apertures. Group differs from others with double row of carinal nodes, as follows: from groups *F. virgosa* and *F. binodata* by having 2 zooecia per fenestrule, instead of 2, 3, and 4 zooecia per fenestrule, and from group *F. plummerae* by having subpentagonal to bean-shaped instead of triangular to rhombic outline of zooecial chamber.

Group appears in Pennsylvanian of America, earliest known representative *F. bispinulata* Moore in Ranger limestone of Canyon group in Texas, correlating with upper part of Missouri Series of Nebraska and Kansas. Next above, *F. compactilis* Condra from basal part of Cass limestone of Douglas group at South Bend, Nebraska. *F. bispinulata* Moore of Ranger limestone apparently related to *F. geminanoda* of lower Graham, Texas, and basal Stanton limestone, Kansas; it could have diverged by stabilization of 2-aperture fenestrules and disappearance of almost all longer fenestrules, as *F. bispinulata* from Nebraska (identified from large specimen in collections at Nebr. Geol. Survey). In Plattsmouth limestone at Plattsmouth, Nebraska occurs *F. compactilis* var. *plattsmouthensis* n. var., with only 2-aperture fenestrules, and very rare addition of 1-aperture and 2½-apperture and 3-aperture fenestrules. Subsequent to 2½-aperture fenestrule in zoarium, row of as many as ten 2-aperture fenestrules usually follows, with no apertures disposed at bases of dissepiments, but all apertures occur in pairs between dissepiments; another single 2½-aperture fenestrule follows, and then normal 2-aperture fenestrules with every other aperture at base of dissepiment. Advanced representative of group is here described as *F. infranodosa* from upper part of Leonard Series, Texas.

Evolutionary advance is manifested by a gradual growth in size, an increased coarseness of meshwork, and a less noticeable progress in gradual elimination of longer fenestrules: they occasionally appear among shorter fenestrules in *F. bispinulata*, become very rare in *F. compactilis*, and disappear entirely in *F. infranodosa*.

Fenestella compactilis Condra

(Plate 1, figures 4–6; Plate 2, figures 1, 2; Plate 12, figures 1–5)

1902. *Fenestella conradi* var. *compactilis* CONDRA, Am. Geologist, v. 30, p. 348, Pl. 22, figs. 1, 2
1903. *Fenestella compactilis* BARBOUR, Nebr. Geol. Survey, v. 1, p. 127
1903. *Fenestella conradi-compactilis* CONDRA, Nebr. Geol. Survey, v. 2, p. 60–61, Pl. 8, figs. 11, 12
not 1941. *Fenestella conradi compactilis* SHULGA, Paleontology U.S.S.R. v. 5, pt. 5, fas. 1, p. 98–99, Pl. 18, figs. 2, 3, Fig. 57 (now identified with *F. infranodosa* n. sp., Elias and Condra)

Holotype: Holotype (Pl. 7, fig. 1) originally illustrated by Condra (1903, Pl. 8, fig. 11) has the reverse exposed; detail of the obverse (1903, Pl. 8, fig. 12) was illustrated from another specimen. In preparation of holotype for redescription lower half was broken off and its obverse cleaned and slightly etched with hydrochloric acid (Pl. 7, figs. 2, 3). Collected west of South Bend, Nebraska, from basal part of Cass limestone, Douglas group, basal Virgil Series, Nebr. Geol. Survey No. 18-3-99.

Description: Holotype large fragment of undulating foliate zoarium, 32 mm long and wider than 20 mm at distal part, so heavily encrusted that all fenestrules sealed, and carina with double row of nodes veneered by thin crust. Nevertheless zooecial apertures are open except at base of zoarium, where closed by encrusting tissue. Bases of several thick, curved pillars arise from the edge and from the reverse of zoarium. Thin section prepared from less-encrusted topotype (Pl. 12, fig. 5) shows branches slightly wider than fenestrules, dissepiments slightly narrower than branches; fenestrules oval, some constricted to hourglass shape by protrusion of zooecial apertures at sides. Outline of zooecial chamber subpentagonal at base, but transverse sides of pentagons strongly inclined distad; at slightly higher level central zigzag line becomes nearly straight, pentagons inclined forwardly become parallelograms, also inclined forwardly; at still higher level, just below apertures, central line becomes zigzag again; vestibulum expands outwardly distad, so that outline becomes bean-shaped. (*see* sketch Pl. 12, fig. 4, drawn from upper part of slide). Two zooecial apertures per fenestrule, with every other aperture stabilized at base of dissepiment; but occasionally stabilization changes to arrangement of 2 apertures symmetrically on either side of dissepiment (Pl. 12, fig. 5, to right of upper central line). In other rare, sporadic departures from stabilization, there may be 2½ zooecia per fenestrule in one or two fenestrules in succession; also there may be only 1 zooecium per fenestrule where an additional dissepiment is developed halfway between two normally developed ones.

Fenestrules range in holotype from 18 per 10 mm in basal part to 18–18.5 in middle part to 19–19.5 in most distal part preserved. In small fragmentary topotype, from which the illustrated thin section was prepared, number of fenestrules varies from 19 to 20 per 10 mm; this fragment represents part of zoarium where subparallel arrangement of branches rapidly changes to outward curving, accompanied by rapid bifurcation.

Meshwork formula: 18–20/18–19.5//18–19.5/34–35; Prevailing number of fenestrules 18.5–19.

Discussion: The history of the study and classification of this species is unusually interesting and instructive. When originally described it was considered a variety of *Fenestella conradi* Ulrich, and named *compactilis* because the holotype of the variety has a thickly encrusted compact zoarium (Condra, 1903, p. 61). Condra, as well as Ulrich, with whom he consulted, believed that the form *compactilis* is a variety of *F. conradi* Ulrich, because both have about the same kind of meshwork, compact zoarium with narrow fenestrules, and wide and short dissepiments. Also they both belong to about the same age: upper Shawnee group of Virgil Series, Pennsylvanian. Another variety of *F. conradi* from the same beds was described simultaneously by Condra with var. *compactilis*, but received no name. It was "quite unlike typical forms of the species," but was "pronounced by E. O. Ulrich a variety of *F. conradi*, or a closely related species" (Condra, 1903, p. 58).

Since these early descriptions and discussions of late-Paleozoic species of *Fenestella* from America the Russian authors Nikiforova and Shulga-Nesterenko have discovered that several forms of *Fenestella* from the lower Permian of Russia resemble closely the American variety *compactilis* but not the typical form of *F. conradi*. Nikiforova (1938, p. 92) pointed out the close resemblance of *F. rhomboidea* Nikiforova to var. *compactilis*, but decided to describe the Russian form as a new species because the internal structure, particularly the shape of the zooecial chamber of the American form, was not known. Subsequently Shulga-Nesterenko (1941), discovered another form from the Permian of Russia which approaches var. *compactilis* even closer than *F. rhomboidea* Nikiforova, particularly in the meshwork dimensions, and decided to identify this form with *F. conradi compactilis*, even though the zooecial chamber of this American form still remained unknown.

The importance of the shape of zooecial chamber in *Fenestella* has been pointed out by Nekhoroshev, and he and his Russian colleagues demonstrated on many examples that this is one of the most essential diagnostic features in the differentiation of the species. For instance, Nikiforova (1933, p. 10–18, 38) described *F. donaica* var. *major* and *F. beschevensiformis* (from two widely different horizons of the Carboniferous), which have the same external appearance and the same dimensions of meshwork, but have distinctly different internal structure of zooecia. *F. virgosa* and *F. pseudovirgosa* also differ only internally. *Fenestella compactilis*, which is here elevated to specific rank, is another example of the indispensability of knowledge of the structure of the zooecial chamber in differentiation and identification of species of *Fenestella*. The types of *F. compactilis* Condra (including the holotype) were sectioned to permit study of the structure of its zooecial chamber: its outline at the base is an elongated pentagon, the short proximal and distal sides of which are inclined to the axis of the branch so that the whole internal structure has a featherlike appearance. At a higher level above the base this featherlike structure is more emphasized, as the outline of the zooecial chamber becomes elliptical, with the long diameter of the ellipsis at an acute angle to the axis of the branch. At a higher level, just beneath the aperture, the elliptical outline of the chamber is dented at the outer side by an upper hemiseptum. Thus internal structure of *F. compactilis* is unlike that in *F. rhomboidea* Nikiforova, and neither is it like that in the *Fenestella* that Shulga-Nesterenko (1941, p. 98–99) identified with *F. conradi compactilis* Condra. The essential feature differentiating the Russian forms from *F. compactilis* is the pronounced triangular outline of the base of zooecial chambers, which results in basal interwedging of adjacent zooecial rows. At a higher level above the base the chamber in these Russian forms becomes rhombic, hence the specific name *rhomboidea*. Only at a still higher level, just beneath the apertures, does the outline of the zooecial chamber look somewhat like that in the American *F. compactilis*. There it becomes nearly oval, inclined to the axis, and indented on the outer side by an upper hemiseptum.

Perhaps the taxonomic significance of this difference may be disputed and the discussed American and Russian forms classified under the same specific name *compactilis* Condra. However, such classification would not be consistent with the practice of differentiation of species of Bryozoa on the combination of both external and internal characters. As paleontologic practice shows, the comprehensive species established on external features alone frequently have wide vertical range and often prove to be artificial polyphyletic groupings, while the narrowly defined species based on the combination of external and internal structures are apt to be more nearly natural taxonomic units. The latter have proved more useful stratigraphically because they have a more limited vertical range. *F. compactilis* Condra, in restricted sense, remains strictly an upper Pennsylvanian form. The externally similar but internally different *F. rhomboidea* described by Nikiforova is probably of early Permian age, because *F. rhomboidea* var. *podtscheremensis* Shulga (P_1^{1a}) and the form identified by Shulga-Nesterenko as *F. conradi compactilis* (P_1^1) are definitely early Permian. The American Permian (Upper Leonard) form *F. infranodosa* n. sp. is identical with the last mentioned Russian form in all respects, and occupies the same or nearly the same stratigraphic position in the lower Permian. Besides the identity of the meshwork, external details of the obverse, and zooecial chamber, these two forms also have in common the well-developed numerous spines on the reverse of the branches, a feature absent in *F. compactilis*, *F. rhomboidea*, and *F. rhomboidea* var. *podtscheremensis*.

When segregating Russian Permian *Fenestella* in natural groups Shulga-Nesterenko made *Fenestella conradi compactilis* Condra a type of a group in which she placed all species just mentioned, and the Russian form which she identified with *F. compactilis*, here referred to the new American Permian species *F. infranodosa*. In view of the fact that *F. compactilis* is a Pennsylvanian form, perhaps it could be assumed that the outline of the zooecial chamber in the group could possibly evolve from basal pentagonal in the Pennsylvanian to basal triangular (and rhombic at a slightly higher level) in Permian. However, in the American upper Pennsylvanian rocks there is another species, *F. plummerae* Moore, which externally is also like *F. compactilis;* but, sectioning of its types reveals that it has a zooecial chamber typical for *F. rhomboidea* and related Permian forms.

In view of this *F. plummerae* is here considered ancestral to *F. rhomboidea* and related Permian forms, and they are placed together in a single genetic group. *F. compactilis* is placed in the group of *F. binodata*. The two groups, one typified by *F. binodata* and the other by *F. plummerae*, are undoubtedly closely related and probably have diverged from a common earlier Pennsylvanian stock.

Fenestella compactilis var. *plattsmouthensis* n. var.

(Figure 15; Plate 12, figures 6, 7)

Types: Two large and a few smaller fragments in same rock specimen, collected at exposure of lower part of Plattsmouth limestone (Upper member of Oread formation, Shawnee group, Virgil Series), are probably parts of one nearly complete zoarium, larger illustrated fragment designated holotype Nebr. Geol. Survey No. 518.

Description: Zoarium long fanlike to foliate expanse, undulating, 6 cm high and 10 cm wide; branches diverge at about same moderate rate throughout. On either side branches curve gently to right and left, but abruptly straighten and run subparallel to lateral margins of zoarium; only on either side of basal part of zoarium do they continue their rapid outward curving, so that those nearest starting point make nearly hairpin turns. The reverse evenly encrusted but, unlike *F. compactilis*, only a few fenestrules are sealed by it, those at the base of the zoarium where a few pillars rise from the edge and seemingly from the obverse. Branches distinctly wider than fenestrules; dissepiments narrower than branches; most fenestrules hourglass-shaped because apertures intrude their sides. Two zooecia per fenestrule, with every other aperture at base of dissepiments well stabilized but occasionally changing to symmetrical disposition of two apertures on either side of dissepiment for distance of few fenestrules. Infrequently two neighboring dissepiments develop half the normal distance apart. Carina prominent, with two rows of zigzagging nodes; dissepiments depressed on the obverse and the reverse, flush with branches where encrusted on the reverse. Thus thickness of crust over the reverse of branches less than over dissepiments, and because of semitransparency of crust it appears whiter over dissepiments than over branches. Narrow barlike crust over branches usually zigzagging, tending to make fenestrules look hexagonal and their lumen circular on the reverse. Surface of the reverse of branches coarsely grooved under crust. Transverse spicules in crust about 3–4μ in diameter.

Zooecial chamber generally as in *F. compactilis* with following modification. Outline at base of chamber less pentagonal than in *F. compactilis;* central wall between two rows of chambers undulates smoothly instead of angular zigzag. Parallelogram outline at top only local and frequently undeveloped. Usually top outline bean-shaped, with central wall nearly straight. Necklike vestibulum extends higher than in *F. compactilis*, and frequently upper hemiseptum invades it posteriorly.

Meshwork formula: 20/18–19//18–19/36–38, sporadically with greater and irregular variation in spacing of fenestrules from 17 to 20.

Discussion: The form is considered a variation of *F. compactilis* because its meshwork is only slightly coarser. The change in the zooecial chamber is of some significance because it indicates a trend toward the stratigraphically higher *F. infranodosa* and *F. quadratopora*, which have distinct upper hemiseptum.

The development and character of the encrustation is not considered by us as specifically important, and the heavily encrusted original *F. compactilis* is placed in the same species with moderately encrusted *F. compactilis* var. *plattsmouthensis*. The tissue which encrusts these species is made of laminated sclerenchyma with only a few spicules or filaments, which are 3–4μ, seldom to 7μ in diameter in *F. compactilis;* Shulga-Nesterenko indicates that *F. infranodosa* (her *F. compactilis*) has two kinds of "capillaries," smaller 2 to 5μ and larger 7 to 17μ in diameter.

Fenestella infranodosa n. sp.

(Plate 12, figures 8–10)

? 1936. *Fenestella conradi compactilis* forma A; Shulga-Nesterenko, 1936, Trudy, Poliarnaia komissia, Akad. Nauk, Leningrad, p. 270 (no illustrations)

1941. *Fenestella conradi compactilis* Shulga-Nesterenko, Lower Permian Bryozoa of the Urals, p. 98–99, Fig. 57; Pl. 17, fig. 3; Pl. 18, figs. 2, 3

Types: Several large fragments obtained by dissolution of limestone from upper Leonard, fossiliferous limestone collected at locality 119 "below and to the west of Clay Slide," Texas (R. E. King, 1930, p. 135); best preserved fragment designated holotype, Nebr. Geol. Survey No. 519.

Description: All fragments from distal part of zoarium: fan-shaped, somewhat undulating longitudinally, stronger undulations accompanied by locally intensified bifurcation. Branches straight to gently and variously curved, slightly narrower than fenestrules; dissepiments usually half as wide as branches, depressed on the obverse and the reverse. Fenestrules hourglass-shaped because of protrusion of zooecial apertures in middle of sides; every other aperture is located at base of a dissepiment. Carina prominent; two rows of nodes at its crest, which locally expand into long cylindrical spines, inclined intermittently right and left.

Thick spines sharply pointed and generally somewhat inclined distad arise from the reverse. Spacing of these spines not as regular as that of carinal nodes on the obverse, although also commonly arranged in two rows but frequently changing to one row. Single row of small, densely spaced upright spines develops occasionally on dissepiments. Sharpness of outline of zooecial chamber dulled by silicification; is broadly triangular at base, changing to elongate oval in featherlike arrangement at higher level (Pl. 12, fig. 10), much like the Russian form (Shulga-Nesterenko, 1941, p. 98, fig. 57) identified with this species.

Meshwork formula: 20/19//19/38, with nearly as many spines on the reverse of branches.

Discussion: The new species is closest to *F. compactilis* Condra, from which it is distinguished by different outline of zooecial chamber. In *F. compactilis* it is pentagonal at the base, changing to a parallelogram and becoming bean-shaped at higher levels. Also, *F. compactilis* has no spines on the reverse. Another similar form is *F. rhomboidea* Nikiforova, which has rhombic outline of zooecial chamber and no spines on the reverse. All these species seem closely related, but their differentiation conforms with the general principles of the taxonomy followed and is stratigraphically justified. Successive species are: *F. compactilis* from the late Pennsylvanian; *F. infranodosa* from the Permian (Leonard) in America and P_1^1 and higher Permian in Russia. Although the exact age of *F. rhomboidea* is unknown (late Pennsylvanian or early Permian), its variety *podtscheremensis* Shulga is from P_1^{1a} of the lower Permian.

F. infranodosa (?) var.

(Plate 12, figures 11, 12)

Description and Discussion: Small fragment of form seemingly identical with *F. infranodosa*, except for lack of spines on the reverse, has been obtained by dissolution of fossiliferous specimen from Fourth limestone of Word group, locality 192, north of junction of Road and Gilliland canyons, section 17, Texas. (R. E. King, 1930, p. 136).

Because the silicification eradicated the outlines of the zooecial chamber, the fragment is only provisionally identified as a variety of *F. infranodosa*, and is distinguished from the typical form by the lack of spines on the reverse.

Meshwork formula: 20–21/18.5 19//19–38, with 2 zooecia per fenestrule stabilized.

Group IX, **Fenestella (Minilia) plummerae** Moore

F. plummerae Moore, **F. rhomboidea** Nikiforova, **F. rhomboidea** var. **podtscheremensis** Nikiforova, **F. clinospina** n. sp., **F. quadratopora** Shulga, and **F. sub-quadratopora** Shulga

1941. Complex *Fenestella conradi compactilis* Shulga-Nesterenko, Paleontology U.S.S.R., v. 5, pt. 5, fasc. 1, p. 44

First two Russian forms listed were originally placed by Shulga-Nesterenko with *Fenestella conradi compactilis* Condra in group believed characterized by Condra's form. However, *F. compactilis* Condra belongs in separate group of species with zooecial chambers elongate oval and arranged in featherlike fashion, while in *F. plummerae* group, where *F. rhomboidea* apparently belongs, zooecial chambers are triangular and interwedge at base, becoming rhombic at higher level. In other important respects it stands close to group *F. compactilis* Condra: both have double row of carinal nodes, and dissepiments stabilized in relation to zooecial apertures. They differ in number of dissepiments per given space. In addition group *F. plummerae* has branches as wide or wider than fenestrules; in group *Fenestella compactilis*, branches are narrower to much narrower than fenestrules, resulting in quadrate form of fenestrules and very diffuse zoarium.

The two Russian species mentioned have practically the same meshwork formula as *F. plummerae* and could be considered at least its varieties rather than different species (*see* discussion under *F. plummerae*). The new American species *F. clinospina* from the Leonard of West Texas is apparently an advanced form derived from *F. plummerae,* as it has coarser meshwork and intense development of carinal spines.

Fenestella plummerae Moore

1929. *Fenestella plummerae* Moore, Jour. Paleontology v. 3, p. 19–20, Pl. 2, figs. 11, 12

Types: Kansas Geol. Survey no. 51–143. Holotype fragment, 4 mm x 3 mm; the obverse and the reverse illustrated. The smallest of three cotypes studied was polished on the reverse in order to study zooecial chambers.

Description: Zooecial chamber broadly triangular at base, tending to interwedge and becoming rhombic at slightly higher level. There is perfect coordination in spacing of dissepiments, zooecial apertures, and carinal nodes, whereby every other aperture is located at base of dissepiment, and at each aperture there is a node, located in diagonal direction backward and inward toward middle of branch. There are twice as many nodes as apertures in single row on both sides of branch. Nodes moderately prominent, possibly only bases preserved; diameter about two-thirds that of apertures. Apertures ornamented by small tubercles. Some apertures circular; others pyriform; looplike extension making this shape extending proximad; dissepiments ornamented by 3 or 4 fine longitudinal ribs, which diverge around apertures at base of dissepiments; carina prominent, smooth, with nodes making two rows, each marginal on narrow crest of carina.

Meshwork formula: Remeasurements of dimensions of cotypes differ slightly from those given by Moore (his formula apparently measured on holotype): 22–24/22//21–22/42–44; based on the cotypes: 20–22/19–21//19–21/38–42.

Discussion: F. plummerae is very close to *F. compactilis* Condra in external features and stabilization of dissepiments in relation to apertures. However, the latter has a coarser meshwork and a differently shaped zooecial chamber. Russian species *F. rhomboidea* and its variety *podtscheremensis*, which belong in the same group with *F. plummerae*, differ from it as follows: *F. rhomboidea* has a coarser meshwork formula: 18–20/18–19//19–20/38–40, which is nearer that of new species *F. clinospina*, while *F. rhomboidea* var. *podtscheremensis*, with formula 18.5–19/20–21.5//21.5–40, has rounded pentagonal outline at base of zooecial chamber, instead of triangular as in *F. plummerae.*

Fenestella clinospina n. sp.

(Plate 13, figures 1–4)

Types: Holotype Nebr. Geol. Survey No. 522 and paratypes obtained by dissolution in hydrochloric acid of limestone from upper Leonard, locality 119, King and King coll., below and west of Clay Slide, Texas (R. E. King, 1930, p. 135; P. B. King, 1930, p. 136).

Description: Largest fragment, designated holotype, about 35 mm wide and 20 mm long, is from middle part of nearly flat, slightly undulating zoarium. Branches about as wide as to slightly narrower than fenestrules; straight to variously curved, bifurcate and diverge in somewhat irregular fashion; zoarium expands rapidly into fan-shaped, foliate growth form. Bifurcations abrupt and nearly always U-shaped; no additional row of zooecia added below points of bifurcation.

In proximal part of zoarium branches above bifurcations are only slightly narrower than parent branch. Hence fenestrules, not branches, change their width considerably at points of bifurcation, from unusually wide below to much narrower above.

In distal part of zoarium branches above bifurcations are only about a half to two thirds as wide as parent branches.

Dissepiments only slightly narrower than branches, about flush with them on the obverse and the reverse; fenestrules rounded rectangular to rounded quadrate, tending to become elliptical and circular. Apertures project into fenestrules only occasionally and slightly; they are circular, seemingly ornamented with pimples, but generally not sufficiently well preserved for study of details. Carina prominent but narrow, with double row of straight spines, slightly inclined right and left, according to right and left position on carina. If fully developed (or fully preserved) each spine bifurcates into two branches, which diverge in plane diagonal to carina. Outline of hollow zooecial chamber becomes observable with variously advanced erosion: triangular and interwedging at base, becoming rhombic at higher level.

Reverse of branches generally roughly tuberculate, in places with thick nodes; their sharp cusps slightly inclined distad along branches, arranged in single straight or somewhat zigzagging row, with about 2 or slightly more nodes per fenestrule.

Several pillars arise in irregular groups from the reverse of holotype. Pillars solid, longitudiaally striated, somewhat curved and irregularly branching at distal parts, where they were apparently attached to some unknown objects. The reverse generally encrusted by thin veneer, segregated at some points into prostrate fascicles, which coalesce and grow into the pillars.

Meshwork formula: 16/17–19//17–19/30–40.

Discussion: Meshwork and double row of spines are similar to those in *Fenestella magnospinata* Shulga (1952, p. 48–49; Fig. 24; Pl. 9, fig. 3) from Schwagerina horizon of Iurak-Tau, Russia. Imperfectly preserved zooecial chamber of *F. clinospina* is also not unlike that of *F. magnospinata*, but the American species differs in having no nodes upon the reverse, while the Russian species has prominently developed nodes in two rows on its reverse. If it were not for this difference the American and Russian forms could be considered conspecific; American form is stratigraphically younger.

Fenestella quadratopora Shulga

(Plate 11, figures 9–12)

1939. *Fenestella quadratopora* Shulga-Nesterenko, Permian Bryozoa, Atlas of characteristic fossil faunas of the U.S.S.R. v. 6, p. 65, Pl. 12, fig. 1
1941. *Fenestella quadratopora* Shulga-Nesterenko, Paleontology of the U.S.S.R., v. 5, pt. 5, fasc. 1, p. 113–114, figs. 73–76; Pl. 25, fig. 4.

Holotype: Slide no. 540, Moscovskii Pedagogicheskii Institut; from Verkhne-Chussovskie Gorodki, borehole 66, depth 405 meters, P_1^1. American material collected at locality 93, Wolfcamp Series, section 24, bed 9, and float from next few higher beds on side of arroyo northeast of Wolf Camp (R. E. King, 1930, p. 131; P. B. King, 1930, p. 54–55). Nebr. Geol. Survey No. 521.

Shulga-Nesterenko mentions many specimens of the species from the bore holes and surficial exposures and gives the following diagnosis for it: meshwork regular, with thin branches, very thin dissepiments, and frequently quadrate fenestrules. Shape of zooecial chamber rounded triangular base; carinal nodes in two rows; capillaries small. She considers as most diagnostic of the species the rhythmic lateral bending of the branches from chamber to chamber (which result in somewhat undulating shape of branches) and very thin dissepiments, especially in comparison with the large zooecial chambers.

Description: Material from the Wolfcamp includes one nearly complete zoarium and many fragments; they add much to understanding of species, originally described from a slide made from a small fragment. Zoarium fan-shaped, 18 mm wide and 9 mm or more high, slightly undulating. Branches straight to variously curved. Manner of bifurcation somewhat unusual for *Fenestella*, resembling that of *Septopora:* instead of equal dichotomy which is customary for *Fenestella*, additional branches arise laterally at an angle. Incomplete holotype illustrated by Shulga-Nesterenko does not show one complete point of birurcation to allow comparative observation. Branches show locally undulating effect as described by Shulga-Nesterenko, and weathering of some allows study of triangular interwedging of zooecial chambers at base of branches. Diffuse meshwork; stability of location of every other aperture at base of dissepiments; slightly zigzag arrangement of nodes along carina, twice the number of zooecia in a row; weak development of crust on the reverse are the same as in Russian holotype.

Meshwork formula: In Russian holotype: 16/16//16/32; and in American specimens 14–19/16–16.5//16–16.5/32. Closer spacing of branching (to 19 per 10 mm) occurs sporadically wherever bifurcations crowd.

Discussion: The diffuse meshwork seems nearest that with subquadrate fenestrules in *Fenestella archimediformis* n. sp., also from the Wolfcamp, but differs from it by having twice as many zigzagging nodes and a coarser meshwork (in *F. archimediformis* 15–17/17–18.5//17–18.5/11–18).

Group X, **Fenestella cylindrica** n. sp.

Unlike other groups of the late-Paleozoic species of *Fenestella*, this group is characterized by its zoarial growth form as well as the meshwork. Its meshwork is with unstabilized 2¼–2½ zooecia per fenestrule, prominent projection of zooecia into fenestrules, low carina, insignificant nodes, and a typical pentagonal zooecial chamber. Its growth form is unique among *Fenestella:* cylindrical bifurcating basket with the poriferous side (obverse) facing outward. The only comparable growth form in Fenestrata has been described by Condra and Elias (1945a, 1945b) for *Bicorbis arizonica.*

Only one species of this group has been collected from the Permian of western Texas, *Fenestella cylindrica* n. sp., but several forms have been collected from the Pennsylvanian of the Mid-Continent. They will be described in a separate paper.

Fenestella cylindrica n. sp.

(Plate 14, figures 1-4)

Holotype: Nebr. Geol. Survey No. 523, from "*Uddenites* zone", Gaptank Series, locality T-88, at Wolf Camp, Texas. University of Texas coll. (R. E. King, 1930, p. 139).

Description: Holotype large fragment from yellowish-brown ferruginous compact (with some fine porosity) calcareous mudstone. Preparatory work revealed its zoarial shape as subcylindrical basket, with the obverse facing outward; basket contracted near middle of upper part, becoming nearly 8-shaped in cross section. In similar growth forms of other species in group as well as of *Bicorbis arizonica* (Condra and Elias, 1945a), 8-shaped cross section of basket precedes bifurcation of zoarium into two branches. Perhaps this is also true in the incompletely preserved *Fenestella cylindrica.*

Meshwork of basket delicate. Branches thin, with little if any encrusting tissue on the reverse. Branches seldom bifurcate, slowly diverge laterally. Third row of zooecia added below points of bifurcation for distance from one to two fenestrules, and even fourth row occasionally added for distance about one fenestrule below bifurcation. This localized departure from two rows of zooecia, results from gradual bifurcation characteristic of species.

Branches average about half as wide as fenestrules; dissepiments slightly narrower than branches. Zooecia average 2¼–2½ per fenestrule, with no fixed position in relation to dissepiments. Apertures circular, with well-developed peristomes, from about their own diameter apart to about two-thirds this distance, protruding conspicuously into fenestrules. Obverse branches slightly convex, with slight indication of thin carina and pimplelike low nodes. Dissepiments only slightly, if at all, below branches on the obverse, and flush with them on the reverse, where branches are slightly grooved. Zooecial chamber pentagonal to nearly rectangular.

Meshwork formula: 26/19.5–21//22–24/27–30, with low carina and insignificant nodes.

Discussion: Apparently the same species was found in Hughes Creek shale, lower Big Blue Series, at Bennett, Nebraska, but the latter form has a well-developed encrustation on the reverse and a few pillarlike braces, which cross-connect the opposite sides of the bifurcating cylindrical growthform. There are other undescribed species of the group from the Virgil Series (Upper Pennsylvanian) of Nebraska in the collection of the Nebraska Geological Survey.

F. cylindrica and other species with a ramose cylindrical growth form, if found in small fragments, may be easily confused with some species of Pennsylvanian group *F. serratula* (not described here), and to a less extent with those of *F. mimica* group. These three groups are seemingly closely related.

Group XI, **Fenestella mimica** Ulrich

F. mimica Ulrich and its varieties, **F. limbata** Foerste, **F. tenax** Ulrich, **F. permica** Shulga, **F. girtyi** Elias, **F. plicata** n. sp., **F. muscus** n. sp.

Part 1937. Group of *Fenestella mimica* Elias, Jour. Paleontology, V. 11, p. 309–318.

Large polyphyletic group includes two conservative long-range species: *Fenestella tenax* and *F. limbata* and several species and varieties of comparatively rapidly evolving lineage of *F. mimica*, type species of group.

Characteristic of group is unstabilized to imperfectly stabilized position of apertures in relation to dissepiments, 2 to 2½ zooecia per fenestrule, more or less pentagonal outline of zooecial chamber, and distinct carina with one row of nodes or spines.

F. mimica is the oldest (Seville limestone, Des Moines Series, Illinois) in *F. mimica* lineage, and, although Ulrich states that each fenestrule contains "generally two [apertures] . . . one . . . opposite each dissepiment and one between" (1890, p. 532), departure from this order is shown in the right side of his Plate 52, figure 7. Tendency toward location of every other aperture at base of dissepiment is evident, but this arrangement does not become stabilized for whole zoarium or its large parts. In some species, such as *F. mimica* var. *rogersi* Elias from the uppermost beds of Missouri Series in Kansas, the number of the apertures average slightly more per fenestrule than in *F. mimica* Ulrich, *F. mimica* var. *raymondi* Elias, and others, but this difference may indicate different position of the fragmentary material in zoarium. All specimens of *F. rogersi* are from distal part of zoaria, as indicated by subparallel branches, in frequent bifurcation, and occasional branch termination. The small

TABLE 9.—*Species of* Fenestella mimica *group*

Species	Principal measurements				Age
	Branches in 10 mm	Fenestrules in 10 mm	Zooecia in 5 mm	Nodes in 5 mm	
F. (*Loculiporina*) *muscus* n. sp.	20	16–17	abt. 20	10–15	Word, West Texas
F. plicata n. sp.	20	19–20	23	abt. 20	Leonard, West Texas
F. girtyi Elias	20–21	16–17	17–18	16–17	Middle Leonard, West Texas
F. permica Shulga, (Elias and Condra)	18–20	16.5–20	17.5–22	17.5–22	Wolfcamp, West Texas
F. permica Shulga	18–20	17–18	18–19	18–19	Lower Permian P_1^1; Russia
F. mimica var. *wellsi* Elias	23	20	20–23	20–23	Garrison shale; Big Blue, Kansas
F. mimica var. *raymondi* Elias	25	21–22	23	32–34	Graham formation; Cisco; Northcentral Texas
F. mimica var. *rogersi* Elias	22–30	20.5–22.5	26–27.5	25–28	Unnamed formation at base of Virgil Series, at Garnett, Kansas (formerly correlated with Lake Creek shale of Nebraska)
F. mimica var. *latirama* Sayre	27	26–27	26–27	37–40	Missouri series, Kansas
F. mimica Ulrich (type)	23–27	22–24	24	32	Seville limestone, Middle Des Moines, Illinois
F. tenax Ulrich, (Elias and Condra)	32	28	26–27	35–40	Lower Leonard; West Texas
F. tenax Ulrich, (Condra and Elias)	30–32	28–29	29–30	20–30	Upper Des Moines, Utah
F. tenax Ulrich, (Condra and Elias)	24–35	25–30	25–31	27–38	Chester, Illinois
F. tenax Ulrich, (Condra and Elias)	28–30	28–29	28–29	30–31	Warsaw, Illinois

fragments on which *F. mimica* Ulrich and its varieties *raymondi* (= var. *texana* Moore 1929, p. 17) and *latirama* Sayre (1930, p. 88–89) are established, belong to proximal or medial parts of zoaria, as indicated by considerable divergence of the branches and their frequent bifurcation.

In a discussion of *F. nodograciosa* from Peru Chronic (*in* Newell, Chronic and Roberts, 1949, p. 118) states that it "seems to be geologically older than members of Elias's evolutionary sequence of species, and does not lend weight to that author's hypothesis of the evolutionary expansion of zoarium in this group." This would be so if *F. nodograciosa* were a member of the group. Chronic correctly compared it with *F. gratiosa* Moore and realized that the South American species differs from typical form of *F. mimica* by "its low median carina and nodes, and its generally more open texture" and then concluded that it "might be considered a South American representative of *F. mimica* (Ulrich) as characterized by Elias" (1937b). However, neither *F. gratiosa* Moore from the Graham formation, Cisco group of Texas, nor *F. nodograciosa* Chronic from the Pennsylvanian of Peru belong to *F. mimica* group because in both carinae are poorly developed and absent in most specimens. They are included here in group XIII characterized by this character.

Hence stratigraphic occurrence of Peruvian form has no bearing on the evolutionary tendency toward expansion or coarseness of meshwork detected in *F. mimica* group, as evident from Table 8. Shulga-Nesterenko detected similar tendency in other groups of *Fenestella*, but there is none in many other groups of the genus.

A small fragment of the species in group *F. mimica*, if it happens to have every other aperture at base of dissepiment, may be easily confused with some species in the groups where such arrangement is fully stabilized. Critical examination of *F. parviuscula* Bassler from the Permian of Timor compels its transfer to *F. spinulosa* group, because its zooecial apertures seem to be stabilized in relation to the dissepiments. Other stratigraphically high Permian species, more nearly related to *F. mimica*, such as *F. permica* (*F. spinilosa* var. *permica* Shulga, 1941, p. 99), *F. plicata* n. sp. from the Leonard, and *F.* (*Loculiporina*) *muscus* n. sp. from the Word are the youngest known representatives of *F. mimica* group. Throughout the group the zooecial chamber remains pentagonal with a tendency toward triangular shape. Its latest American representatives develop a more complex, shrublike zoarial growth form, and a superstructure similar to that in *Hemitrypa*, *Loculipora*, and similar Devonian and Carboniferous fenestellid genera.

The two more conservative stocks of the group *F. limbata* and *F. tenax* range from lower Des Moines to Big Blue (Elias, 1937a, p. 318–319) and from Warsaw to lower Leonard, respectively, surviving to Permian time without appreciable change.

Fenestella mimica var. **rogersi** Elias

(Plate 14, figures 9, 10)

1937. *Fenestrellina mimica* mut. *rogersi* ELIAS, Jour. Paleontology, v. 11, p. 312–313, figs, 3 f–h (holotype) (Generic name *Fenestrellina* has been substituted for *Fenestella* at the request of the editor of the Journal of Paleontology, when the manuscript was submitted for publication).

Holotype: Kansas Univ. no. 221, "Rock Lake shale, Stanton formation, Missouri Series, Pennsylvanian." Recent work on the Stanton formation in Nebraska and Kansas by Elias indicates that the rocks with *F. mimica* var. *rogersi* at Walchia quarry 7 miles northwest of Garnett, Kansas, formerly correlated with the Rock Lake shale and South Bend limestone of Nebraska, are likely to belong at the very base of the Virgil Series locally developed upon differentially eroded Capitan limestone of the Stanton formation.

Discussion and description: This variety was introduced on a small fragment, 1½ x 1½ mm; the measured spacing of its elements had to be much extrapolated when referred to 10- and 5-mm distances (Elias, 1937b, Table 1, p. 315). The newly collected well-preserved topotypes include several larger specimens, and on them new data on spacing were taken for 10- and 5-mm distances. Thus, instead of the spacing of the branches and fenestrules, zooecia and nodes previously given as 27–28 and 20–21 per 10 mm and 28–29 and 28–30 per 5 mm, respectively, the new measurements are: 22–30/20½–22½//26–27½/25–28 (specimen Pl. 14, figs. 9, 10). The abundant new material also allowed observation of zooecial chamber, which is subpentagonal at its base. Peristomes of circular apertures range from inclined to horizontal, but are below the crest of prominent carina. Dissepiments half as wide as branches, striate, much depressed on the obverse, flush with branches on the reverse. Carina wide, prominent, with round stout nodes.

Fenestella permica Shulga

(Plate 14, figures 5–8)

1936. *Fenestella spinulosa* var. *permica* SHULGA-NESTERENKO, Poliarnaia Komissiia Akademii Nauk, Trudy, v. 28, p. 276

1942. *Fenestella spinulosa* var. *permica* SHULGA-NESTERENKO, Paleontology U.S.S.R. v. 5, pt. 5, fasc. 1, p. 99–101; Pl. 16, fig. 4; Pl. 18, fig. 2

Types: Holotype slide no. 532, Moscovskii Pedagogicheskii Institut; from Verkhne-Chusovskie Gorodki bore hole 61, depth 410-416 meters, Permian P_1^1. Although the form averages 2 to slightly more than 2 zooecia per fenestrule, the relationship of apertures to dissepiments is not stabilized. Peristome tuberculate; chamber pentagonal, rarely triangular.

Meshwork formula: 18–20/17–18//18–19/18–19. Our specimen is Nebr. Geol. Survey No. 524, from the middle of the Wolfcamp Series, Schuchert coll. 93-S (19a) (R. E. King, 1930, p. 140); and King and King coll. no. 93-12 (R. E. King, 1930, p. 134; P. B. King, 1930, p. 54–55).

Description and *Discussion:* Two fragments obtained by dissolution of limestone specimen 93-S, represent different parts of large, irregularly undulating foliate zoarium. Rapid divergence and frequent bifurcation of marginal branches in smaller fragment indicate its position in proximal part of zoarium. Apparently correlated with this position is finer meshwork with 19 fenestrules per 10 mm. Larger fragment, with slowly diverging, rarely bifurcating branches, and only 16 to 16.5 fenestrules per 10 mm, is distal part of large zoarium. The latter is nearest to type of *F. permica*. Common to both are character of bifurcation, width of branches, character of fenestrules, and shape of zooecial chamber, which is faintly visible through semitransparent encrustation of the reverse in our specimen. Fine irregularly scattered tubercles on the reverse, about twice as high as broad, seemingly correspond to the "capillaries" of Russian descriptions. Peristome seldom preserved, but in few places its remnants are ornamented with sharp tubercles. Carina with one row of nodes usually poorly preserved. Stabilization of apertures in relation to dissepiments as imperfect as in holotype, averaging 2 slightly more than 2 zooecia per fenestrule in both proximal and distal parts of zoarium. Diameter of apertures increases slightly in distal parts of meshwork; their spacing in relation to fenestrules does not change.

Two other fragments from the King and King collection 93-12 have the reverse exposed; one has been etched out by hydrochloric acid to expose its obverse. Judging by moderate frequency of bifurcation and moderate divergence of branches, harmonious with number of fenestrules (17–18 per 10 mm), its place seems intermediate between proximal and distal parts of zoarium. This is a good match to Russian holotype.

Reverse of 93-12 thinly encrusted; locally encrustation is absent, exposing grooved surface of the reverse. Silicification olbiterated fine structure of encrustation, but in specimens of related *F. girtyi* (?) from the Leonard, structure is sufficiently preserved for point by point comparison.

Fragments of American specimens permit restoration of zoarium of *F. permica* as fan-shaped, more or less flat to undulating, with gradual change from more closely set fenestrules and zooecia at initial part to looser spacing in peripheral part.

Meshwork formula: 20/16.5–17//17.5–18/17 in distal part of zoarium and 20/19.5–20//20–22/? in its proximal part, both no. 93-S (19a). In specimens 93-12 it is 18–19/17–18//18–19/18–19, characteristic of middle part of zoarium. Summarized formula for the whole zoarium: 18–20/16.5–20//17.5–22/17.5–22.

Fenestella girtyi (?) Elias

(Plate 4, figure 1; Plate 15, figures 1–3)

? 1908. *Fenestella spinulosa* (?) Girty, U. S. Geol. Survey Prof. Paper 58, p. 137–138, Pl. 19, figs. 4, 4a

? 1937. *Fenestella girtyi* Elias, Jour. Paleontology, v. 11, p. 314–316

Holotype: From "Dark Limestone", Pine Spring, (station 2930), illustrated by Girty (1908, Pl. 19, figs. 4, 4a).

Types: Several fragments Nebr. Geol. Survey No. 525 obtained by dissolution in hydrochloric acid of rock specimen from middle of Leonard Series, locality 123, section 17, bed 14 (R. E. King, 1930, p. 135; R. B. King, 1930, p. 140). Russian representatives of related *F. permica* known from both P^1_1 and P^2_1 horizons.

Description: Largest fragment, about 4 by 7 mm, apparently distal part of wavy foliate zoarium, with the obverse generally convex. Branches straight, average about as wide as fenestrules; prominent carina with strong nodes, slightly fewer in number than zooecia in adjacent row; disposition of zooecia in relation to fenestrules imperfectly stabilized, but averages little more than 2, occasionally 3, zooecia per fenestrule. Frequently one aperture is at point of departure of dissepiment; next aperture in middle of fenestrule, slightly projecting into it. Bifurcations of branches frequent and abrupt without addition of third zooecial row below points of bifurcation and with slow divergence of two separated branches above. Width of branches above bifurcations usually reduced, slightly below normal to nearly half normal. Zooecial apertures circular to oval, with thick peristomes ornamented by fine tubercles. Dissepiments narrow, faintly ribbed; their surface below level of apertures on the obverse, much depressed on the reverse. Zooecial chambers not distinct, nearly pentagonal.

The reverse of branches covered with longitudinal ribs, about 10 μ wide; distance between their crests ranges from 20 μ to 60 μ. Both crests of ribs and spaces between are covered with densely spaced tubercles, finest about 8 μ and coarsest about 12 μ in diameter. Tubercles tend to be in longitudinal rows. The obverse and lateral sides of branches also covered with tubercles, but most are small and irregularly arranged. Peristomes also ornamented with small and large tubercles, up to 30 μ in diameter. Tubercles not regularly arranged, grow on inner and outer sides of peristomes. Only finest tubercles thickly cover the obverse, reverse, and sides.

Meshwork formula: 20–21/16–17//17–18/16–17, with 2 to somewhat more, rarely to 3, zooecia per fenestrule.

Discussion: The species compares well with *F. permica* from the Permian of Russia and the Wolfcamp of Texas, but has fewer fenestrules and zooecia per unit space; fenestrules and zooecia are larger in the species from the Leonard. *F. girtyi* has more branches per 10 mm than *F. permica,* which seems to result from abnormal crowding of branches owing to frequent bifurcation not accompanied by lateral divergence.

The tubercles of the obverse and the reverse are nearly the same size and arrangement as the "capillaries" in *F. permica* of Russia, which are 7 μ and 15 μ in diameter. Shulga-Nesterenko described tubercles on peristomes of *F. permica,* but it seems likely that all fine ornamentation over the surface of branches, dissepiments, and peristomes is of the same nature. All tubercles are about as high as, or slightly higher than, their width (*see* profiles along edges of lateral sides of branches, dissepiments, and peristomes, Pl. 15, fig. 3). There is little regularity in arrangement and localization of the tubercles of different sizes.

The species was originally described as "*Fenestella spinulosa* (?)" from the "Dark limestone" of the Guadalupian, (Girty, 1908, p. 137), and was later named *F. girtyi* (Elias, 1937b, p. 314), its similarity to *F. parviuscula* being pointed out (p. 316). Comparison of Girty's description and photographs with those of *F. permica* from Russia and with the described specimens of *F. permica* from the Wolfcamp shows the following common features: prominent carina, single row of well-developed nodes, and imperfectly stabilized relationship between zooecia and dissepiments. Girty's measurements of the elements in the specimen from the "Dark limestone" were incomplete. The complete meshwork formula based on his figures and augmented by measurement of his illustrations is: 16–17/17//15–17/17.

Crockford (1945, issued 1946, p. 125, 132) identified *Fenestella girtyi* Elias with *F. aspratilis* Bassler when describing the latter from new material collected from the "Lower Permian" of Lake's Creek Quarry, near Rockhampton, Queensland. She illustrated *F. aspratilis* by a single sketch of the obverse of a small fragment and gave no information on its internal structure. Bassler's photograph of a large fragment of the original *F. aspratilis* from Basleo (1929, Pl. 17, fig. 15) show perfect stabilization of apertures, every other one located at base of a dissepiment and the intervening apertures protruding prominently into the middle of the fenestrules. The fragment which is identified with *F. aspratilis* by Crockford shows imperfect stabilization of the position of the apertures in relation to the dissepiments; in the upper part of the sketch the fenestrules are shown to contain 2½ and even 3 apertures (left side). Also, the apertures are shown to protrude into the fenestrules slightly or not at all. Crockford's specimen is more nearly like *F. tschernovi* Shulga (1941), which has moderately protruding apertures, and practically identical meshwork formula, 15–17/14–16//16–17/17.5, indicating slightly more than 2 zooecia per fenestrule. *F. girtyi* differs from *F. aspratilis* by spacing of dissepiments: in *F. aspratilis* Bassler there are 14 fenestrules per 10 mm, while in *F. girtyi* Elias their number per same length is 16–17 on our material from Middle Leonard and 17 on Girty's type.

Many species of *Fenestella* from Australia and some described from timor need additional study, especially regarding their zooecial chambers, which will provide verification of their relationship to the better known American and Russian forms.

Subgenus **Loculiporina** n. subg.

Generotype: Fenestella (Loculiporina) muscus n. sp.

One of the most interesting and unique forms of late-Paleozoic bryozoans, with zoarium consisting of two, externally almost identical meshworks, one directly above and parallel to the other. Closer study reveals that only lower meshwork contains zooecia; the meshwork is a typical fenestellid expanse, with two rows of zooecia in a branch and regularly spaced fenestrules; branches carinate and extend upward into stout nodes that tend to fuse into solid wall-like crest. Series of occasionally fused nodes support upper "sterile" meshwork, consisting of longitudinal, somewhat flattened bars, that almost perfectly imitate position, shape, and thickness of zooecial branches beneath; bars are transversely connected by numerous regularly spaced shorter bars disposed exactly above dissepiments of zooecial meshwork, looking much like them. As branches of zooecial meshwork bifurcate so do the longitudinal bars of sterile meshwork above. Silicification of whole structure destroyed finer features of external sculpture; observed rugosity is granulation due to silicification.

Both species of this subgenus came fom Word Series. Although they have the same type of superstructure, their meshwork and zoarial growth are different so they must be placed in two groups: one with *Fenestella mimica* and the other, which has twice as many zooecia in long and narrow fenestrules, with *Fenestella veneris*. Thus the superstructure that typifies the new subgenus *Loculiporina* has developed independently, though at about the same geologic time, in two phyletically different groups of *Fenestella*, and this makes the new subgenus polyphyletic. The development of similar superstructure over the obverse of many Devonian and Carboniferous species of *Fenestella* has been considered of generic significance, and recognition of different structural types among these superstructures led to establishment of many genera: *Hemitrypa* Phillips, *Semicoscinium* Prout, *Loculipora* Hall, and others, all of which have fenestellid zooecial meshwork. Perhaps each of the two species with the superstructure like *Loculiporina* should be a separate genus or subgenus, if not referred to *Loculipora*, whose structure is nearest theirs, but the two are not closely related phyletically, and *Fenestella plicata* n. sp. is transitional between *Fenestella* (*Loculiporina*) *muscus* n. sp. and the earlier *F. mimica* and its varieties. As a part of taxonomic compromise the name *Loculiporina* is introduced here as a subgenus for a group of phyletically not closely related species that attain the same stage of evolution. Because this stage has been reached by them at about same geologic time (Wordian), the subgeneric designation *Loculiporina* has stratigraphic importance, much like that of *Schwagerina* (in old sense) among Fusulinidae. As analyzed by Dunbar and Skinner (1936) the phyletically not closely related *Pseudoschwagerina* and *Paraschwagerina* reached the same evolutionary stage of tightly coiled juvenarium and expanded outer volutions, typical of *Schwagerina* in old sense, at about the same geologic time (Wolfcampian = Sakmarian). In our opinion this stage could be appropriately called the Schwagerina evolutionary stage, just as here the *Loculiporina* is an evolutionary stage in some species of *Fenestella*.

Fenestalla plicata n. sp.

(Plate 16, figures 3–6)

Holotype: Nebr. Geol. Survey No. 526, Schuchert's coll. S-7, Leonard Series, Glass Mountains, Texas.

Description: Holotype, only known specimen, nearly 4 cm by 4 cm, complicatedly folded and shrubby, similar to some living *Retepora* or Jurassic *Diastopora*. Generally the obverse faces outward. Unfortunately, silicification of zoarium resulted in obliteration of finer structural details by crystalline quartz, but principal features, including position of zooecial apertures and carinal nodes, are observable. Initial part of zoarium either not preserved, or, possibly, hidden in the maze of numerous intricate small folds and zoarial outgrowths, enveloping its starting point on a fragment of another bryozoan, *Stenopora* (?). Branches of meshwork bifurcate frequently and diverge rapidly in plane of bifurcation in all parts of zoarium; meshwork remains essentially same all over, so that, if detached fragments were found, it would be impossible to say to which part of zoarium they belong. Dissepiments average about half as wide as branches. Fenestrules generally oval; slightly more than 2 zooecia per fenestrule, their apertures apparently circular. Carina wide and high, with strong nodes not preserved or not developed over greater part of zoarium. Where present, nodes not only strong but expanded apically along and across branches, resembling crest of rail beam, an apparent tendency toward superstructure like in subgenus *Loculiporina*. Microsculpture obliterated by coarse silicification. Branches as wide to somewhat wider than fenestrules. Dissepiments somewhat depressed on the obverse, flush with branches on the reverse, half as wide to nearly as wide as branches; fenestrules narrow to oval to nearly circular. Zooecial chamber, judging from rough outlines, seems pentagonal.

Meshwork formula: 20/18-20//21–23/probably about 20.

Discussion: Localized development of supercarina is the principal distinction from similar species of the genus. Unique feature is also the intricately folded, shrublike zoarium, differing from the ordinary zoaria of *Fenestella* and related genera. It resembles the zoarium of *Retepora* from Nordgaard, as illustrated in Canu and Bassler (1920, fig. 140-W, p. 499).

Fenestella (Loculiporina) muscus n. sp.

(Plate 16, figures 7–11)

Holotype: Nebr. Geol. Survey no. 527, King and King coll. no.T-144a, Word Series, ravine 3 miles east of Hess Tank, Glass Mountains, Texas (R. E. King, 1930, p. 140).

Description: Holotype, only specimen collected and subsequently etched from rock matrix, is distal portion of complex shrublike plicated zoarial growth form. Resembles closely related *Fenestella plicata*, but plications much gentler, seemingly because of more complete development of superstructure that stiffened its meshwork. Because of gentle plication, fan-shaped design of expanse is distinct. Two fan-shaped, frontally concave expanses grew parallel face to face, their margins coming into contact along the edges, as if they were sewed together as a flattened bag. No bracing pillars present inside or outside this bag, but the reverse seems encrusted. Coarsely granular silicification of originally calcareous zoarium destroyed microstructure. Growth form complicated by development of subsidiary smaller expanses in subparallel orientation.

The obverse of zoarial meshwork in all parts of complex zoarium shielded by superstructure, imitating almost perfectly poriferous meshwork under it, making it difficult to study the latter, except by removing superstructure. Meshwork can be observed at distal edges of expanse, where the obverse is occasonally seen because development of superstructure lags behind underlying poriferous meshwork.

Branches of poriferous meshwork frequently bifurcating and rapidly diverging; wide as, or somewhat wider than fenestrules. Dissepiments average as wide as branches; fenestrules oval, a few nearly circular; slightly more than 2 zooecia per fenestrule; disposition of apertures in relation to dissepiments not stabilized. Zooecial chamber pentagonal to almost rectangular, except lateral septa turned at an angle distad. Nearly straight course of medial septa between two rows of zooecial chambers possibly consequence of strong development of carina. Superstructure as follows: carina extends upward into nodes which tend to fuse and form solid but not thick wall. Crest of this wall expands like flanges of rail beam, as wide as width of branch underneath. Where branches bifurcate so do beams and their crests above. Crests are also interconnected by dissepimentslike transverse links as wide as dissepiments and disposed exactly above them. Meshwork of superstructure exactly like that of underlying zoarial expanse, except it has no zooecia and is somewhat thinner than the latter.

Meshwork formula: 20/16–17//about 20/about 10, the number of uprights which rise from the keel and support the superstructure.

Discussion: The superstructure of this species is essentially the same as in *Fenestella pavonia* n. sp., and on this ground the two species are classified in the same subgenus, *Loculiporina.* However, their underlying meshworks are considerably different, and they are placed in different groups of the genus *Fenestella.* There is also considerable difference between the growth forms of the two species. Thus the subgeneric name *Loculiporina* does not indicate genetic closeness of the two but designates a stage or "platform" in the evolutionary development (building of superstructure) reached independently in two phyletic lines within the comprehensive genus *Fenestella.*

The peculiar growth form and the development of the superstructure easily distinguish *F. muscus* from other species of *Fenestella* that have similar meshwork.

Fenestella tenax Ulrich

(Plate 16, figures 1, 2)

1888. *Fenestella tenax* ULRICH, Bull. Denison Univ., v. 4, p. 71
1890. *Fenestella tenax* ULRICH, Geol. Survey Illinois, v. 8, p. 546, Pl. 51, figs. 2–2e
? 1906. *Fenestella tenax* (?) CUMINGS, Ind. Dept. Geol. Nat. Res., 30th Ann. Rept. (1905), p. 1279, Pl. 30, fig. 1, Pl. 21, figs. 1–16
not 1926. *Fenestella tenax* NEKHOROSHEV, Comité Geol. Leningrad Bull. v. 43, p. 1248, Pl. 19, fig. 12; Pl. 20, fig. 1 (Probably referable to *Fenestella serratula* Ulrich)
1944. *Fenestella tenax* CONDRA and ELIAS, Geol. Soc. America Spec. Paper 53, p. 99–102, Pl. 21, figs. 1–3

1952. *Fenestella submicroporata* SHULGA-NESTERENKO, Trudy Paleont. Inst. t. 37, p. 35–36, fig. 15; Pl. 4, fig. 2.

Types: Specimens illustrated by Ulrich, (1890, Pl. 51, figs. 2, 2a, 2b) from Warsaw formation are considered typical of species (*see* Condra and Elias, 1944, p. 99). Plesiotype Nebr. Geol. Survey no. 528 from lower part of Leonard Series, locality 124, hill south of forks of Hess Canyon, south of road to Word Ranch, Texas (specimen 124, R. E. King, 1930, p. 135).

Description: Single fragment of delicate zoarium disclosed by breaking limestone specimen; also containing large undulating foliate fistuliporid bryozoan[16].

Fracture which exposed the described bryozoan occurred generally along its curved zoarium so that parts of the zoarium remained on one and other parts on the other fragment. Thus, portions of both the obverse and the reverse sides of one zoarium were exposed.

Fragment of zoarium, about 12 mm wide and 8 mm high, represents middle part of foliate zoarium, with moderately rapid expansion, curved to form flaring funnel or semifunnel with the obverse facing outward. Branches about as wide as fenestrules; dissepiments slightly narrower than branches, making subrectangular fenestrules slightly longer than wide. Slightly less than 2 zooecia per fenestrule with tendency toward occasional stabilization of every other circular aperture at base of dissepiment. Carina rather narrow but prominent and bearing a single row of distinct, numerous, low, round nodes. Scraping, polishing, and slight etching of portions of reverse shows outline of chamber pentagonal tending toward triangular. Zoarium thin; its reverse thinly encrusted, obscuring longitudinal grooving of branches.

Meshwork formula: 32/28//26–27/35–40.

Discussion: This is a late holdover of the well-known and common upper Mississippian species. Condra (1903, p. 52–53) doubtfully referred to this species some Nebraska specimens of "a coarse variety", not quite typical for *F. tenax*. In the extensive collections at the Nebraska Geological Survey there are some specimens (from the Brentwood, Morrow Series, of Arkansas) whose meshwork is finer than that of *F. serratula* but somewhat coarser than typical of *F. tenax*; and others with still coarser zoaria from higher beds of the Morrow at Ardmore, Oklahoma, and elsewhere. Delicate zoaria with meshwork as fine as that in the upper Mississippian representatives of *F. tenax* occur in the Oquirrh formation (late Des Moines age) of Utah (*see* Condara and Elias, 1944, Table 83). A similar form occurs in the Plattsmouth limestone (Oread formation) of Shawnee group, Virgil Series, at Lecompton, Kansas, and a coarse variety of *F. tenax* was found in the Hughes Creek shale of the lower Big Blue Series at Bennett, Nebraska. However, Pennsylvanian and lower Permian occurrences of *F. tenax* and its coarse variety are rare, especially compared with the abundance of this species in the upper Mississippian rocks. The present record of the form in the lower Leonard constitutes the youngest known occurrence of the species. It is of some interest, therefore, to note that this late example of the species shows hardly any changes from the Mississippian type. The only distinctive features are the larger number of nodes and a tendency toward stabilization of position of every other aperture at the base of dissepiments in the specimen from the Leonard. Thus, occurrences of *F. tenax* in the Pennsylvanian and Permian indicate persistence but not abundance of this conservative form along side many more advanced forms of *Fenestella*.

Group XII. **Fenestella spinulosa** Condra

F. spinulosa Condra, **F.** (**Cervella**) **aspera** Chronic, **F. moorei** Sayre, **F. pectinis** Moore, **F. parviuscula** Bassler, **F. parviuscula** var. **libellus,** n. var., **F. archimediformis** n. sp., **F. aspratilis** Bassler, **F. nikiforovae** Shulga, **F.** (**Cervella**) **cervoidea** Chronic, **F.** (**Cervella**) **cruciformis** n. sp., **F. pulcherima** Shulga, **F. tschernovi** Shulga, **F. tschernovi** var. **usiensis** Shulga, **F. shulgae** n. sp.

Group characterized by nearly stabilized to perfectly stabilized disposition of zooecia: one at base of dissepiment, and other at middle of fenestrule. Differs from other groups with same or nearly same stabilization of zooecia by having only one row of nodes on well-developed carina, and by pentagonal to triangular to interwedging zooecial chamber.

[16] This is one of the few specimens of the Leonard limestone in which the fossils are not silicified; therefore, bryozoans cannot be liberated from the rock matrix by its dissolution in hydrochloric acid.

TABLE 10.—*Species of* Fenestella spinulosa *group*

Species	Principal measurements				Age
	Branches in 10 mm	Fenestrules in 10 mm	Zooecia in 5 mm	Nodes in 5 mm	
F. tschernovi var. *usiensis* Shulga	16–17	14.5	14.5	14.5	Usinsk ser. P_1^2, Permian; Russia
F. tschernovi var. *usiensis* Shulga	15	14–15	14–15	13–14	Word; West Texas
F. nekhoroshevi n. sp.	12–14	12	12	12–15	Lower Permian, Lipovaia Gora, Russia
F. aspratilis Bassler	15	14	14	abt. 14	Basleo, Timor.
F. tschernovi, Shulga	15–17	14–16	16–17	16–17	Lower Permian P_1^1, Russia
F. tschernovi, Shulga, (Elias and Condra)	13–15	14.5–16	14.5–16	11–14	Middle Leonard, West Texas
F. cf. *parviuscula* Bassler, (Elias and Condra)	20–24	17–18	18	19–23	Lower Leonard, West Texas
F. parviuscula var. *libellus* n. var.	17	15.5–17	16–17	19–21	Wolfcamp Series, West Texas
F. parviuscula Bassler	20	18	18	18	Bitauni, Timor
F. cervoidea Chronic	24–25	22	22	23	Lower Permian, Peru
F. cruciformis n. sp.	24–25	21–22	21–22	25–28	Lower Leonard, West Texas
F. nikiforovae Shulga	18–20	18–21	20–21	18–19	Lower Permian, Russia
F. nikiforovae Shulga, (Elias and Condra)	20	19–21	20	17–18	Wolfcamp Series, West Texas
F. archimediformis n. sp.	15–17	17–18.5	17–18.5	11–18	Wolfcamp Series, West Texas
F. cornuta n. sp.	21–23	18–20	18–20	18–20	Wolfcamp Series, West Texas
F. aspera Chronic	19–23	16–24	22–26	17–21	Lower Permian, Peru
F. pectinis Moore	20–21	20–22	20–22	24	Graham formation, Cisco, Northcentral Texas
F. moorei Sayre	24–30	24	24	24	Missouri Series, Kansas

Fundamental growth form fan-shaped, foliate or undulating, tending to grow to a large size, 5 cm by 5 cm or more.

The oldest known representative of this group is *F. moorei* Sayre from the Missouri Series in Kansas. Next in age is *F. pectinis* Moore from the latest Pennsylvanian of Texas, then *F. spinulosa* from the Neva of the Big Blue Series of Nebraska. There are several species and varieties of the group in about the same age and younger beds of Permian in western Texas, the Wolfcamp and the Leonard. Some of them are distinctly related to *F. spinulosa* from Nebraska, and some more nearly like the contemporaneous Russian and Timor forms. Perhaps the Russian and East Indies Permian forms evolved from the original early stock in the Carboniferous of America. The differences between the various species of the group are not striking, but the evolutionary trend toward larger forms with coarser meshwork is obvious, especially in the earlier forms. Most species from the Leonard and equivalent horizons elsewhere also have a distinctly coarser meshwork than those from the Wolfcamp and its age equivalents. The coarsest meshwork is in *F. aspratilis* Bassler (1929, p. 76) from Basleo of Timor and *F. pulcherima* Shulga (1941, p. 117) from P_1^1 of Russia, which is possibly identical with *F. tschernovi* var. *usiensis* Shulga (1941, p. 102) from P_1^2, the Usinsk Series of Russia and with *F. aspratilis* Bassler (1929, p. 76) from the Basleo of Timor. *F. crusiformis* n. sp. from the Leonard has a finer meshwork comparable to that in *F. pectinis*. This variety and *F. cornuta* n. sp. of the Wolfcamp have developed complicated carinal spines.

Fenestella spinulosa Condra

(Plate 17, figure 2)

Part 1902. *Fenestella spinulosa* CONDRA, Am. Geologist, v. 30, no. 6, p. 343–344, Pl. 31, figs. 4–6
Part. 1903. *Fenestella spinulosa* CONDRA, Nebr. Geol. Survey. v. 2, pt. 1, p. 55–56, 110–111, Pl. 10, figs. 1–5

Types: Condra indicated two specimens as types (1903, p. 56). Because first is lost, second mentioned, Nebr. Geol. Survey No. 4-7-4-00 is now designated holotype, from Neva limestone of Grenola formation, 1 mi. north of Roca, Nebraska. Because only its reverse exposed, we select a supplementary type, topotype Nebr. Geol. Survey specimen no. 10-7-4-00 (39), which has the obverse exposed. Imperfectly preserved large fragment of zoarium from Wolfcamp Series, bed 9, section 24, northeast of Wolf Camp, Texas, is referred to this species (Pl. 17, fig. 2.)

Description: Zoarium foliate, nearly flat; dissepiments closer spaced in proximal part; branches with frequent bifurcation and fanlike divergence, more distantly spaced and nearly parallel in distal part; zooecial chamber triangular at base. Specimen from the Wolfcamp (Pl. 17, fig. 2) has subparallel branches indicative of position in distal part of large, somewhat transversely undulating zoarium. Spacing of dissepiments, 19 per 5 mm, also indicative of distal position in the zoarium.

Meshwork formula: 19–20/19.5–21.5//19.5–21.5//21–25, remeasured on holotype and topotypes.

Discussion: Because nearly all the numerous specimens of *F. spinulosa* from the Neva at Roca, Nebraska, have the reverse exposed and the few with obverse exposed have the details either somewhat weathered or obscured by adherent particles of matrix, it is difficult to compare the details of the obverse with that in the other species of *F. spinulosa* group, here described. Evidently *F. spinulosa* is closely related to its probable direct ancestors *F. pectinis* Moore and *F. moorei* Sayre from the Upper Pennsylvanian of the Mid-Continent. They could be considered as varieties or early mutations (in Waagen's sense), and the comparison of their meshwork formulae (see Table 9) indicates an evolutionary trend from a finer to coarser mesh.

Fenestella cornuta n. sp.

(Plate 17, figures 3–9; Plate 18, figure 6)

Holotype: Nebr. Geol. Survey No. 529, King and King coll., locality 93-12x, Wolfcamp Series, section 24, bed 9 (P. B. King, 1930, p. 55). Originally zoarium was embedded in rock with its reverse exposed. The obverse was liberated from covering rock by dissolution in weak hydrochloric acid, and zoarium broke into four large fragments.

Description: Cone-shaped zoarium, up to 3 mm across, in neanastic or full-grown stage, a foliate fan-shaped expanse, with small circular base, curled and fused into open funnel somewhat compressed laterally (Pl. 17, figs. 3, 4). Line of contact and fusing of lateral edges of funnel somewhat ragged and angular (Pl. 17, fig. 3). The obverse faces inside.

Branches straight and bifurcate occasionally and abruptly, with no third row of zooecia added below bifurcations. Bifurcation much more frequent near base of funnel, accompanied by rapid fanlike divergence of branches at edge of curling expanse. Branches about as wide as fenestrules, with thin well-developed carina carrying thin upright spines, that are seldom preserved. Full-grown spines are about 0.2 mm long and expand at apices transversely into thin, symmetrical, repeatedly bifurcating, antlerlike structures (Pl. 17, figs. 8, 9); hence, the name *cornuta*.

Dissepiments average half as wide as branches, usually grooved, upper surfaces about flush with adjacent zooecia; fenestrules subrectangular with rounded corners, and slight, occasional projection of apertures located at middle of fenestrules; zooecia round, with solid peristomes slightly less than own diameter apart, commonly disposed so that one occurs at base of dissepiment and other opposite center of fenestrule. Dissepiments, besides those regularly disposed, rarely developed.

Dense crust covers branches, dissepiments, and zooecia, and envelops the spines and their delicate antlerlike superstructure; the latter however is distinctly visible through the semitransparent crust, and the sharp apical points of the antlers occasionally project beyond the crust (Pl. 17, fig. 9).

A group of 11 straight to gently curving, tapering, striate, and barbed pillars arises from the inner surface (which is the obverse) of the funnel near its base (Pl. 17, fig. 9, left; Pl. 18, fig. 6, center).

Meshwork formula: 21–23/18–20//18–20/18, with well-stabilized disposition of 2 zooecia per fenestrule. Variability in spacing of dissepiments, which determines number of fenestrules per given space, is correlated with zoarial growth. Densest spacing of dissepiments is 19 to 20 per 10 mm at base of funnel and they become less densely spaced with a well-stabilized number of 18–19 per 10 mm along the distal part of the funnel.

Discussion: The new species differs from *F. spinulosa* by its slightly coarser meshwork and fewer and more nearly stabilized number of nodes equaling the number of zooecia in a row. Its nodes average thinner than in *F. spinulosa* and have complex antlerlike apices. However, because the character of the apex of the nodes in *F. spinulosa* is unknown, this latter difference may be only apparent. *Fenestella ornata* Shulga (1942, p. 88–89) from the Permian of Russia (P_1^1 and P_1^{1a}) has similar apical outgrowths of the nodes but belongs to a different group of forms, as it has unstabilized 2.5 to 3 zooecia per fenestrule, tuberculate peristomes, and other features unlike those in *F. spinulosa* and *F. cornuta*. The curling of the zoarium into funnel form distinguishes *F. cornuta* from that of *F. spinulosa*; however, because the funnel is wide open, its distal parts are only slightly curved to nearly flat, and, therefore, fragments cannot be distinguished from *F. spinulosa*. Besides, the zoarial growth form is variable in some Fenestrata and not generally used in differentiation of species or genera, except in *Archimedes*, *Lyropora*, and similar complex forms.

If the barbed pillars in *F. cornuta* are integral part of the colony, their prominent development and position in the funnel is difficult to explain. Only 2 or 3 of the group of 11 pillars contact the opposite sides of the funnel and therefore could be considered to function as braces, serving the purpose of strengthening the growth form; but most of them have free, perfectly developed, delicate apices and show no tendency to serve as diagonal braces. The intense and regular development of barbs on each pillar serves no apparent purpose. The somewhat similar barbs on the radicles in some rare living Bryozoa (Pl. 17, fig. 11) have been explained as a device for anchorage in soft or fluffy substratum, such as provided by some sponges to which they were found attached (Peach, 1878, p. 240); but this could not possibly be the purpose of the barbed pillars inside the zoarium of *F. cornuta*. There are only four stumps of broken pillars on the outer (which is the reverse) surface, near the base of the zoarial funnel, and these could and probably did serve its anchorage. Yet, the one outer pillar that was saved from breaking because it was bent down to the outer surface of the funnel and became fused to it shows no barbs on its smooth surface. The barbed pillars are more nearly like barbed branches of the Red Alga *Asparagopsis armata* than like the barbed radicles of the living Bryozoa (Pl. 17, fig. 11). The barbed branches in this living alga serve the purpose of vegetative propagation, through proliferation upon attachment to the substratum and subsequent breaking from parent plant. When the barbed pillars in the described *Fenestella cornuta* touch the opposite side of the funnel, they adhere to it by an apparent delicate proliferation but do not tend to develop mechanically strong contact.

Fenestella archimediformis n. sp.

(Plate 18, figures 1–5; Plate 19, figures 1–10)

Holotype: Nebr. Geol. Survey No. 530, King and King Coll., locality 93, Wolfcamp Series, section 24, bed 9 (R. E. King, 1930, p. 134; P. B. King, 1930, p. 55). Supplementary type Nebr. Geol. Survey No. 529a, same collection, horizon, and locality.

Description: Nearly complete coiled part of zoarium liberated from matrix by dissolution in hydrochloric acid selected for holotype. This spirally coiled funnel-shaped expanse (Pl. 18, fig. 1–3) could have been easily mistaken for part (slightly more than one coil) of *Archimedes*, except for the absence of any trace of a screwlike shaft in the center. In the place where an *Archimedes* screw should be, there is a small open space, 1 mm diameter. Branches of expanse radiate from central hole in manner typical of *Archimedes*, and branches and dissepiments near hole are encrusted on the reverse by tissue, which becomes distinctly thinner few fenestrules away from center. Several supporting pillars rising subperpendicularly from encrustation around hole are reminiscent of manner in which similar pillars frequently depart from flanges of *Archimedes*, particularly near its base. However, in *Fenestella archimediformis* encrusting tissue, though distinctly thicker at center does not tend to seal fenestrules and thus does not produce real flange typical of *Archimedes*. The whole coiled zoarium closely resembles topmost part of large *Archimedes*, where coiling is less tight, and screwlike shaft and adjacent flange gradually weaken and disappear, while meshwork remains coiled. However, holotype could not have been apical part of *Archimedes*, because zoarial branches curving downward do not show convergence toward would be shaft but indicate its probable direct continuity with what may be visualized as less-coiled main part of large, foliate expanse, from whose margin spiral growth form probably arose: compare similar, smaller marginal coiling of nearly flat zoarium, accompanied by local development of encrustation and supporting pillars, in supplementary type (Pl. 19, fig. 5, 6). Supplementary type shows also two-floor or even three-floor development of zoarial expanse; floors probably parts of single complex growth form not wholly preserved. Similar growth form, made of meshwork above meshwork, all facing same way, was described for *Fenestella plebeia* from the English Lower Carboniferous by Vine (1879). Identity of meshwork in all three floors is emphasized by presence of fine serration along middle of reverse of branches, with variable number of sharp cusps, about 30 to 40 per 5 mm; and carinal nodes on the obverse of all floors are equally poorly developed.

Essential character of meshwork remains same in all parts of zoarial growth, except for some variation in spacing of elements. However, this variability does not affect perfect stabilization of zooecial apertures and dissepiments: every other aperture at base of dissepiment. Only exception is occasional development of additional dissepiment between pairs of opposite apertures for succession of two to four apertures in row (Pl. 18, fig. 5).

Zoarial branches narrower than fenestrules, straight, occasionally abruptly bifurcating, with no additional zooecia developed below bifurcation; occasionally branching lateral instead of ordinary U-shaped bifurcation. Dissepiments average about half as wide as fenestrules, lower than branches on the obverse and the reverse; fenestrules almost square, with tendency toward hourglass outline because of projection of zooecia from middle of sides; zooecial apertures circular, with weakly developed peristome, spaced about own diameter apart; carina usually distinct, narrow, elevated and commonly ornamented with strong nodes but, some without nodes. Where fully developed and preserved (Specimen 1-1A3) nodes up to 0.4 mm long and slightly inclined distad. Reverse of branches coarsely grooved, but sharp longitudinal ribs of the reverse are commonly covered by encrustation. Outline of zooecial chamber triangular at base, where central zooecial wall sharply undulates from side to side.

Meshwork formula: Although meshwork measurements within a zoarium fairly constant, meshwork formulae differ somewhat for different zoaria. Holotype meshwork formula 15–17/17//17/17. In specimen 93S three successive floors of growth form have following meshwork, starting with upper: (1) 17/17.5–18.5//17.5–18.5/11–12; (2) 16–17/16–17//16–17/11–17; (3) 16–17/20–21//20–21/14. In fragments liberated by dissolution in hydrochloric acid of specimen 1-1A3, 15–16/18//18/3–4. In these fragments serration on the reverse not developed or feeble, while nodes on the obverse particularly well developed, strong, and uniformly inclined distad.

Discussion: The various examples just described may be considered genetic variations of a single species, but it seems that they are rather its phenotypic variations, whose meshwork dimensions apparently varied considerably in changed environment. Thus a summarized formula for the variable species may be written as follows: 15–17/16–21//16–21/11–17.

The transverse spacing of branches is the least variable among the four values in the formula, which is in accord with the general observation by Shulga-Nesterenko, who claims that in the related Permian species from Russia the number of fenestrules (per 10 mm), not the number of branches, is most variable (*see* chapter on Varability of Meshwork).

The reverse of specimens covered evenly by crust about 0.2 mm thick and ornamented by thin and sharp tubercles about 10 μ in diameter. Occasionally, without any semblance of order, small groups of pillars arise from crust. In specimen 93S pillars, which start from the reverse of upper floor, bifurcate in distal parts one, two, or three times, or divide at single point into three, four, or more short branches, some connected to the obverse of first floor. Where edge of upper floor locally curved and elevated, short pillar rising from the reverse of elevated part divides at single point into five short branches, radiating in nearly same plane and occasionally delicately connected to carinae of underlying floor. Branches of pillars bear scattered inverted hooks. From single point on the reverse of the lower floor three pillars arise in greatly inclined position (Pl. 19, fig. 10); two broken short distance from base, and one sends off lateral branch; another, nearly 5 mm long, carries four whorls of inverted hooks, two to three hooks in each whorl; distance between whorls gradually diminishing distad, from 1.5 mm between lower two whorls to 0.5 mm between third and fourth; its terminal broken off.

Discussion: Many described species are comparable to *F. archimediformis* in having the same or nearly the same meshwork, nearly stabilized to quite stabilized, 2 zooecia per fenestrule, and one row of nodes. They differ from it as follows: *Fenestella pectinis* Moore (1929, p. 18–19) has wider branches, imperfect stabilization of 2 zooecia per fenestrule, and a larger number of distally inclined nodes; *F. nikiforovae* Shulga (1941, p. 73) has wider branches and pentagonal zooecial chamber; *F. tschernovi* Shulga (1941, p. 101) has much wider branches; *F. pulcherrima* Shulga (1941, p. 117) has coarser meshwork, and thick complex encrusting tissue—its variety *magnospinata* has comparable meshwork formula, but its encrusting tissue is still more complex (Shulga-Nesterenko, 1941, p. 118). *F. perelegans* Meek, as identified and described by Condra (1903, p. 56–57), *F. parviuscula* Bassler (1929, p. 79), and *F. spinulosa* var. *permica* Shulga (1941, p. 99) have wider branches and imperfect stabilization of 2 zooecia per fenestrule. *Fenestella spinulosa* Condra has wider branches but in other respects is nearer to *F. archimediformis* than any other species described. *F. cornuta* here described has wider branches and structurally complex spines. *F. quadratopora* Shulga (1941, p. 133) from the Permian of Russia, which has delicate branches and dissepiments and subquadrate and somewhat hourglass-shaped fenestrules as in *F. archimediformis* differs from the latter in having a double row of nodes and a coarser meshwork. *F. subquadratopora* Shulga (1952, p. 47–48; Pl. 9, fig. 5) from Burtzevka horizon of Russia has somewhat different meshwork (18/16–17//17–18) indicative of not quite stabilized position of zooecia resulting in occasional occurrence of up to three per fenestrule (holotype; Pl. 9, fig. 5, low at left edge). *F. archimediformis* could have been considered a variety or mutation of *F. spinulosa*, but it seems more nearly correct to regard it as a new species. It differs from *F. Spinulosa* by narrower branches, more nearly square fenestrules, different character of variability of meshwork, and a much more complex zoarial growth form. Perhaps some phenotypic varieties could be differentiated from *F. archimediformis* in its suggested scope, but at the present it seems best to refrain from naming such varieties pending collection of more complete zoaria, apparently very large.

F. parviuscula var. **libellus** n. var.

(Plate 22, figures 1–7)

Types: Holotype Nebr. Geol. Survey No. 531, 11 mm by 11 mm, is fragment of two-storied zoarium from middle part of Wolfcamp Series, Schuchert coll., locality 93-S (19), from stream bank northeast of Wolf Camp (R. E. King, 1930, p. 140). Two fragments of ordinary foliate zoarium from same horizon and locality, liberated from another piece of limestone by dissolution in hydrochloric acid.

Description: Holotype unique among growth forms of *Fenestella*: consists of two foliate expanses disposed closely, one above other, with subparallel surfaces of two expanses and with initial parts and fanlike spreading of branches almost identical and placed exactly one above other. Two expanses interconnected by numerous, irregularly disposed, short, stout pillars. Fewer stumps of similar pillars arise from the reverse of lower expanse near initial point. Rapid curving of initial parts of upper and lower foliate expanses is reminiscent of shape and disposition of a wineglasslike or lilylike flange in some species of *Archimedes*: *A. grandis*, *A. halli*, *A. meekanus*, and others. However in described *Fenestella* there is no complete solid sealing of fenestrules by crust in curved part corresponding to flange, and there is no indication of *Archimedes*-like shaft or of possible spiral-like connection between upper and lower foliate expanses. Exact relationship between initial points of two expanses remains unknown, because earliest initial zooecia are broken off; it seems that upper expanse grew from lower by additional budding in inclined upward direction, and subsequent ordinary budding in plane parallel to lower expanse. Thus, it repeats at higher level normal budding of foliate expanse below. So similar are upper and lower expanses that when viewed at exact 90-degree angle to surfaces (from above or below) lumens of fenestrules seen exactly one above other over whole or nearly whole expanse. Near initial points lumens become smaller to almost completely sealed by encrustation; but along greater, nearly flat parts of both expanses branches average as wide as fenestrules, and frequently bifurcate so that branches spread out rapidly and zoarium looks like plant leaflet. Dissepiments average slightly narrower than branches; fenestrules rectangular to elliptical, with almost no tendency toward hourglass shape; most zooecia well stabilized, with 2 per fenestrule, every other aperture at base of dissepiment. However, near points of bifurcation apertures occasionally unstabilized. Apertures roughly circular, with indistinct (possibly not preserved) peristomes, from own diameter to nearly 1½ times diameter apart. Outline of zooecial chamber triangular, with deep interwedging at base; carina wide and high, with poorly developed nodes, about 2 per fenestrule; dissepiments at level of aperture on the obverse and almost on level with branches on the reverse; the reverse of branches somewhat unevenly, moderately to heavily encrusted; from this layer arise numerous stout pillars, variable in diameter, oriented perpendicular to expanse at points of attachment in irregularly distributed groups. Encrusting tissue and pillars faintly striate; striae about 50 μ apart. At or near points of attachment of pillars striae occasionally stand out in slight relief, tending to group into fascicles. Pillars apparently start as small conical elevations, gradually increase in height and width; some becoming slender stiff structures, growing variously inclined to zoarial surface, cylindrical at base, rapidly changing to triangular prismatic shape distad, and ornamented with reverted hooks along prismatic edges (Pl. 22, figs. 5–7). One proliferates at apex and along lateral side near apex (Pl. 22, figs. 5, 7) for apparent purpose of attachment to the obverse of expanse, approaching it at acute angle. Another slender triangular prism penetrates through fenestrule of same expanse and projects slightly above it (Pl. 22, fig. 6).

Meshwork formula: 17/15.5–17//16–17/19–21 with only slight variability.

Discussion: The variety is nearest *F. parviuscula* from Basleo of Timor and *F. tschernovi* of P_1^{1b}, or uppermost Artinskian, of Russia in having the same type of stabilization of 2 zooecia per fenestrule with only slight local irregularities, the same width of branches and shape of fenestrules, and the same structure of zooecial chamber. In its dimensions it is intermediate between these two species, though slightly nearer to *F. tschernovi*, whose formula is 15–17/14–16//16–17/16–17.

The combination of the prolific development of the encrustation and two kinds of uprights, stout, unsculptured pillars, and slender barbed prisms has not been previously observed.

Fenestella nikiforovae Shulga

(Plate 17, figure 1; Plate 20, figure 6; Plate 21, figures 5, 6)

1936. *Fenestella nikiforovae* SHULGA-NESTERENKO, Trudy, Poliarnaia Komissia, v. 28, p. 270–271, Figs. 1–4; Pl. 1, fig. 3

1941. *Fenestella nikiforovae* SHULGA-NESTERENKO, Paleont. U.S.S.R., v. 5, pt. 5, fasc. 1, p. 73–74, Figs. 29–32, Pl. 10, fig. 4;

Types: Holotype no. 565, Lower Permian P_1^{1a}, from point 4 of exposure 40 on left side of Podcherem River, Pechora Basin. To this species is referred large, somewhat weathered fragment from Wolfcamp Series, Nebr. Geol. Survey No. 532, locality 93 (-12) of King and King coll. section 24, bed 9, and float from a few next higher beds, northeast of Wolf Camp, (R. E. King, 1930, p. 134; P. B. King, 1930, p. 54–55.)

Description: Species characterized by regular meshwork, pentagonal shape of basal part of zooecial chamber, and presence of one row of nodes on carina. Specimen indicates zoarium large, slightly curved, fan-shaped, with uniform meshwork throughout. Fenestrules average narrower than branches; dissepiments narrower than branches; nodes disposed in one row.

Meshwork formula: 18–20/18–21//20–21/18–19 (after Shulga-Nesterenko); measured on our specimen: 20/19–21//20/17–18.

Discussion: The presence of one row of nodes on the carina and the nearly stabilized disposition of every other aperture at the base of dissepiment, with 2 zooecia per fenestrule, indicate close affinity to the American *F. spinulosa*, though Shulga-Nesterenko does not discuss this similarity. The chief differences between the two are the pentagonal shape of the chamber and the wider dissepiments in the Russian form in distinction from the triangular chamber and narrower dissepiments in *F. spinulosa*. *F. nikiforovae* is also distinguished by the enlargement of branches below bifurcation. The tuberculate peristome is another specific character of *F. nikiforovae*, but insufficient preservation of the details in ornamentation of *F. spinulosa* precludes comparison between the two in this respect. Only small fragments of *F. nikiforovae* were described from Russia; their slowly diverging branches indicate distal position in full-grown stage of comparatively large zoarium. Larger fragment from the Wolfcamp indicates that complete zoarium was about 5 cm by 5 cm, a fan-shaped growth form.

Fenestella (Cervella) cervoidea (Chronic)

1949. *Cervella cervoidea* CHRONIC; NEWELL, CHRONIC, and ROBERTS, Upper Paleozoic of Peru, N. Y., Columbia Univ. p. 124–125, Pl. 23, figs. 3a–7
1953. *Cervella cervoidea* CHRONIC; NEWELL, CHRONIC, and ROBERTS, Geol. Soc. Am. Mem. 58, p. 118–119, Pl. 23, figs. 3a–7 (identical descritpion and illustrations with those of 1949).

Types: Holotype Am. Mus. Nat. Hist. no. 26975/2:1, from localities 298, bed 54, illustrated by Chronic (Pl. 23, figs. 3a, b); a beautifully preserved silicified young zoarium about 1 cm long. Additional illustrated fragments indicate that adult zoarium was perhaps 5–6 cm across.

Description: The species resembles closely *Fenestella nikiforovae* Shulga and even more so the new species *F. cruciformis*. Its meshwork formula is close to that of *F. cruciformis*, 24–25/21–22//21–22/26–28, but the spines are spaced much closer in the latter. Spines are of different shape: the two lateral branches in *F. cervoidea* transversely directed and diverging repeatedly resemble the antlers of a deer; in *F. cruciformis* the lateral branches of the spines depart ascendingly, and only at tips do they occasionally diverge into two short points.

Meshwork formula: 20–24/20–22//20–23/15–24, calculated from Chronic's measurements of the fragment from bed 54.

Discussion: It seems that the difference in shape and spacing of the carinal nodes justifies specific differentiation of *F. cruciformis* from *F. cervoidea*, the latter possibly geologically younger.

Chronic describes *F. cervoidea* from beds (41 and 54) in one geologic section, which are separated stratigraphically by more than 1200 feet plus an "intraformational diastem" between beds 47 and 48 (Newell *et al.*, 1953, p. 30). Because the spacing of the elements in the zoaria from these two bryozoan-bearing beds was measured separately, it is possible to calculate two separate formulae for the two samples of *F. cervoidea*: 22–25/22–24//20–25/22–26 from bed 41; and 20–24/20–22//20–23/15–24 from bed 54. The spacing of the fenestrules is wider in the sample from bed 54 and seems to be correlated with the greater stability of the zooecia in relation to the dissepiments. In these two qualities the sample from bed 54, containing holotype of *F. cervoidea*, is closer to *F. cruciformis* than the sample from bed 41.

Fenestella (Cervella) cruciformis n. sp.

(Plate 20, figures 1–5; Plate 21, figures 1–4)

Holotype: Nebr. Geol. Survey No. 533, King and King coll. from locality 123, section 17, richly fossiliferous horizon near middle of Leonard Series (R. E. King, 1930, p. 135).

Description and Discussion: Several fragments liberated by dissolution in hydrochloric acid; largest, measuring 15 mm by 15 mm, designated holotype. Zoarium moderately large, slightly flexuous, fan-shaped, foliate. Branches straight to gently curved, averaging as wide as fenestrules; bifurcation abrupt; branches above bifurcations usually narrower for length of several fenestrules; dissepiments somewhat variable in width and length, averaging as wide and short as in *F. nikiforovae;* fenestrules oval, narrowing in middle like hourglass; zooecia almost perfectly stabilized, with every other aperture at base of dissepiment, but in some parts of zoarium, usually near bifurcations, apertures slightly offset from this position; apertures circular, small, more than own diameter apart, with very thin peristomes, ornamented by few sharp spines; carina wide and high, with row of stout upright nodes, spaced denser than zooecia and in single row; carinal nodes complex, dividing into three branches at apex; central branch continues straight upward, only about half as thick as node below; lateral branches about as thick as upper branch, departing at slightly ascendant angle to horizontal plane, tend to bifurcate in horizontal plane at their tips. Viewed along direction of branches complex nodes resemble a row of crosses on single long grave, hence the name *cruciformis*. Dissepiments slightly depressed on the obverse, more so on the reverse. Reverse of branches covered by thick crust with irregularly tuberculate surface; along middle there is one row of thick, cone-shaped nodes, slightly less than 1 to about 2 per fenestrule. Because lateral walls that separate zooecial chambers were destroyed, exact outline of zooecial chamber impossible to determine; slight polishing of the reverse disclosed faint zigzag line in middle of branches, which indicates that chamber was probably pentagonal at base.

Primary grooved surface of the reverse of branches and dissepiments covered by crust about 0.2

mm thick; grooves observable where encrustation unusually thin or removed artificially. Encrustation ornamented with densely spaced tubercles of nearly uniform size, 12 μ to 15 μ in diameter, tending to line up in longitudinal rows along branches and dissepiments; smaller tubercles, less than 10 μ in diameter, scattered between larger ones. The reverse also ornamented with larger nodes, spaced more or less regularly along middle of unequally developed branches, ranging from knobs barely raised on surface to stout, slightly tapering nodes from 0.05 to 1 mm in diameter and 0.2 mm in height. Nodes usually inclined about 60°–70° toward distal part of zoarium. Centers of nodes hollow, like in carinal nodes of the obverse. Their spacing variable, but tends to become regular and stay so for distance of few fenestrules. Ordinarily as many nodes as dissepiments; frequently nodes opposite dissepiments, but occasionally spaced farther apart, with only 2 nodes per 3 fenestrules, or even 1 node per 2 fenestrules; occasionally 2 adjacent nodes nearly fused.

On right side of holotype several branches in a row depart abnormally at about 45-degree angle to normal branch; some portions of abnormal and normal branches occasionally somewhat elevated above neighboring branches on the obverse, crosslike nodes particularly thick and more completely developed along elevated branches.

Meshwork formula: 20–26/21–22//21/22–25–29, with about 20 stout nodes per 5 mm on the reverse.

Discussion: The general character and details of the described form seem to indicate its close relationship to the Russian *Fenestella nikiforovae* and its representative from the Wolfcamp. However, it differs distinctly from both by its finer meshwork, more densely spaced and elaborately developed nodes on the obverse, and by the development of another set of nodes on the reverse. The size and complexity of the nodes on the obverse are not constant characters even within the same zoarium; the largest specimen and some smaller fragments possess only small nodes on the obverse, though they are as densely spaced as the large and complex nodes of the holotype. The stout nodes on the reverse have been observed on all specimens studied. Similar nodes with diameter of 0.08 mm were observed by Shulga-Nesterenko (1941, p. 74) along the central line of the reverse of the branches in one Russian specimen of *F. nikiforovae*. Her description and illustrations of "capillaries" and of "additional pores" (Shulga-Nesterenko, 1941, p. 73) in the slides of the same species show the fine sculpture observed on the reverse of the American specimens of the species. Shulga-Nesterenko's measurement of larger "capillaries" is 10 μ, which is slightly smaller than 12 μ to 15 μ, as measured on tubercles of our specimens, but the spacing of the large "capillaries" and of the smaller ones between s similar to that of the larger and smaller tubercles.

Fenestella tschernovi Shulga

(Plate 23, figures 4–7)

1936. *Fenestella tschernovi* SHULGA-NESTERENKO, Poliarnaia Komissiia Akad. Nauk, Trudy, v. 28, p. 277

1941. *Fenestella tschernovi* SHULGA-NESTERENKO, Paleontology U.S.S.R., v. 5, pt. 5, fasc. 1, p. 101, Pl. 27, fig. 1

? 1945 (1946) *Fenestella aspratilis* CROCKFORD, Proc. Linn. Soc. N. S. W., v. 70, p. 131–132, Fig. 5

Holotype: Slide no. 532, MGPI. Verkhne-Chusovskie Gorodky, borehole 61, depth 410–416 meters, Permian, higher horizon of P_1^1.

Plesiotypes: Nebr. Geol. Survey No. 534, Leonard Series, etched specimen from King and King coll. locality 300 (not listed in R. E. King, 1930, p. 137).

Description: Shulga-Nesterenko (1941, p. 107) diagnosed species as having "regular meshwork with straight wide branches. Zooecial chamber triangular and pentagonal; apertures almost circular; carinal nodes in one row; capillaries small (5 μ), not densely spaced." Meshwork formula 15–17/14–16//16–17/about 16–17.

Several fragments from the Leonard, largest 7 mm by 7 mm, confidently referred to *F. tschernovi* in spite of imperfect preservation precluding comparison of details of sculpture and shape of zooecial chamber. Preservation is most peculiar, original calcareous skeleton being replaced by aggregate of small quartz crystals. However, in spite of imperfection, silicified bryozoan retained faithfully general outline of meshwork and position of zooecial apertures and even of nodes, large and distantly spaced.

Zoarium fan-shaped, foliate, with frequent bifurcation of rapidly expanding branches, as wide as elliptical fenestrules; locally, especially near bifurcations, fenestrules wider and subquadrate.

Dissepiments variable, from narrower to nearly as wide as branches; carina prominent, with straight stout and high nodes; disposition of apertures in relation to dissepiments well stabilized, every other aperture at base of dissepiment.

Meshwork formula: 13–15/14.5–16//14.5–16/11–14.

Discussion: Shulga-Nesterenko noticed the close external similarity of this species to *F. quadratopora*, which has double row of nodes, a character indicating its place in *F. compactilis* group, distinct from *F. spinulosa* group (Shulga-Nesterenko placed it in *F. quadratopora* complex, distinct from her *F. conradi compactilis* complex). According to Shulga-Nesterenko's formula the number of branches and fenestrules per given space is quite variable.

F. aspratilis Bassler and *F. pulcherrima* Shulga (1941, p. 117) have nearly the same meshwork formulae as *F. tschernovi*, but differ from the latter in about same way that it differs from *F. quadratopora*.

All our fragments are from proximal to middle parts of zoarium, which is indicated by frequent bifurcation and divergence of branches. Russian holotype is apparently from middle or distal part of zoarium. Taking this into account and considering the possible slight increase in length of fenestrules toward the periphery of a zoarium, the examples from the Leonard may have a slightly coarser meshwork than Russian holotype.

Shulga-Nesterenko meshwork formula for *F. tschernovi* indicates an average of slightly more than 2 zooecia per fenestrule, apparently observed on larger fragment than illustrated holotype, which shows exactly or nearly exactly 2 zooecia per fenestrule throughout, with every other aperture at base of a dissepiment. In the description of the variety *usiensis* Shulga-Nesterenko indicates in the measurements exactly twice as many zooecia as fenestrules. In our material of the species and its variety the number of zooecia is invariably twice that of fenestrules, and their position in relation to dissepiments is stabilized, every other located at base of a dissepiment. Thus *Fenestella tschernovi* and its variety *usiensis* are placed in the group of *Fenestella spinulosa*, which is characterized by stabilized disposition of zooecia, 2 per fenestrule.

Crockford's *F. aspratilis* from the lower Permian of Australia is probably identical with *F. tschernovi*, but the identification needs verification through study of the zooecial chamber in the Australian form (*see* also the discussion of *Fenestella girtyi*).

Fenestella tschernovi var. usiensis Shulga

(Plate 23, figures 1–3)

1936. *Fenestella tschernovi* Shulga, Forma A. Poliarnaia Komissiia Akad. Nauk, Trudy, v. 28, p. 277
1941. *Fenestella tschernovi* Shulga far. *usiensis* Shulga, Paleontology U.S.S.R., v, 5, pt. 5. fasc. 1, p. 102, pl. 19, fig. 3

Types: No. 610, MGPI, Shchugor River, exposure 48 on left side; P_1^2. Plesiotype, Nebr. Geol. Survey no. 535, Word Series, etched specimen from locality 192, R. E. King coll. Highest (4th) limestone in Word Series, north of junction of Road and Gilliland canyons, Glass Mountains, Texas.

Shulga-Nesterenko's diagnosis (1941, p. 102) of variety indicates similarity to *F. tschernovi* except for densely spaced capillaries and coarser meshwork formula: 16–17/14.5//14.5/14.5. Single fragment, 9 mm x 4 mm, from the Word is strongly curved part of left marginal portion of foliate zoarium. Branches sturdy, thickly encrusted on the reverse, with heavy carina on the obverse carrying moderately prominent nodes, regularly spaced in one row, slightly less numerous than zooecia. Poorly preserved apertures crowded by wide carina into oblique position not projecting into fenestrules; every other aperture at base of dissepiments, spacing of 2 zooecia per fenestrule stabilized; dissepiments narrower than branches, sturdy, depressed on the obverse to level just below carina; fenestrules subquadrate, from slightly narrower to wider than branches; the reverse of dissepiments slightly depressed; zooecial chamber indistinct, probably pentagonal or triangular.

Coarse silicification obliterated the finer structural details, such as sculpture of encrustation and of apertures.

Meshwork formula: 15/14–15//14–15/13–14 (also about 21 spines per 5 mm on reverse).

Discussion: Generally the variety *usiensis* is very much like *F. tschernovi*, and differs from it essentially only in the coarser meshwork. The respective position in Glass Mountains of *F. tschernovi* and its variety *usiensis* (an advanced Waagen's or time mutation of the former) corresponds also to the stratigraphic relationships of same forms in Russian Permian; var. *usiensis* is stratigraphically higher than *F. tschernovi*.

Fenestella shulgae n. sp.

(Plate 23, figures 8–11)

Holotype: Single collected specimen with the reverse exposed, but faint impression of the obverse discernable in the matrix where zoarium exfoliates; Nebr. Geol. Survey No. 536 from lower Permian of Lipovaia Gora, near Vavilovo, west-central Urals, Russia. Collected by G. E. Condra, locality B-9.

Description: Observation of obverse handicapped by difficulty of preparation of thin section from fragil meshwork. However, study of faint impression of the obverse upon rock matrix, and of a small thin section prepared and observation of persistent slight inward bulging at middle of sides of fenestrules seen on the reverse, indicate that apertures are stabilized at bases of dissepiments and halfway between them, 2 zooecia per fenestrule. This and single row of carinal nodes place new species in group XII.

Apparently zoarium small; holotype perhaps nearly complete zoarium, elongate, foliate, about 20 mm x 10 mm, somewhat cylindrically curved longitudinally, the obverse being convex. A few central branches run subparallel throughout, while lateral branches on both sides diverge symmetrically at about 40° to central branches. Branches slightly narrower than fenestrules; dissepiments half as wide as branches. Fenestrules slightly rounded, subrectangular to subquadrate. At distal part of zoarium branches more crowded and fenestrules narrower. Sharply outlined carina carries one row of elongated nodes, about as many as zooecia; the reverse of prominently grooved branches also ornamented by nodes, broad at base and pimplelike, about 2–2½ per fenestrule. Zooecial chamber triangular, with considerable interwedging, hence tendency to become trapezoid in outline.

Meshwork formula: 12–14/12//12/12–15.

Discussion: The species is nearest *Fenestella pulcherrima* Shulga, having the same character of zoarium, stabilization of apertures, nodes, zooecial chamber, and even the same kind of nodes on the reverse. It differs from the latter, however, by much coarser meshwork, the formula in *F. pulcherrima* being 14–14.5/15//14.5.

Shulga-Nesterenko collected a variety of the latter species from the higher Permian rocks at Iurak-Tau Mountains at Sterlitamak, naming it *magnospinata*. This variety has finer meshwork, and Shulga-Nesterenko considers that its evolution was through diminution of the elements of the meshwork. If true, this would constitute an exception to the generally observed evolutionary trend toward the increase of size in many species of *Fenestella*, as observed by Ulrich (1890, p. 545), Elias (1937), and Shulga-Nesterenko (1941, p. 63–64, *F. foraminosa* and others), and by Nekhoroshev (1926a, p. 794) for *Fenestella*-like *Reteporina* in the highest Devonian of Altai. *Fenestella quadratoporaeformis* Shulga-Nesterenko from Schwagerina horizon of Tra-Tau Mountain of Russia (1941, p. 114; Pl. 25, fig. 1; 1952, p. 52–53, fig. 29; Pl. 8, fig. 5) has nearly the same meshwork formula (11–13/12//12.5–13) as *F. shulgae* but has narrower branches and different zooecial chamber. Its meshwork formula should indicate equal number of fenestrules and zooecia, 2 zooecial per fenestrule shown stabilized in both 1941 and 1952 photographs by Shulga.

Addendum to Group XI

Fenestella girtyi var.

(Plate 13, figures 5–8; Plate 15, figures 4, 5)

Types: three fragments from Word group, "Fourth" limestone, section 17, north of junction of Road and Gilliland canyons (R. E. King, 1930; P. B. King, 1930, p. 139).

Description: Largest fragment (Pl. 13, figs. 4–8) represents median part of zoarium, with numerous pillars aligned in single file across zoarial branches on the reverse; pillars branch laterally mostly at 90°. Smaller fragments represent median (Pl. 15, fig. 5) and distal (Pl. 15, fig. 4) parts of zoarium. Triangular chamber distinguishes it from *F. girtyi*.

Meshwork formula: 16–25/16–17//15–16/16–17, which indicates slightly wider spacing of zooecia than in *F. girtyi* from the Leonard Series.

BIBLIOGRAPHY

ADAMS, JOHN EMERY (1939) Standard Permian section of North America. Am. Assoc. Petroleum Geologists Bull., v. 23, p. 1673–1681.

ALEXANDROVA, E. (1939) On the diagenesis in the upper Paleozoic reef limestones from the western slopes of Urals. Geol. Oil Inst. Trans., ser. A, fasc. 115, Russian, p. 189–205, 3 pls., English summary, p. 204.

BARROIS, J. (1877) Recherches sur l'embryologie des bryozoaires. Paris and Lille, 305 p., 16 pls.

BASSLER, R. S. (1929) Permian Bryozoa of Timor. Paläontologie von Timor, Ergebnisse d. Expeditionen G. A. F. Molengraff, J. Wanner, u. F. Weber, Leif. XVI, p. 37–90, pls. 225(1)–247(23)

———(1935) Pars 67: Bryozoa, in Fossilium Catalogus, 1. Animalia. 229 p. W. Junk, Grawenhage, Denmark

——— (1953) Bryozoa. Part G, Treatise on Invertebrate Paleontology, ed. R. C. Moore, p. xiii, 253, 175 figs.

BEISSEL, IGNAZ (1865) Ueber die Bryozoen der Aachener Kreidebildung. Naturkundige Verh. v.d. Hollandsche Maatschappij d. Wetenschappen te Haarlem, 2 verz., 22 de., Haarlem, 92 p., 10 pls.

BIGBY, J. KEITH (1956) *Acanthocladia guadalupensis* Girty, a possible algal-bryozoan symbiont (Abstract). Progr. AAPG-SEPM Annual Meeting, 1956, Chicago, Ill., Program, p. 82.

BOLKHOVITINOVA, M. O. (1915) Sur les coraux et les bryozoaires carbonifères du gouvernement de Moscou. Moscow Soc. Amis Sci. Nat., geol. ser., Bull. 3 (1914–1915), p. 61–68, pls. 5, 6

BORG, FOLKE (1926) Studies on recent cyclostomatous Bryozoa. Zoologiska Bidrag från Uppsala, v. 10, p. 181–504, 14 pls., 109 figs.

——— (1933) A revision of the recent Heteroporidae. Zoologiska Bidrag från Uppsala, v. 14, p. 253–394, 29 figs., 14 pls.

——— (1942) On the structure and relationships of Crisina (Bryozoa Stenolaemata). Arkiv for Zoologi, v. 33A, no. 11, p. 1–44, 4 pls., 16 figs.

BUSK, GEORGE (1875) Catalogue of marine Polyzoa in the collection of the British Museum, pt. 3, Cyclostomata, p. viii, 39, pls. 1–35

——— (1884) Report on the Polyzoa collected by H. M. S. CHALLENGER. Rept. Sci. Res. H. M. S. CHALLENGER, Zoology, v. 10, pt. 30, xxiv and 216 p., 36 pls.

CALVET, L. (1900) Contribution à l'histoire naturelle des Bryozoaires ectoproctes marins. Trav. Inst. Zool. Univ. Montpellier, n.s., Mem. 8, 488 p., 13 pls.

CANU, F. C., AND BASSLER, R. S. (1920) North American early Tertiary Bryozoa. U. S. Nat. Mus. Bull. 106, xx and 879 p., 162 pls., 279 figs.

CHAPMAN, F. (1900) On some new and interesting Foraminifera from the Funafuti Atoll. Jour. Linn. Soc., Zoology, v. 28, p. 1–27, pls. 1–4, 2 figs.

CONDRA, G. E. (1902) New Bryozoa from the Coal Measures of Nebraska. Am. Geol., v. 30, p. 337–359, pls. 18–25

——— (1903) The Coal Measure Bryozoa of Nebraska. Nebr. Geol. Survey, v. 2, p. 11–163, 21 pls., 1 frontispiece

CONDRA, G. E., AND BUSBY, C. E. (1933) The Grenola formation. Nebr. Geol. Survey, 2d ser., Paper 1, 31 p., 2 figs.

CONDRA, G. E., AND ELIAS, M. K. (1941) *Fenestella* Lonsdale and *Fenestrellina* d'Orbigny. Jour. Paleontology, v. 15, p. 565–556

——— (1944) Study and revision of *Archimedes* (Hall). Geol. Soc. America Special Paper 53, ix and 243 p., 41 pls., 6 figs.

——— (1945a) *Bicorbula*, a new Permian bryozoan, probably a bryozoan-algal consortium. Jour. Paleontology, v. 19, p. 116–125, pls. 13–16, 1 fig.

——— (1945b) *Bicorbis arizonica* Condra and Elias, new name for *Bicorbula arizonica*. Jour. Paleontology, v. 19, p. 411

CONDRA, G. E., AND REED, E. C. (1943) The geological section of Nebraska. Nebr. Geol. Survey Bull. 14, vii and 82 p., 1 pl. correl. chart, 24 figs. including geol. map

CONDRA, G. E., AND UPP, J. E. (1931) Correlation of the Big Blue Series in Nebraska. Nebr. Geol. Survey, 2d ser., Bull. 6, 74 p., 15 figs.

CROCKFORD, JOAN M. (1941) Permian Bryozoa of eastern Australia. Royal Soc. N.S.W. Jour. and Proc., v. 74; pt. 1, p. 397–418, figs. 1, 2, pl. 18, 19; pt. 2, p. 502–519, figs. 1–3, pls. 20, 21

——— (1944) Bryozoa from the Permian of Western Australia, Pt. 1, Cyclostomata and Cryptostomata. Linn. Soc. N.S. Wales Proc., v. 76, p. 139–175, 52 figs., 2 pls.

——— (1945) [1946] A bryozoan fauna from the Lake's Creek Quarry, Rockhampton, Queensland. Proc. Linn. Soc. N. S. W., v. 70, p. 125–134, 12 figs.

CUMINGS, E. R. (1904) Development of some Paleozoic Bryozoa. Am. Jour. Sci., 4th ser., v. 17, p. 49–78, 83 figs.

——— (1905) Development of *Fenestella*. Am. Jour. Sci., ser. 4, v. 20, p. 189–177, 3 pls.

——— (1906) Description of the Bryozoa of the Salem limestone of southern Indiana. Depart of Geol. and Nat. Res. of Indiana, 30th Ann. Rept., p. 1274–1296, pls. 27–40

CUMINGS, E. R., AND GALLOWAY, J. J. (1915) Studies of morphology and histology of the Trepostomata or monticuliporoids. Geol. Soc. Am. Bull., v. 26, 349–374, pls. 10–15

DUNBAR, C. O. (1940) The type Permian: its classification and correlation. Am. Assoc. Petroleum Geologists Bull., v. 24, p. 237–281, 9 figs.

DUNBAR, C. O., AND SKINNER, J. W. (1936) *Schwagerina* versus *Pseudoschwagerina* and *Paraschwagerina*. Jour. Paleontology, v. 10, p. 83–91, pls. 10, 11

DUNCAN, P. M., AND JENKINS, H. M. (1869) On *Palaeocoryne*, a genus of tubularine Hydrozoa from the Carboniferous formation. Royal Soc. London Philos. Trans., v. 159, p. 693–699, pl. 66

EDSON, FANNY CARTER (1945) Subsurface geological cross section from Ford County to Wallace County, Kansas. Kansas Univ., Geol. Survey Oil and Gas Inv., Prelim. Cross sec. 1.

EICHWALD, E. (1860) Letaea Rossica, or Paléontologie de la Russie. Ancienne Période. Stuttgart, v. 1, 682 p.; Atlas of 59 pls.—Bryozoa, p. 355–419, 434–435, 450–452, 475–494; pls. 23–27, 30, 32

ELIAS, M. K. (1937a) Depth of deposition of the Big Blue (late Paleozoic) sediments in Kansas. Geol. Soc. America Bull., v. 48, p. 403–432, 1 pl., 4 figs.

——— (1937b) Stratigraphic significance of some late Paleozoic fenestrate bryozoans. Jour. Paleontology, v. 11, p. 306–336, 3 figs., 6 tables

——— (1946) Fossil symbiotic algae in comparison with other fossil and living algae. Am. Midland Naturalist, v. 36, p. 282–290, 2 pls.

——— (1950) *Fenestella deissi* (new name) from the Middle Devonian of Michigan, and related forms. Jour. Paleontology, v. 24, p. 390–392

FOERSTE, A. F. (1887) Flint Ridge Bryozoa. Denison Univ., Sci. Lab. Bull. 2, pt. 1, p. 71–88, pl. 7

FOSLIE, M. (1895) The Norvegian forms of Lithothamnion. Det. k. norske Vidensk. Selskabs Skrifter

FREDERICKS, GEORGE (1913) Bemerkungen über Bryozoa der Steinkohlenablagerungen von Russland. Ueber die Gattungen *Fenestella* Lonsdale und *Polypora* McCoy). Kazani Prot. obsc. jest., v. 44, 1912–1913. Beilage no. 288, p. 1–8, 2 pls.

——— (1915) La Faune paléozoique supérieure des environs de la ville de Krasnoufimsk. Comité Geologique, Mém. 109 n. s.

GIRTY, G. H. (1908) The Guadalupian fauna. U. S. Geol. Survey Prof. Paper 48, 651 p., 31 pls.

GROZDILOVA, L. P. (1938) Fusulinidae from the oil-bearing limestone of Ishimbaievo oil field. Geol. Oil Inst. Trans., ser. A, fasc. 101, p. 90–141, 5 pls., 4 figs. (diagrams), 3 tables, Russian

HARMER, S. F. (1898) On the development of Tubulipora, and on some British and northern species of this genus. Micro. Sci. Quart. Jour., n. s., v. 41, p. 73–157, pls. 8–10

——— (1900) A revision of the genus *Steganoporella*. Micro. Sci. Quart. Jour., n. s., v. 43, p. 225–297, pls. 12, 13

——— (1903) On the morphology of the Cheilostomata. Micro. Sci. Quart. Jour., n. s., v. 46, p. 263–350, pls. 15–18

——— (1934) Polyzoa of the Siboga Expedition. Pt. III. Cheilostomata Ascophora. I. Family Reteporidae. p. viii and 503–640, pls. 25–41, 25 figs.

HENBEST, LLOYD G. (1937) Keriothecal wall-structure in *Fusulina* and its influence on fusuline classification. Jour. Paleontology, v. 11, p. 212–230, pls. 34, 35

Johnson, J. Harlan. (1951) Permian calcareous algae from the Apache Mountains, Texas. Jour. Pal., v. 25, p. 21–30, pls. 6–9.

Kay, G. Marshall (1941) Classification of the Artinskian Series in Russia. Am. Assoc. Petroleum Geologists Bull., v. 25, p. 1396–1404, 4 figs.

King, P. B. (1930) The geology of the Glass Mountains, Texas, Pt. 1, Descriptive Geology. Univ. of Texas Bull. 3038, 167 p., 43 figs., 15 pls., 1 geol. map

——— (1937) Geology of the Marathon region, Texas. U. S. Geol. Survey Prof. Paper 187, ix and 148 p., 24 pls., 33 figs. and maps

King, R. E. (1930) Geology of the Glass Mountains, Texas, Pt. 2. Faunal summary and correlation of the Permian formations with description of Brachiopoda. Univ. of Texas Bull. 3042, 245 p., 44 pls., 5 figs. (charts and tables)

King, W. A. (1849) On some families and genera of corals. Ann. Mag. Nat. Hist., ser. 2, v. 3, p. 388–390

——— (1850) A monograph of the Permian fossils of England. Palaeontographical Soc. London Mon. 3, 258 p. 28 pls. Bryozoa, p. 28–49, pls. 2–5

Knight, J. Brookes (1940) Are the "Omphalotrochus Beds" of the U.S.S.R. Permian? (with discussion by C. O. Dunbar). Am. Assoc. Petroleum Geologists Bull., v. 24, p. 1128–1133

Korn, Hermann (1930) Die cryptostomen Bryozoen des deutschen Perms. Leopoldina (Berichte Leopoldinischen Deutsche Akademie der Naturforscher zu Halle), VI Band, p. 341–377, 9 figs., pls. 1–3

Levinsen, G. M. R. (1909) Morphological and systematic studies on the cheilostomatous Bryozoa. Copenhagen, p. vii and 431, 24 pls., 6 figs.

——— (1925) Undersögelser over Bryozoerne i den danske Kridtformation. Kgl. Danske Vidensk. Selsk. Skrift., nat.-mat., Afd., 8 Rkke., v. 7, p. 283–445, 28 figs., 8 pls.

Likharev, B. (1926) Quelques bryozoairies du Permien supérieur du gouvernement de Vologda. Bull. Com. Géol., Leningrad, v. 43 (for 1924), p. 1011–1036, pls. 14–15, 6 figs., (Russian. Résumé in French, p. 1032–1034)

McCoy, Frederick (1844) A synopsis of the characters of the Carboniferous fossils of Ireland. Dublin. Bryozoa, p. 194–207, pls. 26–29

McFarlan, A. C. (1942) Chester Bryozoa of Illinois and western Kentucky. Jour. Paleontology, v. 16, p. 437–458, pls. 65–68, 7 tables

Marcus, E. (1924) Zur vergleichenden Embryologie der Bryozoen. Mitteil. Zool. Mus. Berlin, Bd. 11, p. 155–166

Miller, A. K. (1938) Comparison of Permian ammonoid zones of Soviet Russia with those of North America. Am. Assoc. Petroleum Geologists Bull., v. 22, p. 1014–1019

Mohr, C. L. (1939) Subsurface cross section of Permian from Texas to Nebraska. Am. Assoc. Petroleum Geologists Bull., v. 23, p. 1694–1711

Moore, R. C. (1929) A bryozoan faunule from the upper Graham formation, Pennsylvanian, of north-central Texas. Jour. Paleontology, v. 3, p. 1–27, 121–156, pls. 1–3, 15–18, 3 figs.

——— (1930) New species of bryozoans from the Pennsylvanian of Texas. Denison Univ. Sci. Lab. Bull. 25, p. 147–163, pl. 26

——— (1940) Carboniferous-Permian boundary. Am. Assoc. Petroleum Geologists Bull., v. 24, p. 282–336, 5 figs.

Moore, R. C., and Dudley, R. M. (1944) Cheilotrypid bryozoans from Pennsylvanian and Permian rocks of the Midcontinent region. Geol. Survey of Kansas Bull. 52, p. 229–403, 48 pls.

Nalivkin, V. D., and Dmitriev, G. (1939) Geology of the middle part of Jurezan River Valley, western slope of the south Urals. Geol. Oil Inst. Trans., ser. A, fasc. 115, p. 3–39, 14 figs. (incl. maps), English summary, p. 38–39

Nekhoroshev, B. (1926a) Carboniferous-Devonian Reteporinae from the Altai Mountains. Bull. Com. Géol., v. 44, p. 785–803, 1 pl., Russian

——— (1926b) On the affinities of some European and North American species of Carboniferous Fenestellidae. Ann. Soc. Paleontology Russia, v. 5, pt. 2, p. 105, Russian

——— (1926c) Lower Carboniferous Bryozoa from the Kuznezk basin. Bull. Com. Géol, v. 43, p. 1237–1290, 2 figs., pls. 19, 20, Russian

——— (1929) Résultats de l'étude des collections de bryozoaires paléozoïques dans quelques musées de l'Europe Occidentale. Bull. Com. Géol., v. 48, p. 105–125 (863–883), Russian

——— (1930) On certain Paleozoic Bryozoa in the British Museum (Natural History). Geol. Mag., v. 67, p. 178–179

NEWELL, N. D., CHRONIC, J., AND ROBERTS, T. G. (1949) Upper Paleozoic of Peru. New York, Columbia Univ., 241 p., 44 pls., 43 figs.

——— (1953) Upper Paleozoic of Peru. Geol. Soc. Am. Mem. 58, vii and 276 p., 44 pls., 43 figs.

NICHOLSON, H. A. (1872) A manual of paleontology. Wm. Blackwood, Edinburgh and London, xvi + 601 p., 399 figs.

NICKOLSON, H. A., AND LYDEKKER, R. (1889) Manual of Palaeontologie. 3d ed., v. 1, Wm. Blackwood, Edinburgh and London, xviii and 885 p., 812 figs.; v. 2, xi and 889–1624 p., figs. 813–1419

NIKIFOROVA, A. I. (1933) Middle Carboniferous Bryozoa of the Donetz Basin. Trans. United Geol. and Prospecting Service of U.S.S.R., fasc. 237, 46 p., 23 figs. 7 pls., Russian

——— (1938a) Types of Carboniferous Bryozoa in the European part of the U.S.S.R. Akad. Nauk S.S.S.R., Inst. Paleontology, Paleontology U.S.S.R., v. 4, pt. 5, fasc. 1, 290 p., 55 pls., 80 figs., Russian, English summary p. 205–281

——— (1938b) Stratigraphic distribution of the bryozoans in the Permo-Carboniferous oil-bearing reef deposits of the Ishimbaiev district, Russia. Geol. Oil Inst. Trans., ser. A, fasc. 10, p. 76–89, 2 pls., 1 fig. 1 table, Russian

——— (1939) New species of the upper Paleozoic Bryozoa from the Bashkirian Urals. Geol. Oil Inst. Trans., ser. A, fasc. 115, p. 70–102, 6 pls., 1 table, Russian

NITSCHE, H. (1871) Beiträge zur Kenntniss der Bryozoen. Pt. IV, Ueber die Morphologie des Bryozooen. Zeitsch. Wiss. Zool. Bd. 21, p. 471–498

OLTMANNS, F. (1923) Morphologie und Biologie der Algen. 2d ed., G. Fischer, Jena, v. 3, vii and 558 p., figs. 618–797

PEACH, C. W. (1878) Observations on British Polyzoa. Jour. Linn. Soc., Zoology, v. 13, p. 479–486, pl. 23

PROUT, HIRAM A. (1859) Third series of descriptions of Bryozoa from the Paleozoic rocks of the Western States and Territories. St. Louis Acad. Sci. Trans., v. 1, p. 443–452, pls. 17, 18

REINKE, JOHANNES (1889–1992) Atlas deutscher Meeresalgen. Berlin, Auftr. d. k. Preuss., Min. f. landw. dom. u. forsten., 2 v., 50 pls.

ROGERS, A. F. (1900) New bryozoans from the coal measures of Kansas and Missouri. Kansas Univ. Quart., ser. A, v. 9, p. 1–12, 4 pls.

SAYRE, A. N. (1930) The fauna of the Drum limestone of Kansas and Missouri. Univ. Kans. Sci. Bull., v. 19, No. 8, (Kans. State Geol. Survey Bull. 17) p. 75–203, 21 pls.

SETCHELL, W. A. (1926) Nullipore versus coral in reef-formation. Am. Phil. Soc. Proc., v. 65, p. 136–140

SHRUBSOLE, G. W. (1880) A review and description of the various species of British Upper Silurian Fenestellidae. Quart. Jour. Geol. Soc. London, v. 36, p. 241–254, pl. 11

——— (1881) Further notes on the Carboniferous Fenestellidae. Geol. Soc. London Quart., v. 37, p. 178–189, pl. 11.

SHULGA-NESTERENKO, M. I. (1931) A Lower Permian bryozoan, *Lyrocladia* nov. gen. from Pechora Land. Ann. Soc. Paleont. de Russie, v. 9, p. 47–86, 13 figs., pls. 4–7, English summary, p. 77–86, Russian

——— (1936) *Fenestella* and *Archimedes* from the middle Pechora region of the North Ural. Akad. Nauk U.S.S.R., Poliarnaia Komissiia, Trudy, v. 28, Russian, p. 233–285, 38 figs., 7 pls., English summary, p. 269–285

——— (1939) Permian Bryozoa. In atlas of index fossil faunas of the U.S.S.R., v. 6, Permian., p. 64–73, 16 figs., 3 pls., Russian

——— (1941) Lower Permian Bryozoa of the Urals. Akad. Nauk S.S.S.R., Paleontological Inst., Paleontology U.S.S.R., v. 5, p. 5, fasc. 1; Russian, 226 p., 67 pls., 177 figs., English summary, p. 229–242

——— (1949a) Opyt filogeneticheskogo analiza mshanok semeistva Fenestellidae. Akad. Nauk S.S.S.R., Paleontological Inst. Trans., t. 20, p. 293–315, illus., Russian

——— (1949b) Funktsionalnoe, filogeneticheskoe i stratigraficheskoe znachenie mikrostruktury skeletnykh tkanei mshanok. Akad. Nauk U.S.S.R., Paleontological Inst. Trans., t. 23, 67 p., illus., Russian

——— (1951) Kamennougolnye fenestellidy Russkoii platformy. Akad. Nauk S.S.S.R., Paleontological Inst., tom 32, 61 p., 57 figs., 34 pls., Russian

——— (1952) Novye Nijnepermskie mshanki Priuraliia. Akad. Nauk S.S.S.R., Paleontological Inst. Trans., tom 37, 84 p., 45 figs., 16 pls., Russian

Silén, Lars (1944) On the formation of the interzoidal communications of the Bryozoa. Zool. Bidr. Uppsala, v. 22, p. 433–488, 59 figs., 1 pl.

Simpson, G. B. (1895) [1897] A handbook of the genera of the North American Paleozoic Bryozoa. N. Y. State Geol. Ann. Rept. 1894, p. 407–608, 25 pls., 222 figs.

Smitt, F. A. (1866) Om Hafs-Bryozoernas utveckling och fettkroppar. Öfvers. K. Vetensk. Akad. Förhandl., Årg. 22

——— (1867) Kritisk Förteckning öfver Skandinaviens Hafs-Bryozoer. Pt. II. Öfvers. K. Vetensk. Akad. Förhandl., Årg. 23

——— (1872) Remarks on Dr. Nitsche's researches on Bryozoa. Quart. Jour. Micr. Sci., n.s., v. 12, p. 246–248

Stach, L. W. (1935) Growth variation in Bryozoa Cheilostomata. Ann. Mag. Nat. Hist., v. 16, ser. 10, p. 645–647

——— (1936) Correlation of zoarial form with habitat. Jour. Geology, v. 44, p. 60–65, 1 fig.

Stuckenberg, A. (1895) Korallen und Bryozoen der Steinkohlenablagerungen des Urals und des Timan. Com. Géol. Mem. 10, fasc. 3, 244 p., 24 pls.

Tomlinson, C. W., *et al.* (1940) Classification of Permian rocks. Am. Assoc. Petroleum Geologists Bull., v. 24, p. 337–358

Trizna, V. (1939) New species of the upper Paleozoic Fenestellidae and Acanthocladiidae from the Bashkirian Urals. Geol. Oil Inst. Trans., ser. A, fasc. 115, Russian, p. 102–144, pls. 1–6, English summary, p. 128–139

Ulrich, E. O. (1882) American Paleozoic Bryozoa. Cincinnati Soc. Nat. Hist. Jour. v. 5, p. 121–175, pls. 6–8, p. 232–257, pls. 10, 11

——— (1888) A list of the Bryozoa of the Waverly group in Ohio, with description of new species. Denison Univ., Sci. Lab. Bull. 4, p. 62–96, pls. 13, 14

——— (1890) Paleozoic Bryozoa. Ill. Geol. Survey, v. 8, pt. 2, p. 283–688, pls. 38–61, 18 figs.

Vaughan, T. W., and Wells, J. W. (1943) Revision of the suborders, families, and genera of the Scleractinia. Geol. Soc. America Special Paper 44, 363 p., 51 pls., 39 figs., 3 tables

Vine, G. R. (1879) On Palaeocoryne and its development of Fenestella. Hardwicke's Science Gossip, v. 15, p. 225–229, 247–249, figs. 181–183, 202–204

——— (1884) Fourth report of the committee appointed for the purpose of reporting on fossil Polyzoa. Part II. Classification of Cyclostomatous Bryozoa. (Rept. of the 53rd Meeting of the British Assoc. for the Adv. of Sci., 1883), p. 175–205

Waagen, Wm., and Pichl, Joseph (1885) Salt Range fossils, Part 5, Bryozoa. Geol. Survey India, Paleontologica Indica, ser. 13, Mem. 1, p. 771–834, pls. 87–96

Waagen, Wm., and Wentzel, Joseph (1887) Salt Range Fossils Coelenterata. Geol Survey India, Paleontologica Indica, ser. 13, Mem. 1, p. 835–982, pls. 117–125

Walther, Johannes (1910) Sedimente der Taubenbank in Golfe von Neapel. Abh. K. Preuss, Akad. Wiss., Phys.-Math. Klasse, Abt. III, p. 1–49, 2 maps

Waters, A. W. (1889) Supplementary report on the Polyzoa collected by H.M.S. Challenger during the years 1873–1876. Rept. Sci. Res. H.M.S. Challenger, Zoology, v. 13, pt. 59, 41 p., 3 pls.

——— (1890) On some ovicells of cyclostomatous Bryozoa. Jour. Linn. Soc. London, Zoology, v. 20, p. 275–280, pl. 14

——— (1891) On cheilostomatous characters in Meliceratidae and other fossil Bryozoa. Ann. Mag. Nat. Hist., ser. 6, v. 8, p. 48–58, pl. 6

——— (1896) On Mediterranean and New Zealand Reteporae and a fenestrate Bryozoa. Jour. Linn. Soc. London., Zoology, v. 25, p. 255–271, pls. 6, 7

——— (1904) Bryozoa. In Expédition Antarctique Belge. Resultats du Voyage de S. Y. Belgica en 1897–1899. Rapports Scientifiques, Zoologie, Anvers, 114 p., 9 pls.

West, Wm., and Annandale, N. (1915) Description of three new species of algae associated with Indian freshwater Polyzoa. Asiatic Soc. of Bengal Jour. and Proc., n. s., v. 7, p. 83–84, pl. 3

Whidborne, G. F. (1895) A monograph of the Devonian fauna of the south of England. Paleontographical Soc. Mon., v. 2, pt. 4, Bryozoa, p. 161–188, pls. 18–20

Williams, J. S. (1938) Pre-Congress Permian conference in the U.S.S.R. Am. Assoc. Petroleum Geologists, v. 22, p. 771–776, 1 chart

Yakovlev, N. N. (1945) On bryozoan and crinoidal reefs of the Permian period in the Urals. Akad. Nauk S.S.S.R. (Dokl.), v. 48, no. 5, p. 352–354, Russian

Young, John, and Young, John (1874) On Palaeocoryne and other polyzoal appendages. Quart. Jour. Geol. Soc. London, v. 30, p. 684–689, pls. 40–43

EXPLANATION OF PLATES

Photographs not retouched except as indicated

PLATE 1.—STRUCTURE OF THE WALL IN FENESTRATA

Figure | Page

1–3. Spicules in laminated sclerenchyma.. 35, 40

1. Cross section of the base of *Thamniscus pinnatus* Condra. Hughes Creek shale, Big Blue Series (Lower Permian), Bennett, Nebraska. From the top down in the photograph the spicules are sectioned successively longitudinally, diagonally, and transversely. × 100.
2. Cross section of a part of dorsal side of *Thamniscus serialis* Waagen and Pichl, Middle Productus limestone, Salt Range, India. Most spicules are sectioned longitudinally, except in the left lower corner, where they are cut diagonally. They bifurcate at the points marked "x". × 100.
3. Cross section of the same specimen as figure 2, photographed in polarized light. Spicules are cut longitudinally. Three spicules marked "a" start within the upper zooecial chamber marked "A" and cut across its wall as they enter laminated sclerenchyma. × 100.

4–8. Colonial plexus and secondary calcification in *Fenestella*........................ 28

4. Cross section near the base of *Fenestella* (*Minilia*) *compactilis* Condra (holotype) photographed in polarized light. Cass limestone, Douglas group, Virgil Series, Pennsylvanian, Plattsmouth, Nebraska. Crystallographic unity of the colonial plexus is indicated by simultaneous blackout of its parts. Only very few spicules are traversing copious laminated sclerenchyma, as compared with the multitude in the similar sclerenchyma of *Thamniscus* in figures 1–3. × 70.

5, 6. Cross section of part of the same specimen (5, ordinary light; 6, polarized light). Inner part of the chamber marked "c" blacks out simultaneously with the core of the colonial plexus. × 140.

7. Cross section of *Fenestella quadratocellata* Shulga. Upper Carboniferous C_1^2b, Podcherem River, Pechora Land, northern European Russia (after Shulga-Nesterenko, 1926, Fig. 30, right side). Colonial plexus, white, continues across the dissepiment between the two branches on the right. × 19.

8. Cross section of *Fenestella ornata* var. *robusta* Shulga, from the Permian P_1^2, Stschugor River, Pechora Land (after Shulga-Nesterenko, 1926, Pl. 14, fig. 3, right side). Colonial plexus, black; inner sclerenchyma, white; and outer laminated sclerenchyma, lighter and darker zones. × 40.

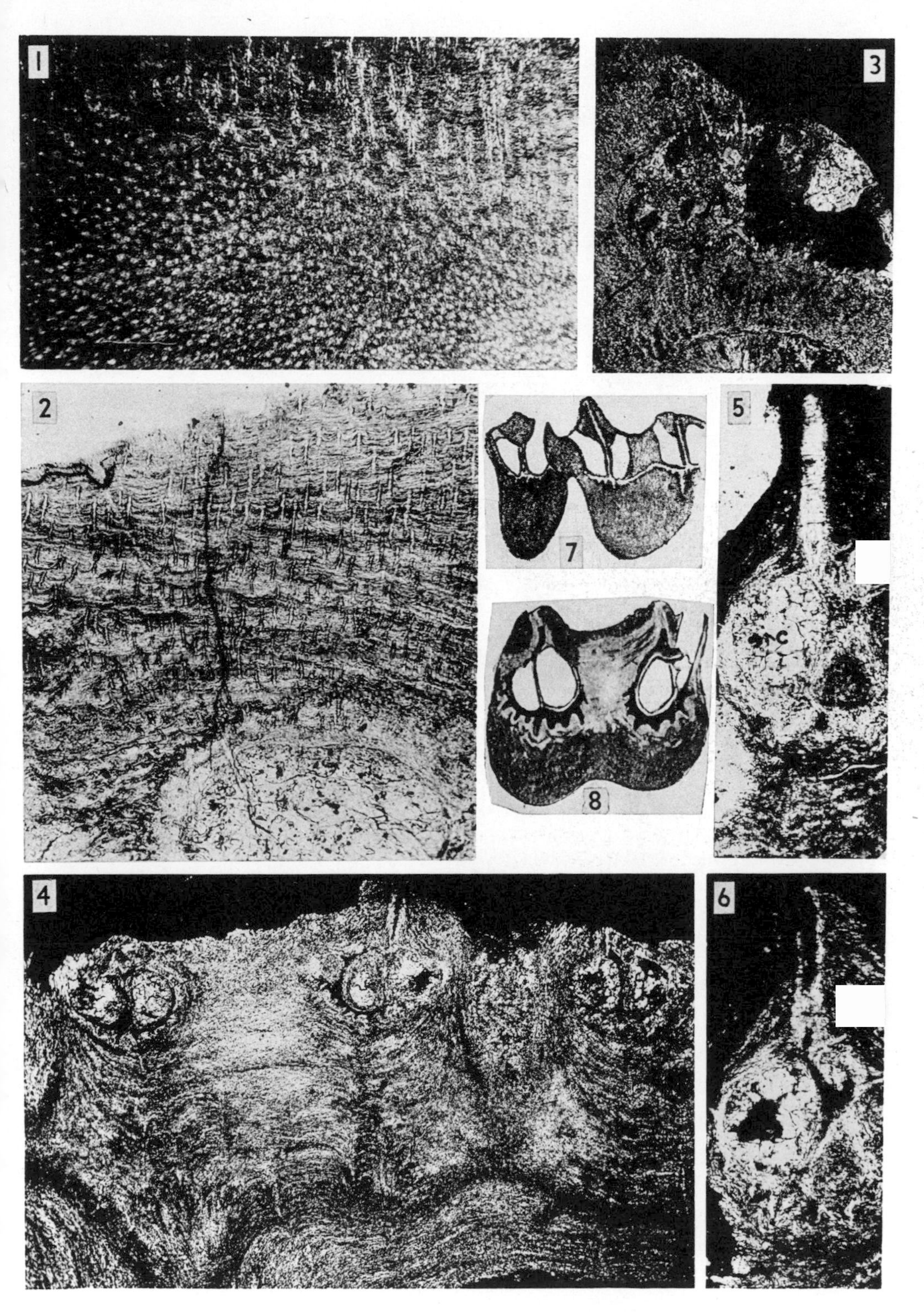

STRUCTURE OF THE WALL IN FENESTRATA

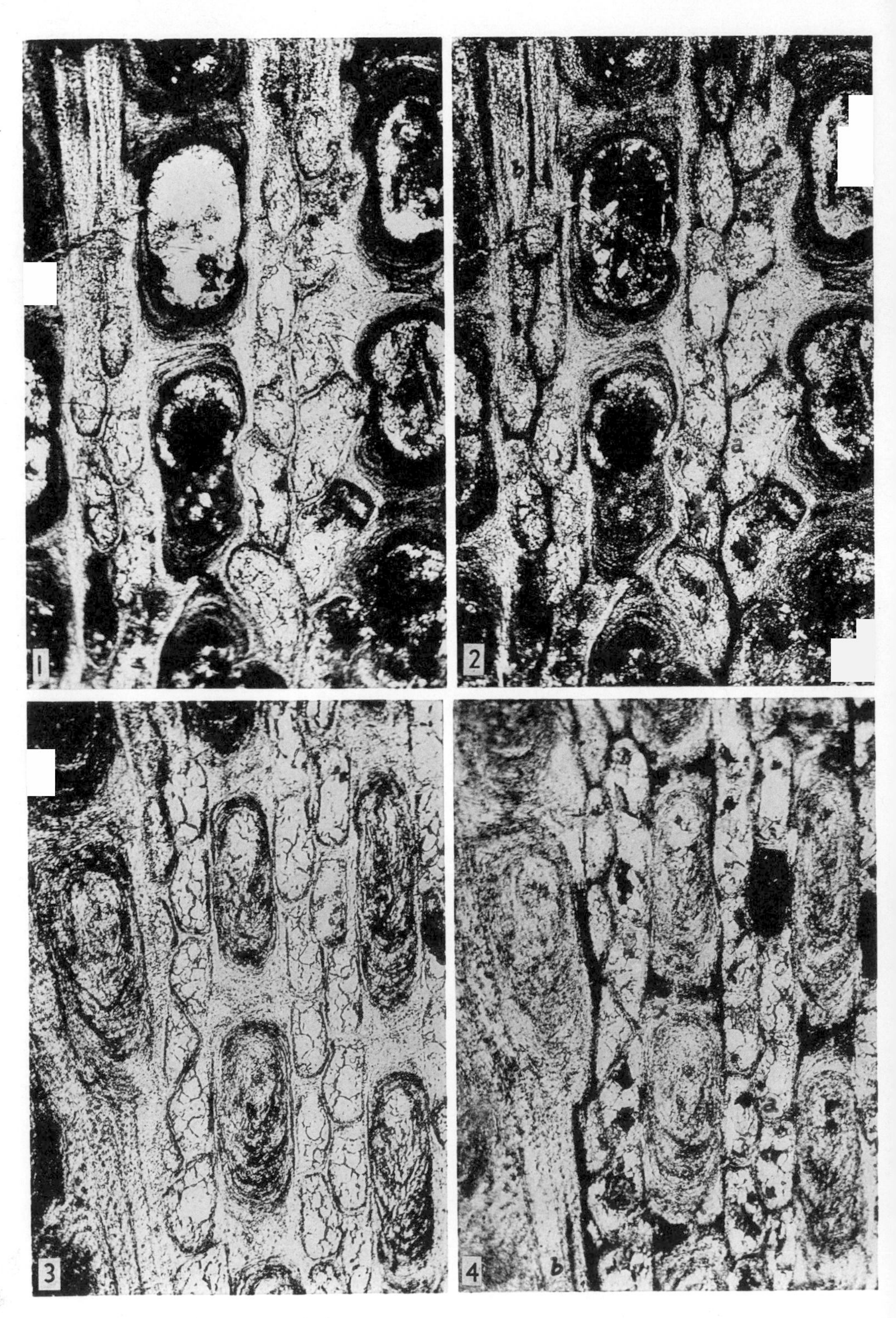

COLONIAL PLEXUS IN POLARIZED LIGHT

Plate 2.—COLONIAL PLEXUS IN POLARIZED LIGHT

Figure | Page

1–2. *Fenestella* (*Minilia*) *compactilis* Condra. Topotype. Cass limestone, Plattsmouth, Nebraska. Detail of the tangential sections illustrated on Figure 4 of Plate 12........ 28
   1. In ordinary light;
   2. In polarized light.

3–4. *Archimedes owenanus* Hall. Lectotype. Koekuk limestone, Adams County, Illinois. Detail of the tangential section of the flange illustrated by Condra and Elias (1944, Pl. 14, fig. 15).. 28
   3. In ordinary light.
   4. In polarized light. All figures *circa* × 70.

The photographs show the colonial plexus which blacks out in polarized light as a crystalline unit, revealing its continuity and contents. It includes the single wall, marked *a*, between the zooecia and the prominent folds ("striae") which rise on their dorsal side, marked *b*. The plexus includes also the flattened core of the dissepiments, as the blacked-out unit enters into them from either side. A slight difference in optical orientation of the calcite in the colonial plexus of the two neighboring branches from which the core starts results in a slight lag of the blackout in the left and right parts of the core, and the contact of the two parts in the middle of a dissepiment is thus revealed (marked x in Figure 4).

PLATE 3.—INTERNAL STRUCTURE OF CYCLOSTOMATA

(p. 41)

Figure | Page

1–2. *Idmidronea maxillaris* (Lonsdale). Middle Jacksonian (Eocene). Lenuds Ferry, South Carolina........ 37

1. Cross section of branch
2. Longitudinal section in the plane of symmetry of branch. *Circa* × 130

In Figure 1 laminated sclerenchyma encrusts both sides of the thin common wall of the zooecia marked *a*. The dorsal part (lower) of the branch is made of "firmatopores," arranged in radial and concentric rows as are the zooecial tubes in the frontal part (above). The two parts of the branches are separated by a partition *b*, which is as thin as the common zooecial wall marked *a*, and is frequently broadly pierced or absorbed (*see c* in Fig. 2). The laminated sclerenchyma grows inward from the common wall between the zooecia and tends to fill them, and at least part of the sclerenchyma of the dorsal side of the branch fills the "firmatopores" similarly.

3–4. *Hornera jacksonica* Canu and Bassler. Middle Jacksonian (Eocene). Castle Hayne, Wilmington, North Carolina........ 37

3. Cross section of branch
4. Diagonal section of branch. *Circa* × 80.

In Figure 3 the laminated sclerenchyma displays an inward drag around the large "vacuoles" marked *a* (pseudopores in terminology of Levinsen and Borg), while a similar drag is outward around the spicules in *Fenestella* and *Thamniscus* (*see* Pl. 1, figs. 2 and 4)

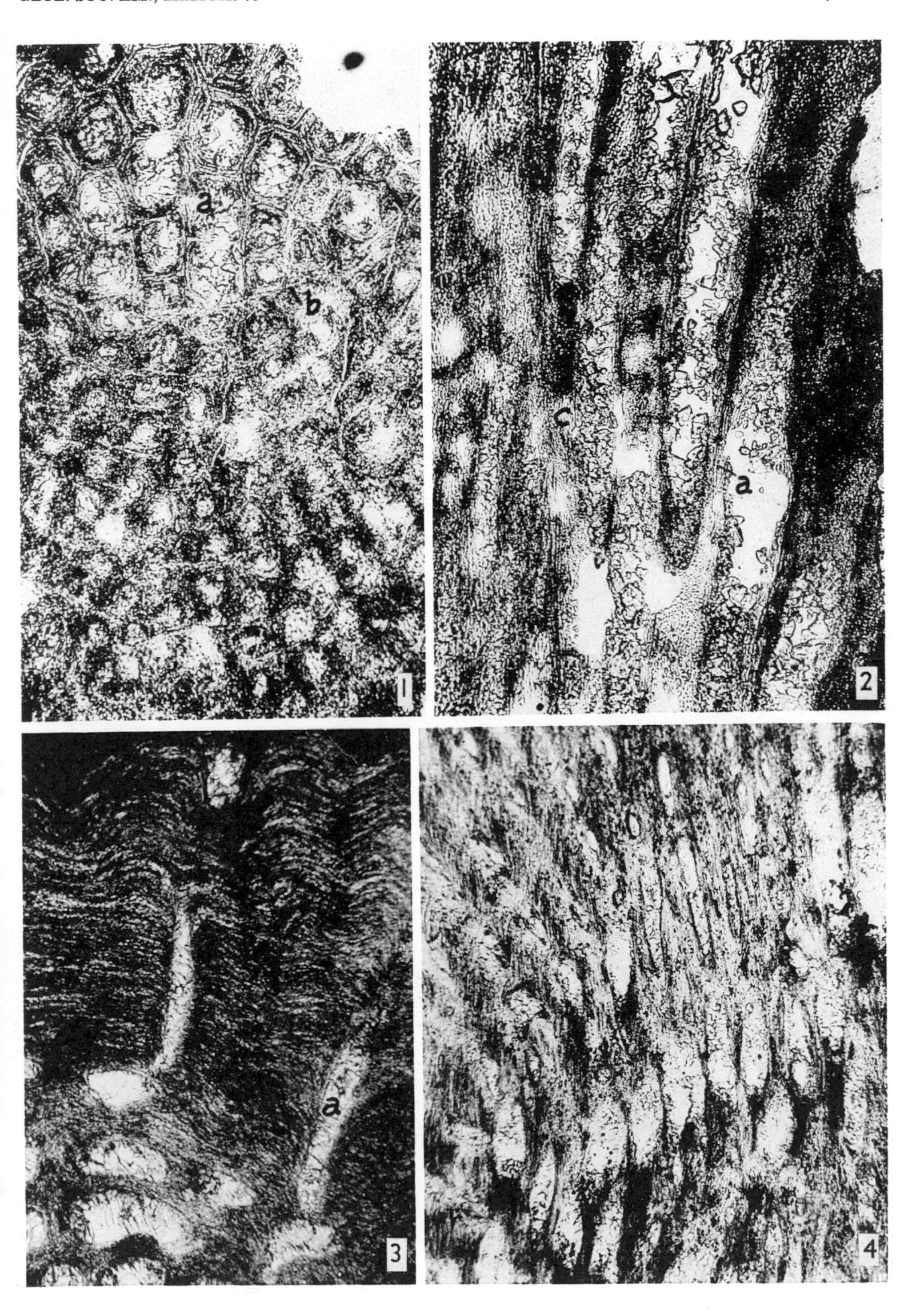

INTERNAL STRUCTURE OF CYCLOSTOMATA

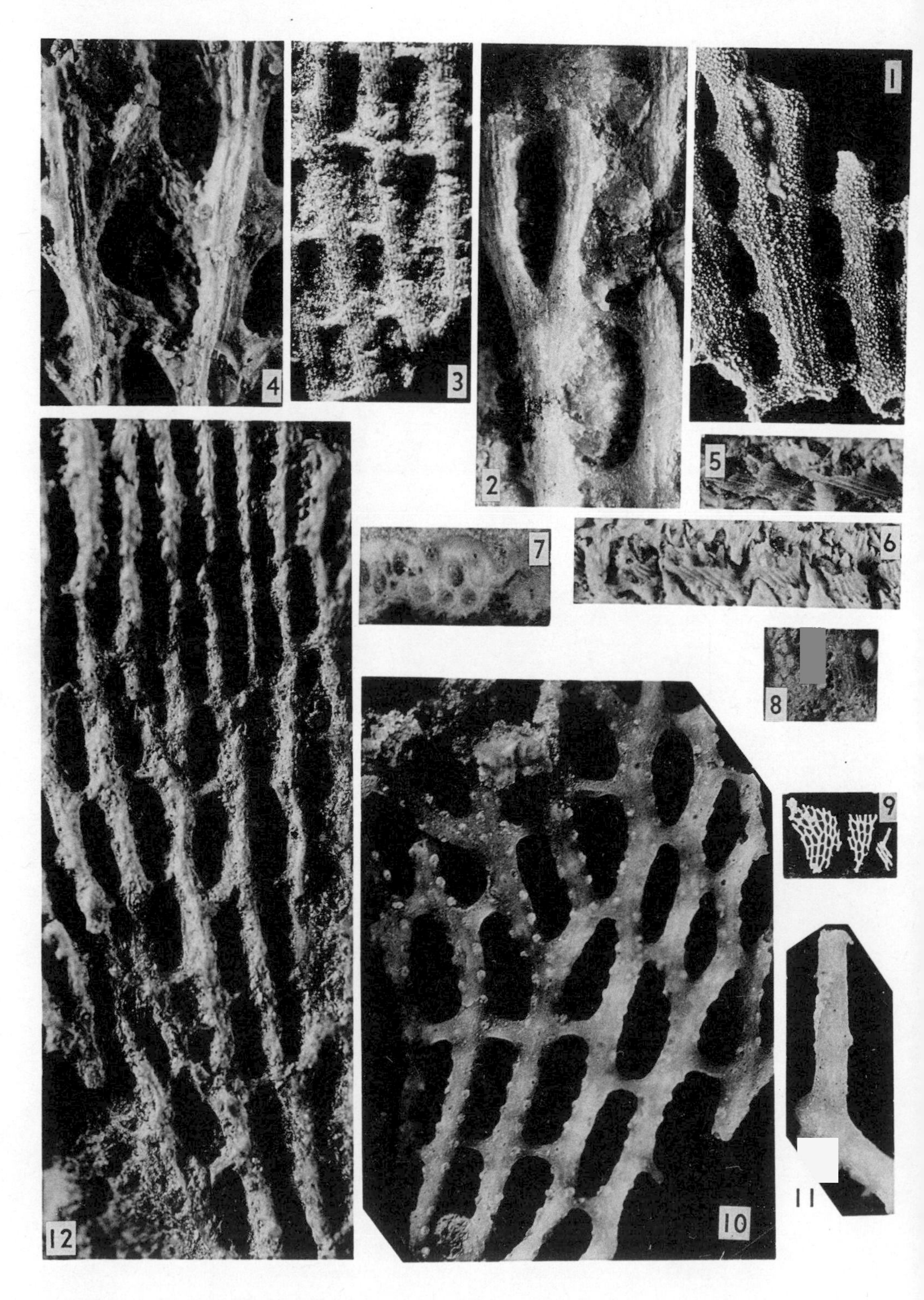

DETAILS OF CALCIFIED COLONIAL PLEXUS IN *FENESTELLA* AND RELATED BRYOZOA

Plate 4.—DETAILS OF CALCIFIED COLONIAL PLEXUS IN *FENESTELLA* AND RELATED FOSSIL BRYOZOA

Figure Page

1. *Fenestella girtyi*(?) Elias. Middle part of Leonard Series, Glass Mountains, Texas. Reverse of a zoarium, with branches covered by narrow ridges and wide depressions over which are numerous tubercles, some aligned along crests of ridges. 28, 29, 103
2. *Fenestella basloensis* var. *shaktauensis* n. var. Detail of the reverse (upside-down orientation) to show grooved surface of branches and dissepiments exposed under exfoliating sclerenchymatous crust. × 10. . . . . .28, 29, 79
3. *Archimedes fragilis* Condra and Elias. Pitkin limestone, Leslie, Arkansas. Reverse of fenestellid expanse, with branches covered by narrow tuberculate ridges, and depressions wider than ridges. 28, 29
4. *Septopora* cf. *pinnata* Ulrich. Hughes Creek shale, Big Blue Series, 5 miles east of Douglas, Nebraska. Details of the reverse of a zoarium; sclerenchymatous crust removed by weathering which exposed two series of narrow ridges (the fewer higher and the more numerous lower ones between them); large circular accessory pores stand out in form of molds; originally they penetrated the sclerenchymatous crust, now removed by erosion. × 20. . . . . .28, 29

5–6. *Archimedes lunatus* Condra and Elias (after Condra and Elias, 1944, Pl. 11, fig. 7). From Pitkin limestone, Leslie, Arkansas. Narrow ridges and U-shaped grooves on reverse of *Fenestella* meshwork, etched from the phytomorphic tissue by differential weathering. × 20. . . . . .28, 29

7–8. *Bicorbis arizonica* (Condra and Elias), Kaibab formation, Permian, Grand Canyon, Arizona. (7) Polished transverse section showing grooved reverse of branches of the colonial plexus of *Polypora* zoarium, encrusted by photomorphic tissue in the consortium *Bicorbis* (Part of Condra and Elias, 1945, Pl. 14, fig. 3. × 20. (8) Polished longitudinal section showing grooved reverse of the colonial plexus on the right side. × 10. The ridges of the colonial plexus have been commonly referred to as "striae" on the reverse of the branches. 28, 29

Group I

9–11. *Fenestella austini* n. sp. Wolfcamp Series, Glass Mountains, Texas. 76

9. Holotype and two paratypes. × 1.
10. Detail of holotype. × 10.
11. Columnar "appendage" or pillar with reverted hooks, arising at about 45-degree angle from the reverse of a branch. × 10.

12. *Fenestella gaptankensis*, n. sp. Holotype, beds with *Uddenites*, Gaptank Series, at Wolfcamp, Glass Mountains, Texas. × 10. 75

PLATE 5.—*FENESTELLA* OF GROUPS I AND II

Group I

Figure | Page

1–2. *Fenestella petschorica* Shulga. Leonard Series, at Word Ranch, Glass Mountains, Texas. C. O. Dunbar coll., no. 5443–5446. 77

1. Basal part, heavily encrusted at elongated base and on the reverse, weathered out on the obverse. × 2.
2. Detail of same. × 10.

Group II

3–6. *Fenestella schucherti* n. sp. Upper part of Leonard Series, at Clay Slide, Glass Mountains, Texas. Scattered octahedrons of magnetite embedded in the silicified fossil (Figs. 3–6), particularly on the reverse. 80

3. Obverse of the proximal part of zoarium, with a group of parasitic coral-like organism
4. Detail of same. × 10.
5. Reverse of part of same. × 10.
6. Tangential view of a part of the reverse of same, showing stumps of a group of columnar "appendages," and double rows of nodes along some branches. × 10.

FENESTELLA OF GROUPS I AND II

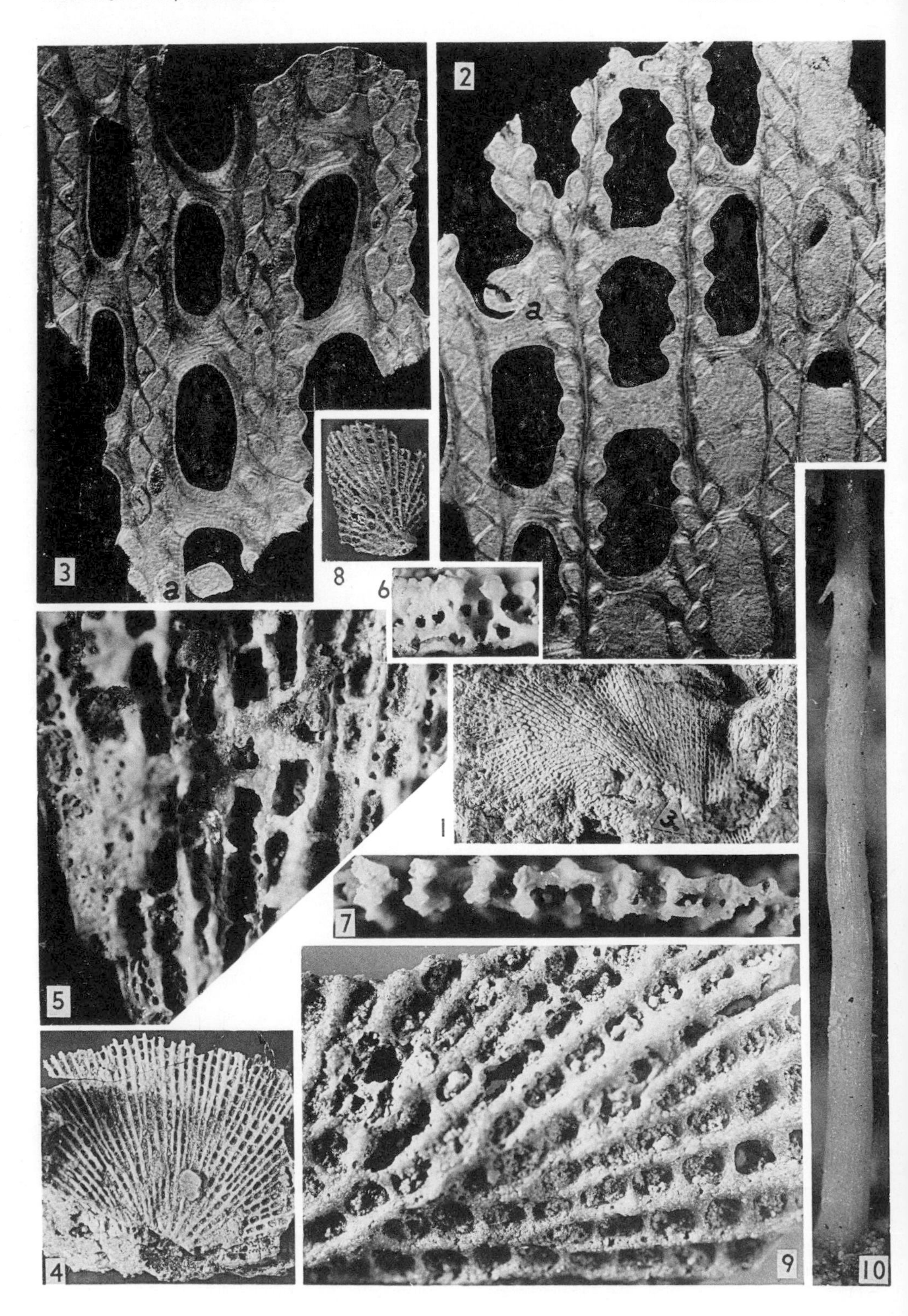

FENESTELLA OF GROUPS II, III, AND IV

PLATE 6.—*FENESTELLA* OF GROUPS II AND III

Group II

Figure | Page

1–3. *Fenestella basloensis* var. *shaktauensis* n. var. Shak-tau limestone reef, Lower Artinskian, Russia........ 79

1. Holotype. × 1.

2, 3. Thin sections of holotype. A third row of four successive zooecia has developed in the second branch from the right in Figure 3. Structures indicated by letter *a* are probably ovicells. × 20.

Group III

4–9. *Fenestella* (*Loculiporina*) *pavonia*, n. subgenus, n. sp. Section 8, basal part of Word group, Glass Mountains, Texas........ 82

4. Holotype, view from the reverse. × 2.

5. Detail of holotype, view from the obverse. × 10.

6, 7. Details of holotype, profile across zoarium; superstructure above is thicker than the poriferous meshwork below. × 10.

8. Paratype, from the reverse. × 2.

9. Detail of paratype, view from the reverse; the circular openings are the locally developed "accessory pores." × 10.

10. Columnar "appendage" or pillar on the reverse of *Fenestella stocktonensis* var. *magnolobata* n. var., illustrated on Figure 1 of Plate 7........ 82

Plate 7.—*FENESTELLA* OF GROUPS III AND IV

Group III

Figure | Page

1–4. *Fenestella stocktonensis* var. *magnolobata* n. var. Holotype, bed 9 of section 24, Wolfcamp Series, northeast of Wolf Camp, Glass Mountains, Texas.................... 82

1. View of the obverse before etching. × 2.

2–4. Details of the obverse (2, 3) and the reverse (4) after etching. Fusing of two neighboring lobes with angular contact of branches is shown on figure 3. × 10.

Group IV

5–7. *Fenestella kingi* n. sp. Holotype, bed 1 or 2, section 11, lower part of Word group, 1½ miles west of Sullivan Peak, Glass Mountains, Texas.......................... 84

5. Side view, showing thick sclerenchymatous encrustation and the stumps of massive columnar "appendages" on the reverse of the zoarium. × 2.

6, 7. Views of the obverse and the reverse. × 10.

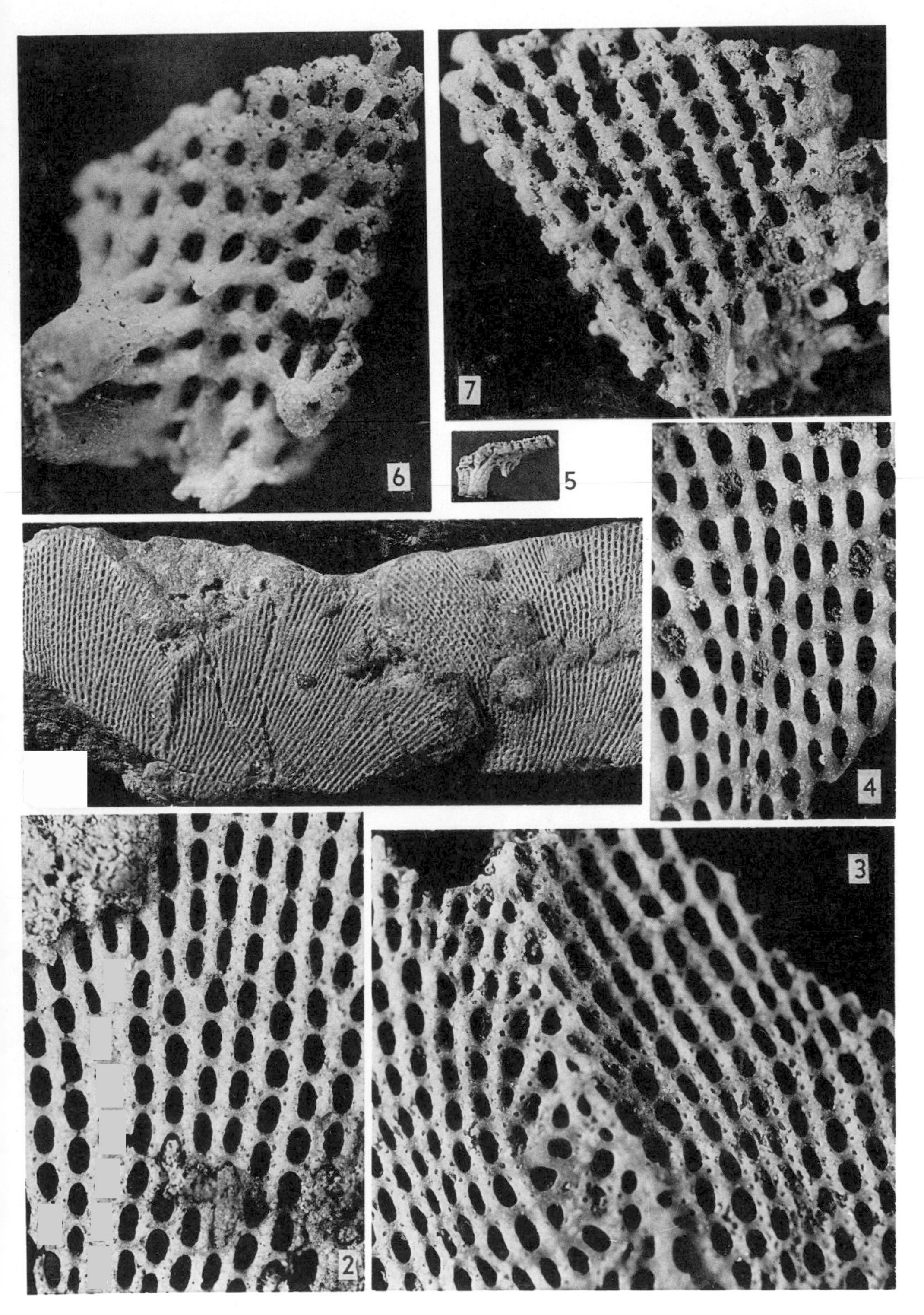

FENESTELLA OF GROUPS III AND IV

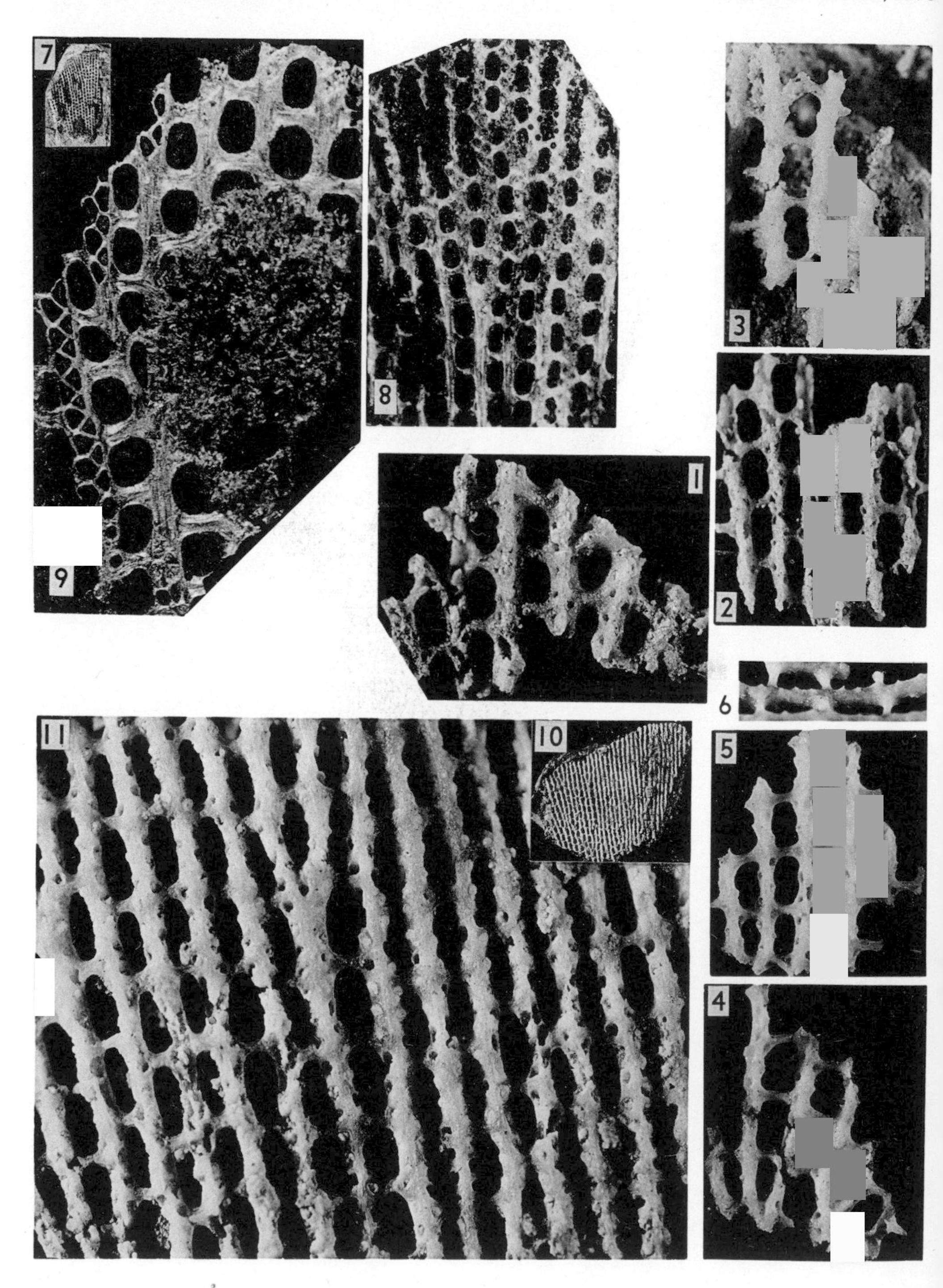

FENESTELLA OF GROUPS V AND VI

PLATE 8.—*FENESTELLA* OF GROUPS V AND VI

Group V

Figure Page

1–3. *Fenestella strukovi* var. *vidrioensis* n. var. Altuda member of Vidrio formation, basal Capitan. South of James Ranch, Del Norte Range, Glass Mountains, Texas. Fan-shaped zoarium. × 10 86
1. Obverse of proximal part
2. Obverse of distal part
3. Reverse of proximal part

4–6. *Fenestella strukovi* var. *tenuiformis* n. var. "Fourth limestone" of Word group, section 17, at junction of Road and Gilliland canyons, Glass Mountains, Texas. Fan-shaped zoarium. × 10 86
4. Obverse of proximal part
5. Obverse of distal part
6. Tangential view of reverse of Figure 4, showing distally pointed spines.

7–9. *Fenestella nalivkini* n. sp. Shale in Artinskian (Lower Permian) at Sims Plants, west-central Urals, Russia 87
7. Holotype, largest fragment, reverse exposed. × 1.
8. Detail of holotype polished and etched. × 10.
9. Thin tangential section of paratype. × 20.

Group VI

10–11. *Fenestella virgosa* var. *dubia* n. var. Bed 9 of section 24, Wolfcamp Series, northeast of Wolf Camp, Glass Mountains, Texas. Large fan-shaped zoarium 89
10. Etched obverse of a distal part. × 1.
11. Detail of Figure 10. × 10.

PLATE 9.—*FENESTELLA* OF GROUP VII

Figure | Page

1. *Fenestella binodata* var. *wolfcampensis* n. var. Lower part of Wolfcamp Series, bed 9 of section 24, northeast of Wolf Camp. Obverse of proximal part of fan-shaped zoarium. × 10.......... 91

2–9. *Fenestella binodata* var. *leonardensis* n. var.......... 91

2–5. Middle part of Leonard Series, bed 14, section 17, Leonard Mountain, Texas

2. Obverse of a distal part. × 2.
3. Detail of the reverse of specimen in Figure 2. × 20.
4. Detail of the reverse of a proximal part. × 20.
5. Detail of the obverse of specimen (holotype) illustrated on Figure 10, of Plate 10. × 20.

6–9. Upper part of Leonard Series at Clay Slide, Glass Mountains, Texas.

6. Proximal and distal parts of a full-grown stage of a fan-shaped zoarium. × 1.
7. Detail of the obverse of the largest specimen. × 10.
8. Diagonal view of a part of the obverse, showing character and disposition of the double row of carinal nodes. × 10.
9. Diagonal view of a part of the obverse, showing unusual development of a carinal node into a tubular trabeculalike connection with a neighboring branch (*see* sketch of it in Fig. 16). × 10.

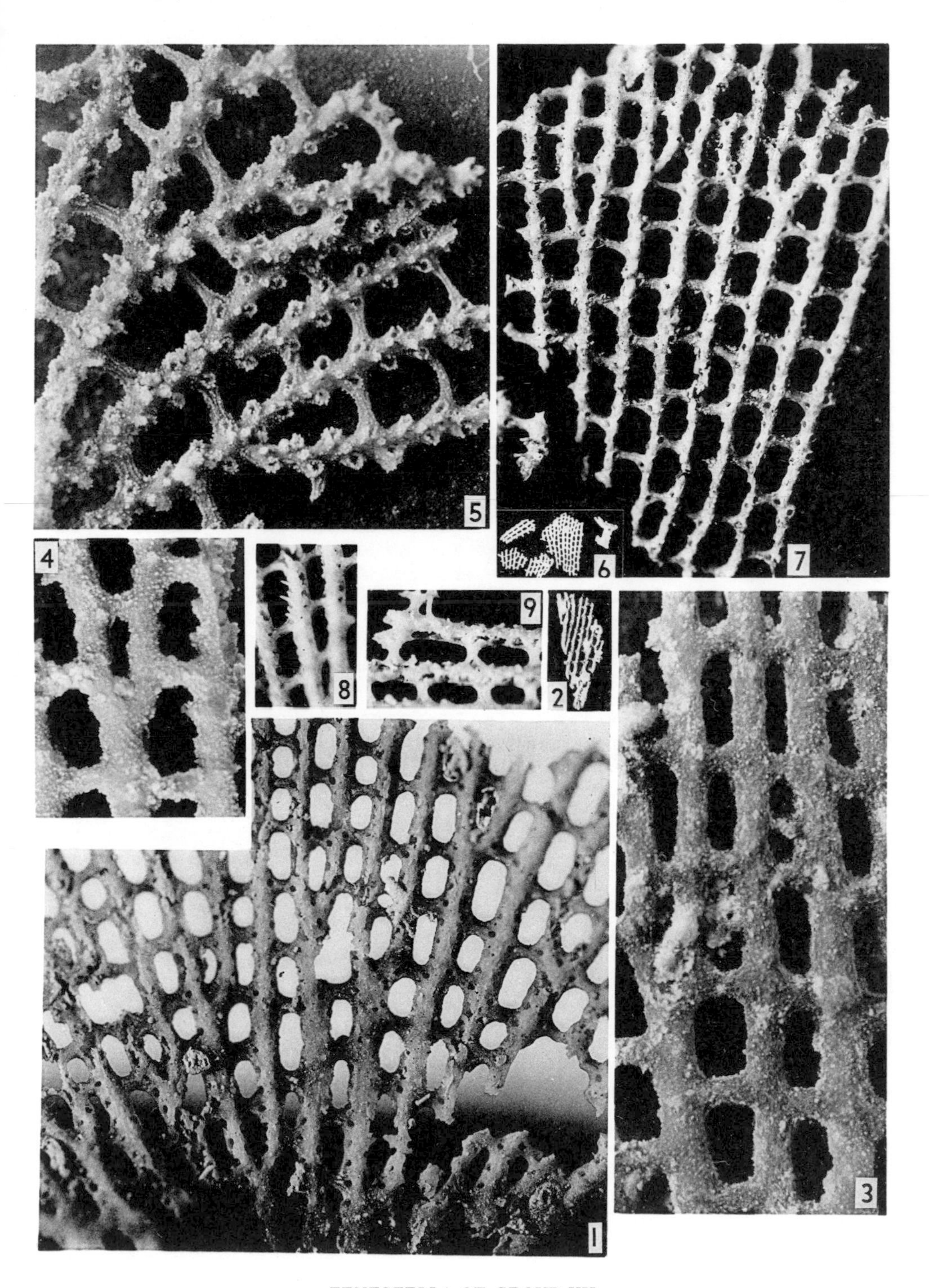

FENESTELLA OF GROUP VII

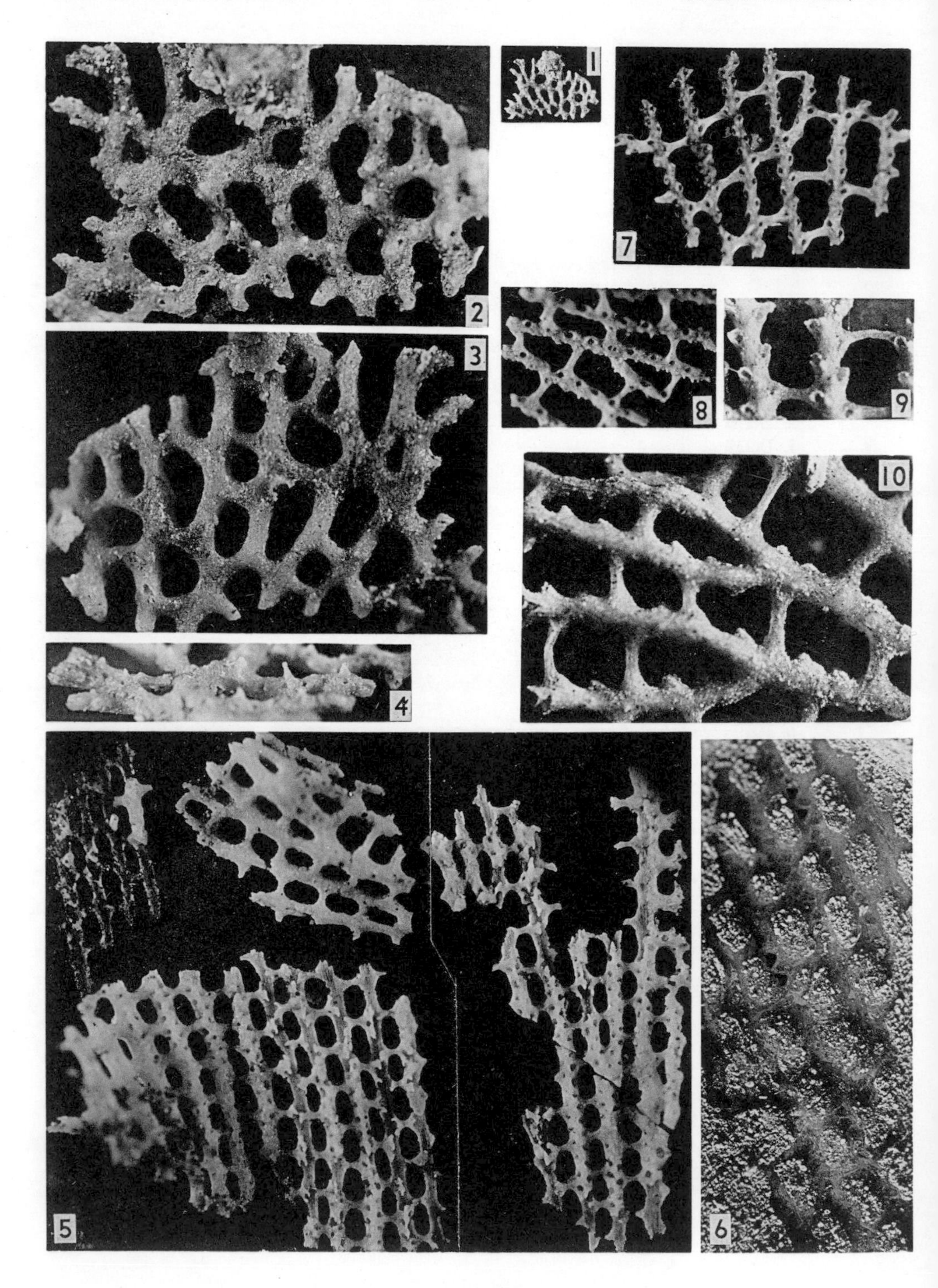

FENESTELLA OF GROUPS I, V, AND XI

PLATE 10.—*FENESTELLA* OF GROUPS I, V, AND XI

Group I

Figure | Page

1–4. *Fenestella varifenestrata* n. sp. Upper part of Leonard Series, at Clay Slide, Glass Mountains, Texas. 77

1. Obverse of a full grown part of a fan-shaped zoarium. × 2.
2. Detail of figure 1, obverse. × 10.
3. Detail of figure 1, reverse. × 10.
4. Detail of figure 1, diagonal view of the obverse, to show the character of the carinal nodes. × 10.

Group V

5–6. *Fenestella inornata* n. sp. Altuda member of Vidrio formation, basal Capitan limestone, locality south of James Ranch, Del Norte Range, Glass Mountains, Texas. 87

5. Four fragments of same zoarium, which broke in the process of etching. Two larger fragments show obverse and impressions of grooved reverse on inside a sclerenchymatous (?) crust. The fragment in the upper left corner shows the remains of the internal zooecial walls and subpentagonal contour of the zooecial chambers. The fragment in the upper center shows the surface of the reverse. × 10.
6. Partially etched reverse, showing the faint interwedging triangular outline (retouched) of the basal parts of the zooecial chambers. × 20.

Group XI

7–10. *Fenestella binodata* var. *leonardensis* n. var. (7, 8) Middle part of Leonard Series, section 17, bed 14. 91

7, 8. Detail of the obverse of paratypes. × 20.

9. Detail of the obverse; zooecial apertures strongly projecting into fenestrules.

10. Detail of the reverse of specimen (holotype) illustrated on Figure 5 of Plate 9, showing the strongly projecting apertures and the finely grooved dissepiments.

Plate 11.—*FENESTELLA* OF GROUPS VII AND VIII

Group VII

Figure | Page

1–4. *Fenestella binodata* var. *leonardensis* n. var. Upper part of Leonard Series at Clay Slide, Glass Mountains, Texas. × 10. 91
1. Obverse of a proximal part (but not the initial part) of a fan-shaped zoarium.
2. Side view of specimen in Figure 1, showing two pillars and their flattened common base, attached to the obverse of another *Fenestella*.
3. Obverse of a fragment from a full-grown stage of zoarium, but showing considerable divergence of branches and their multiplication by an intense lateral branching which is comparable to that in *F. quadratopora*, Figures 11 and 12.
4. Reverse of specimen in Figure 3, viewed diagonally, showing distally pointed spines upon the reverse of the branches.

5–7. *Fenestella binodata* var. *wordensis* n. var. "Fourth" limestone of Word group, section 17, north of junction of Road and Gilliland canyons, Glass Mountains, Texas. × 10. 92
5. Obverse of a proximal part of a fan-shaped zoarium, with frequent bifurcation of the crowded branches. Localized development of sclerenchymatous crust is indicated by the evenly rounded contours of the narrowed fenestrules, and a whiter color caused by the lesser transparency of the thickened branches and dissepiments.
6. Obverse of a full-grown part of zoarium, the single bifurcation accompanied by crowding of the branches instead of their divergence. Short fenestrule developed in the right lower part of the figure. Diagonally developed sclerenchymatous crust, indicated by a slightly thicker and whiter branches and dissepiments, from the upper left to the lower right part of the figure.
7. Reverse of Figure 6, viewed diagonally, to show a series of columnar appendages that arise from the diagonally developed sclerenchymatous crust.

8. *Fenestella geminanoda* Moore. Lower Stanton limestone, upper Missouri Series, east of Bonner Springs, Kansas. To show side-by-side development of shorter (containing two apertures) and longer (containing three apertures) fenestrules and the few one-aperture fenestrules. Probable ancestral form of the two groups: group VII, *F. binodata*, and group VIII, *F. compactilis*. × 2. 89

Group VIII

9–12. *Fenestella quadratopora* Shulga. Wolfcamp Series, bed 9, section 24, northeast of Wolf Camp, Glass Mountains, Texas. 99
9. Obverse of probably nearly complete small zoarium, characterized by frequent multiplication of the branches by lateral branching. × 2.
10. Detail of Figure 9. × 10.
11. Two fragments of another example. × 1.
12. Detail of Figure 11, showing obverse (below) and reverse (above) views of full-grown stage of zoarium, characterized by lateral branching. × 10.

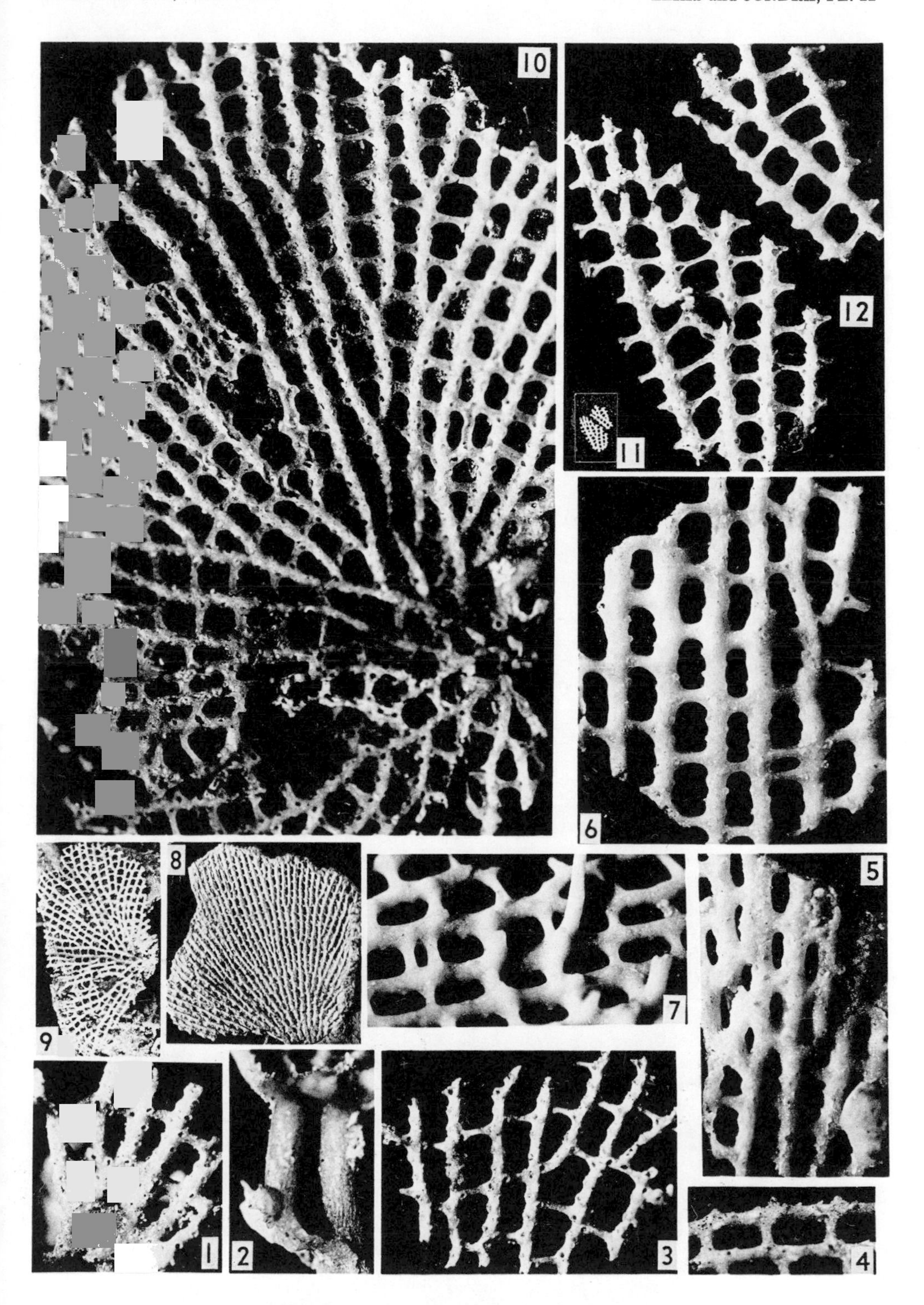

FENESTELLA OF GROUPS VII AND VIII

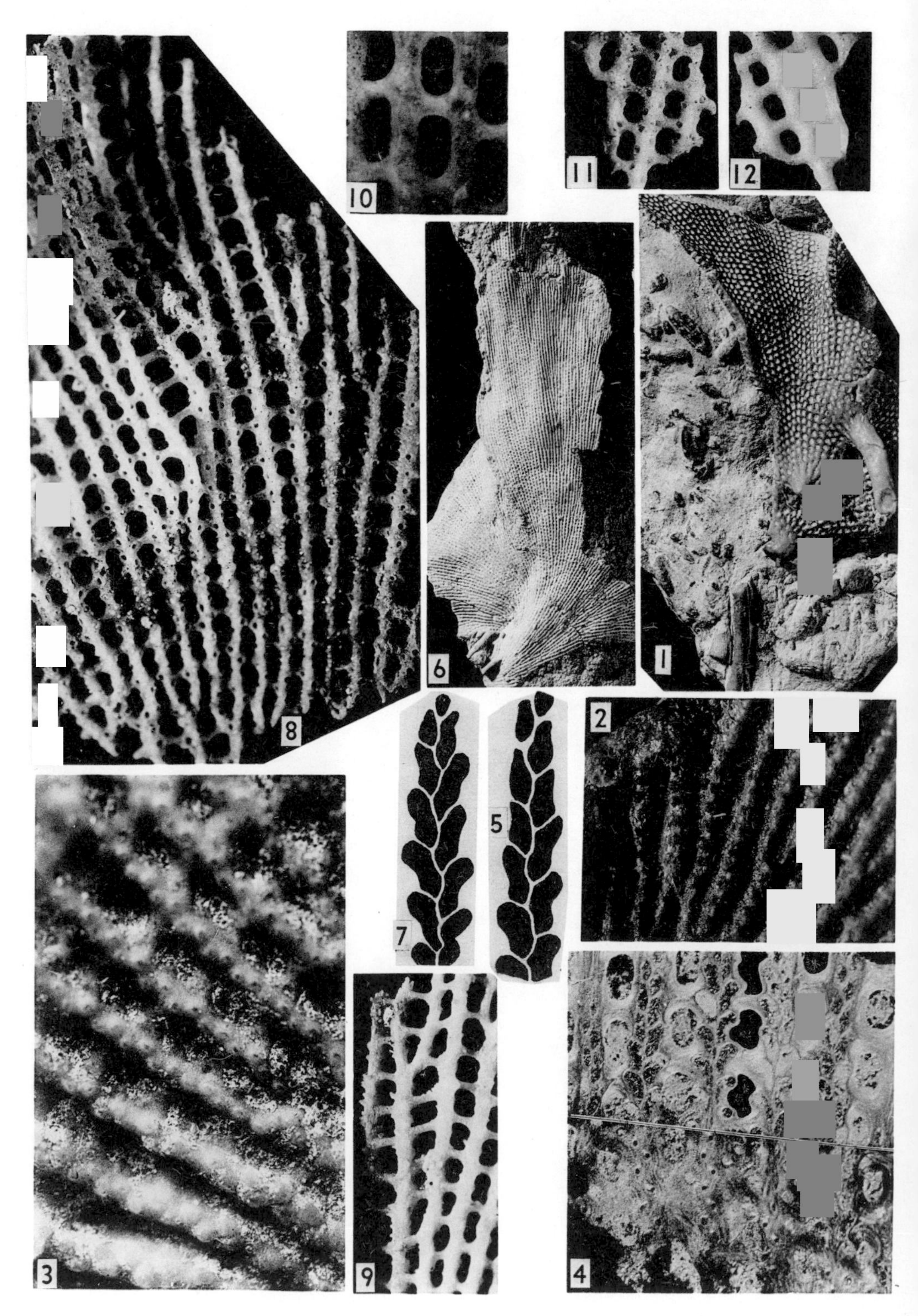

FENESTELLA OF GROUP VIII

Plate 12.—*FENESTELLA* OF GROUP VIII

Figure	Page

1–5. *Fenestella compactilis*. Condra. Holotype (1, 3–5) and topotype (2), Cass limestone (middle Douglas group, Virgil Series), South Bend, Nebraska. 93

1. Reverse of holotype (illustrated by Condra, 1903, Pl. 8, fig. 11), showing uniform sclerenchymatous encrustation of the reverse and the localized growth of the thick columnar "appendages" or pillars in the proximal part of the fan-shaped zoarium. × 2.
2. Obverse of topotype (detail of the obverse illustrated by Condra, 1903, Pl. 8, fig. 12). × 10.
3. Obverse of holotype, from the proximal part of the zoarium removed from matrix and slightly etched by acid; shows two rows of zigzaging carinal nodes and the faint apertures. × 20.
4. Two parts of thin section from topotype, Figure 2. Lower part shows fine undulating, septate threads of sclerenchymatous crust, which is submerging the zigzaging nodes on the obverse. × 20.
5. Shows change in outline of the zooecial chamber from bottom (above) to near level of apertures (below); sketched from left upper part of photograph Figure 4. × 40.

6–7. *Fenestella compactilis* var. *platsmouthensis*, n. var. Plattsmouth limestone (Upper Oread), lower Shawnee group, Virgil Series, Plattsmouth, Nebraska. 95

6. Obverse of a greater part of a fan-shaped zoarium. × 1.
7. Shows change in outline of zooecial chamber, from about the same series of levels as those of Figure 5; sketched from the thin section prepared from the zoarium of Figure 6 to show the difference in the zooecial chamber in comparison with that in *F. compactilis* Condra. × 10.

8–10. *Fenestella infranodosa* n. sp. Upper part of Leonard Series, Clay Slide, Glass Mountains, Texas. 96

8. Obverse of a full-grown part of a fan-shaped zoarium. × 10.
9. Reverse of Figure 8, showing vigorous development of nodes on the reverse of branches and dissepiments. Nodes on branches are locally arranged in two zigzaging rows (left upper side of the figure), pointing distad. × 10.
10. Polished section of the reverse of specimen in Figure 8, showing faint outline of the poorly preserved zooecial chamber. × 20.

11–12. *Fenestella infrandosa* (?) var. "Fourth" limestone of Word group, section 17, north of junction of Road and Gilliland canyons, Glass Mountains, Texas. Fragment from a full-grown stage of a zoarium. × 10. 97

11. Obverse
12. Reverse

PLATE 13.—*FENESTELLA* OF GROUPS IX AND XI

Group IX

Figure | Page

1–4. *Fenestella clinospina* n. sp. Upper part of Leonard Series, Clay Slide, Glass Mountains, Texas. Holotype.......... 98
- 1. Reverse of a large middle portion of a full-grown fan-shaped zoarium, with a group of pillars on the right side. × 2.
- 2. Detail of the obverse of specimen in Figure 1. × 10.
- 3. Detail of a shorter columnar appendage on the left side of the group. × 10.
- 4. Detail of a longer pillar on the right side of the group, showing the manner of attachment to the reverse and the nodes upon the reverse of the branches pointing slightly distad. × 10.

Group XI

5–8. *Fenestella girtyi* Elias var. "Fourth" limestone, upper part of Word group, section 17, north of junction of Road and Gilliland canyons, Glass Mountains, Texas........ 117
- 5. Reverse of a lateral part of a full-grown fan-shaped zoarium, with a group of pillars attached to the obverse more or less along a diagonal line. × 2.
- 6. Detail of the obverse of specimen in Figure 5. × 10.
- 7, 8. Details of the pillars, showing manner of giving off occasional lateral branches perpendicular to the main branch. × 10.

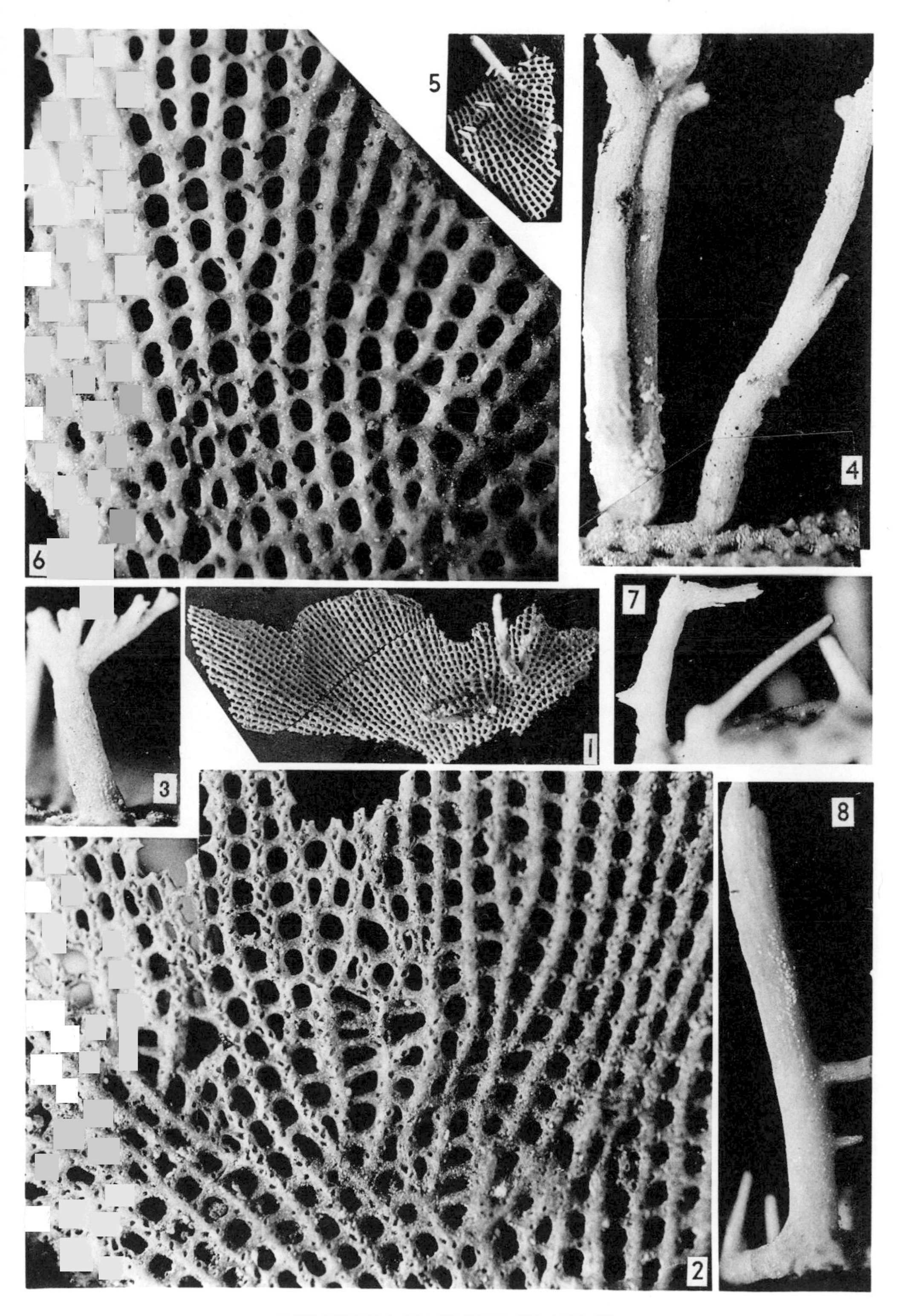

FENESTELLA OF GROUPS IX AND XI

FENESTELLA OF GROUPS X AND XI

PLATE 14.—*FENESTELLA* OF GROUPS X AND XI

Group X

Figure | Page

1–4. *Fenestella cylindrica* n. sp. Beds with *Uddenites* in Wolfcamp Series, at Wolf Camp, Glass Mountains, Texas. 100

1–3. Bottom, side, and top view of a large fragment of cylindrical zoarium, which tends to bifurcate into two nearly equal cylindrical zoarial branches. × 2.

4. Detail of the obverse, which faces outward. × 10.

There is no observable sclerenchymatous encrustation and no columnar braces to connect the opposite reverse sides of the zoarium. Such were observed, however, in an undescribed species of the group.

Group XI

5–8. *Fenestella permica* Shulga. Middle part of Wolfcamp Series, northeast of Wolf Camp, Glass Mountains, Texas. 102

5, 6. Two fragments, smaller (5) from the proximal, and larger (6) from the distal parts of a full-grown fan-shaped zoarium. × 2.

7, 8. Details of the obverse of the proximal (7) and distal (8) fragments of Figures 5 and 6. × 10.

9, 10. *Fenestella mimica* var. *rogersi* Elias, unnamed limestone from base of Virgil Series, 7 miles northwest of Garnett, Kansas. 102

9. Obverse of fragment from middle part of zoarium. × 2.

10. Detail of same obverse. × 10.

PLATE 15.—*FENESTELLA* OF GROUP XI

Figure | Page

1–3. *Fenestella girtyi* (?) Elias. Middle of Leonard Series, bed 14, section 17, north of Leonard Mountain, Glass Mountains, Texas. × 20. 103

1. Detail of the obverse of the proximal part of a full-grown fan-shaped zoarium. Bifurcation of several branches at about the same level results in the more crowded and somewhat narrower branches above the points of bifurcation. Apertures tend to be stabilized at the base of dissepiments in some parts of the zoarium.
2. Obverse of slightly more distal part of a zoarium, with no evidence of stabilization of the apertures.
3. Reverse of a proximal part of a zoarium. Abundance of tubercles of about equal size over all surfaces with concentration along the crests of the ridges on the dissepiments and on the reverse of the branches.

4–5. *Fenestella girtyi* var. "Fourth" limestone of the upper part of Word group; north of junction of Road and Gilliland canyons, Glass Mountains, Texas. Details of the obverse of the distal part of a zoarium. On Figure 4 two neighboring branches end abruptly, and above them the branches on either side are connected by a long dissepiment (a). × 10. 117

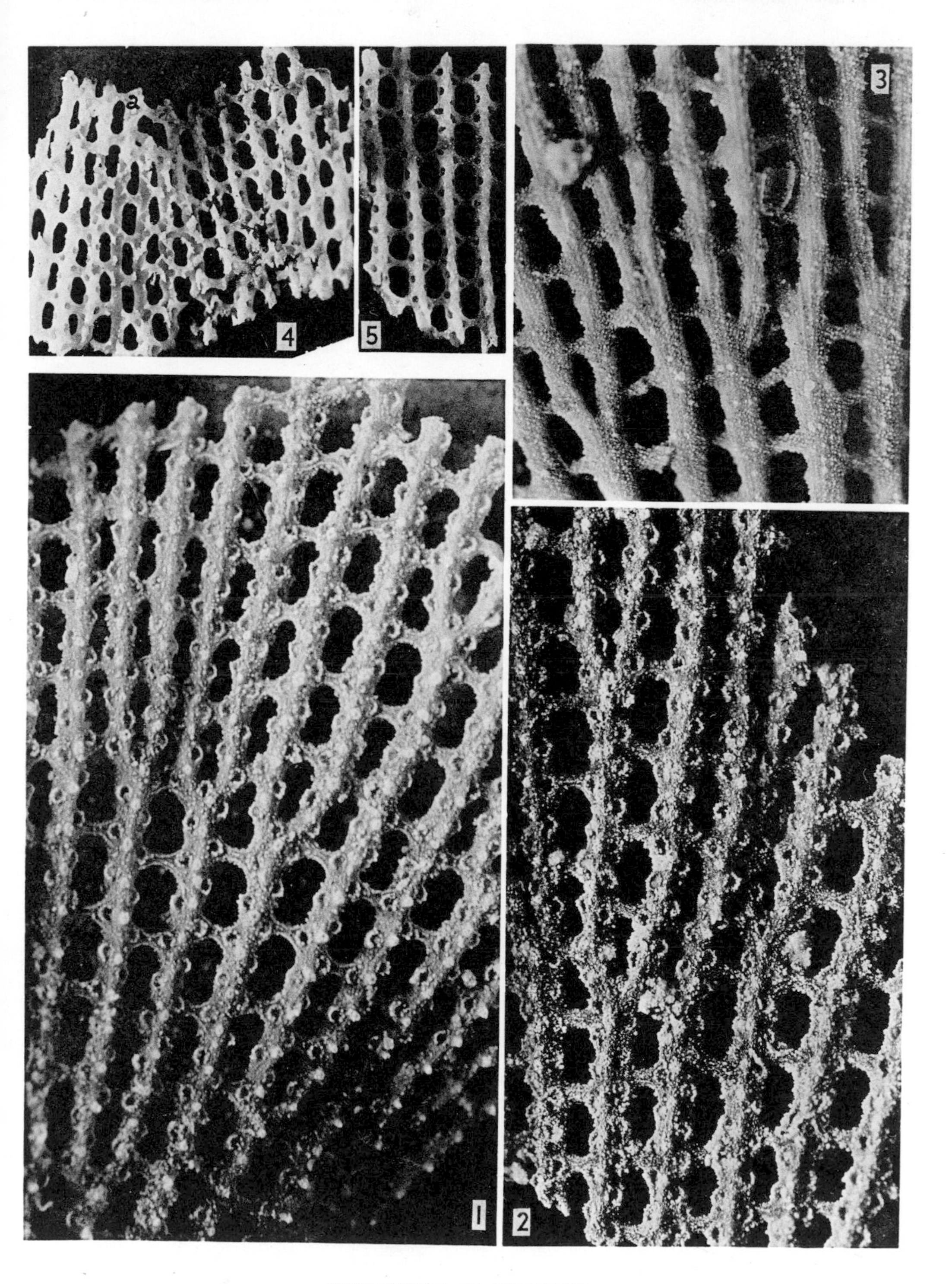

FENESTELLA OF GROUP XI

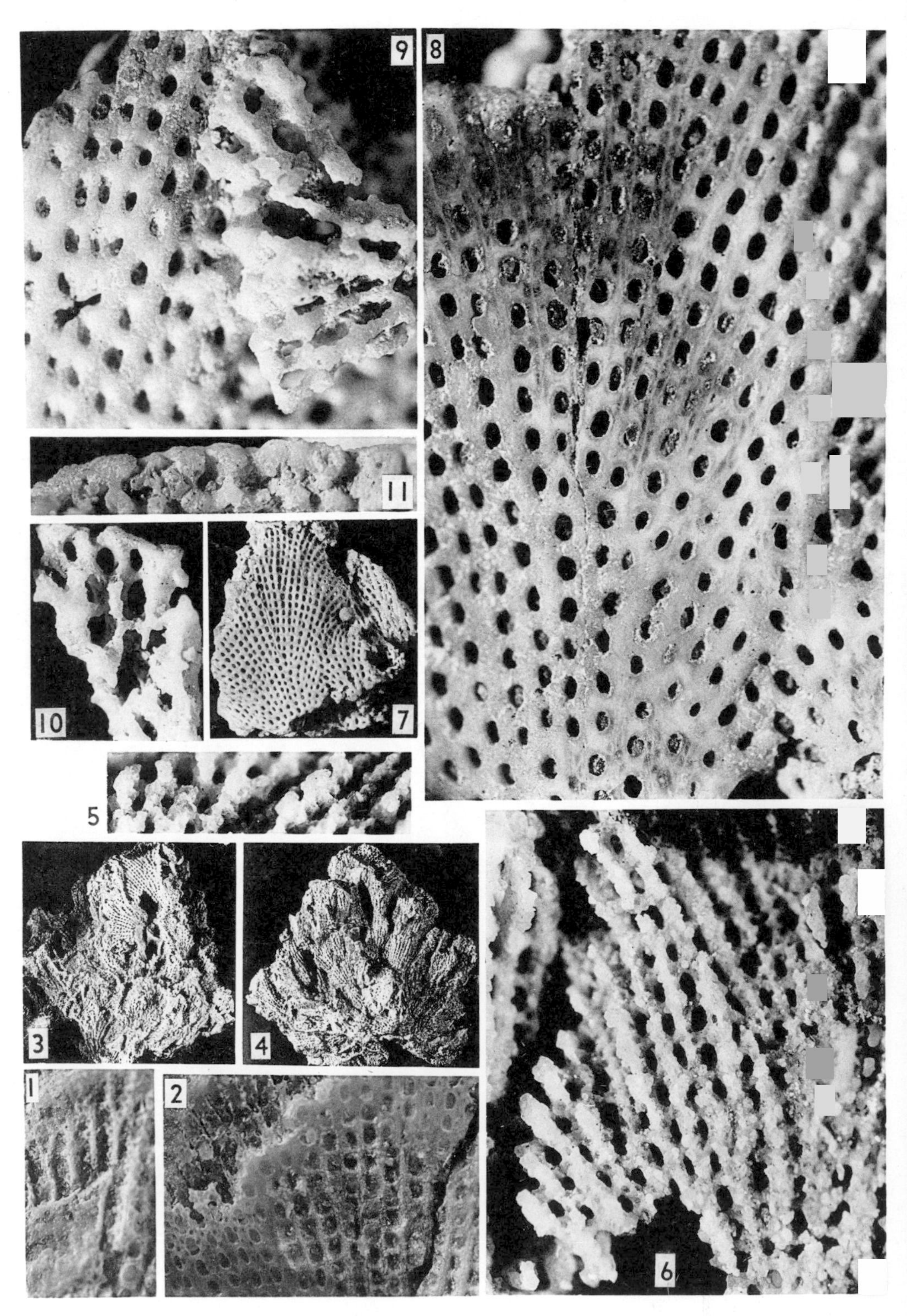

FENESTELLA OF GROUP XI

PLATE 16.—*FENESTELLA* OF GROUP XI

Figure | Page

1–2. *Fenestella tenax* Ulrich. Lower part of Leonard series, south of the forks of Hess Canyon, Glass Mountains, Texas. × 10. 106

1. Detail of the obverse of a small fan-shaped zoarium
2. Polished and slightly etched cut of a part of zoarium of Figure 1 to show the faintly visible outline of its zooecial chamber

3–6. *Fenestella plicata* n. sp. Leonard Series, exact location unknown. 105

3, 4. Lateral views of the opposite sides of holotype, to show its intense plication and general shrub-like growth form.

5, 6. Details of the obverse of specimen illustrated on Figures 3, 4, to show localized tendency to develop superstructure along some branches of zoarium. × 10.

7–11. *Fenestella* (*Loculiporella*) *muscus* n. subg., n. sp. Word group 3 miles east of Hess Tank, Glass Mountains, Texas. 106

7. Side view of the reverse of the holotype. × 2.
8. Detail of the reverse partly cut and polished to show the outline of the zooecial chamber. × 10.

9, 10. Details of the obverse near proximal edges of the small adventitious lobes of a zoarium, where the development of the superstructures lags slightly behind the growth of the zooecial meshwork. × 10.

11. View of a break across zoarium, showing profile of the zooecial meshwork and the superstructure, which faces interior of the zoarium (downward on this photograph). × 10.

Plate 17.—*FENESTELLA* OF GROUP XII

Figure / Page

1. *Fenestella nikiforovae* Shulga. Wolfcamp Series, bed 9, section 24, northeast of Wolf Camp, Glass Mountains, Texas. Obverse of the distal part of a full-grown zoarium. × 2. 113
2. *Fenestella spinulosa* Condra. Horizon and locality same as Figure 1. Reverse of the distal part of a full-grown zoarium. × 2. 109

3–9. *Fenestella cornuta* n. sp. Horizon and locality same as figure 1. 109

3. Bottom view of an elongated funnel-shaped zoarium. Arrow indicates the line of fusion of the most distal part of the curling meshwork to its most proximal part preserved, the initial part was broken along the same line of fusion. × 2.
4. Top view of zoarium in Figure 3 (the obverse facing inside) from the bottom of which arises a dozen of variously oriented, straight to very gently curved columnar appendages or pillars with reverted hooks. × 2.
5. Distal part, broken from zoarium in Figure 3. To show the adherent layer of silt above the obverse, with the rows of holes opposite the branches of the zoarium, each hole corresponding to a carinal spine. × 2.

6, 7. Details of Figure 5. × 10 and × 20.

8. Detail of Figure 5, to show (at the left) a delicate antlerlike apex of a carinal spine (in most others not preserved). × 20.
9. Detail of the bottom of zoarial funnel of Figures 3, 4. View along the branches of the zoarium, with antlerlike apices of carinal nodes preserved in central part only, where they are nearly submerged by the sclerenchymatous crust. This crust spreads around bases of barbed pillars on the left. Spreading of the crust covers some zooecial apertures, but others are left open (*see* foreground). × 20.
10. Tip of one of the barbed pillars, which splits into three branches diverging in a plane, with about 25 degree angle of divergence between each pair
11. Grapnel radicle of living bryozoan *Scrupocellaria* (*Cauda*) *reptans* (After Hinks, 1880, Pl. 7, fig. 6, about × 45). Structurally it is a simple tube with hollow hooks or barbs, while fossil barbed pillars are solid with stellar core similar to that of the colonial plexus of a zoarium to which they are attached.

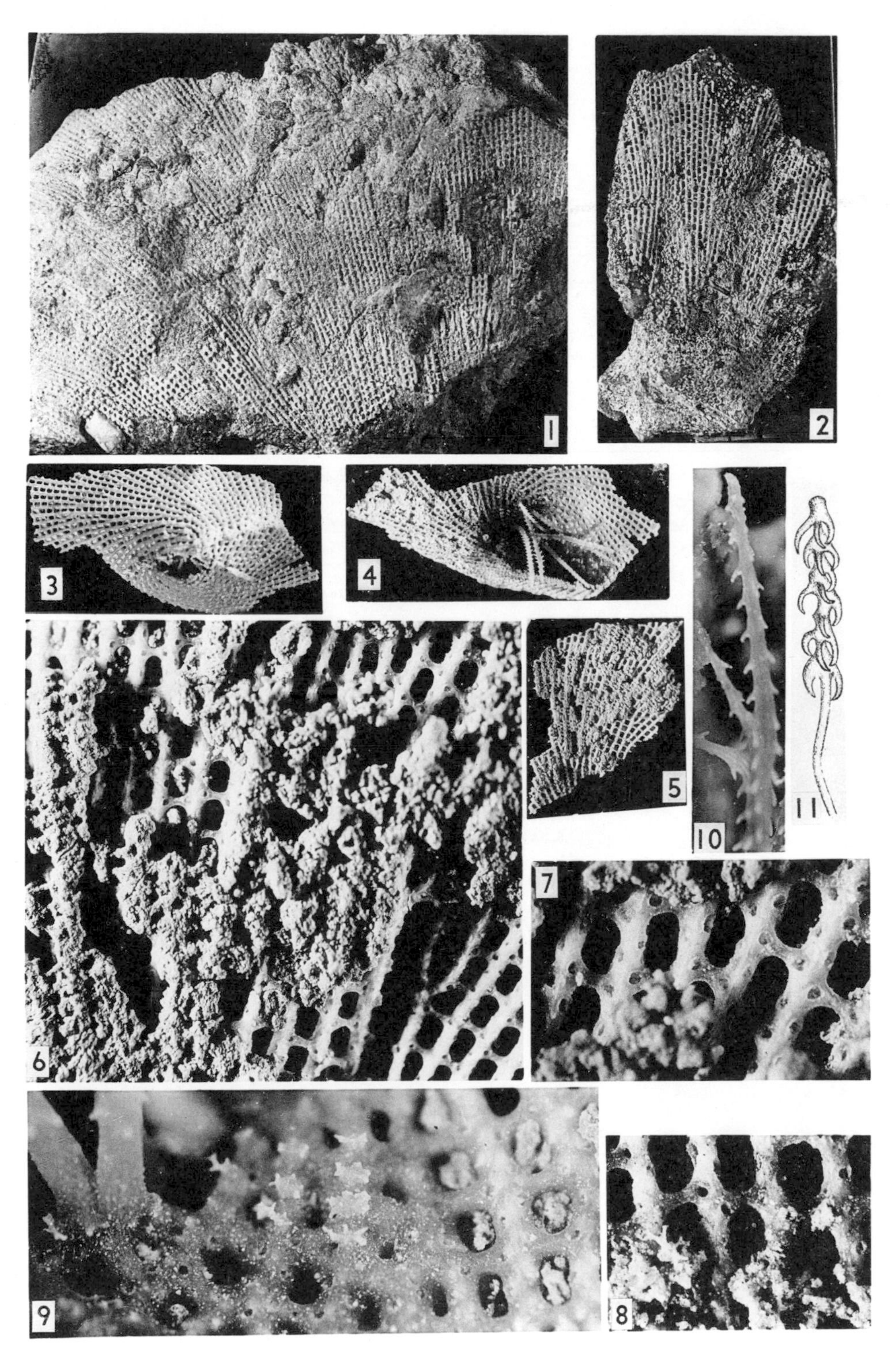

FENESTELLA OF GROUP XII

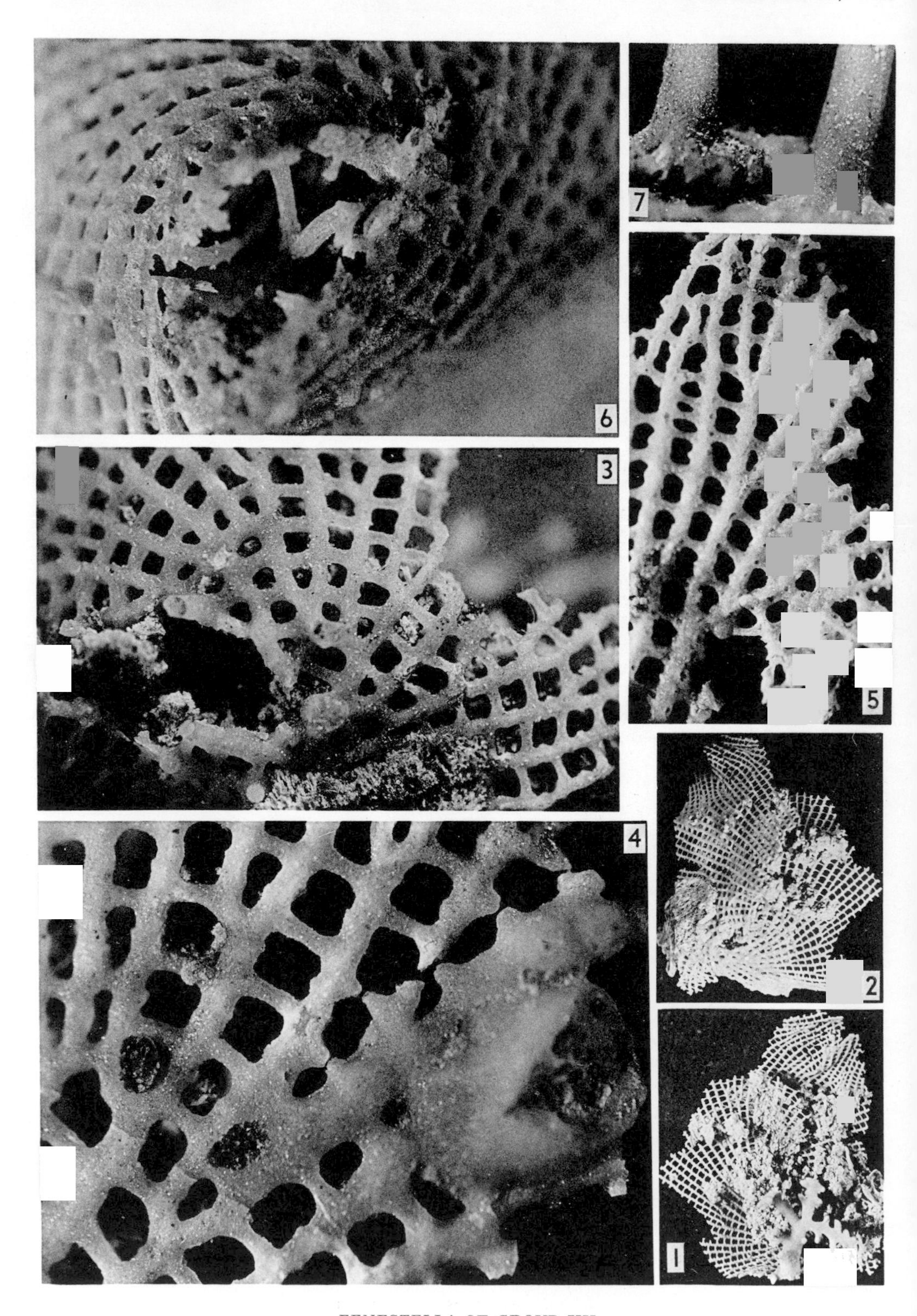

FENESTELLA OF GROUP XII

PLATE 18.—*FENESTELLA* OF GROUPS XII AND III

Group XII

Figure | Page

1–5. *Fenestella archimediformis* n. sp. Holotype. Wolfcamp Series, bed 9, section 24, west end of Wolf Camp Hills, Glass Mountains, Texas. 110

1. Top view, showing obverse facing inward of coiled zoarium. In lower center *Thamniscus guadalupensis* adnate on the obverse of *Fenestella* and growing face to face with it. × 2.
2. Bottom view, showing bottom hole in the center of a coiled zoarium in place of solid shaft in *Archimedes*. × 2.
3. Detail of the center of coiled zoarium, showing stumps of several smooth pillars growing upon the reverse and outward of coiling.
4. Detail of the reverse at a point of attachment of *Thamniscus* (on the right). Base of *Thamniscus* has sagged *Fenestella* meshwork and encrusted it with additional amount of sclerenchymatous tissue. A rosette of the initial zooecia of *Thamniscus* is seen inside its broken base. × 20.
5. Detail of obverse in a fragment apparently broken from slightly coiled lateral edge of zoarium, showing many irregularities in the development of the dissepiments. × 10.

6. *Fenestella cornuta* n. sp. Same zoarium as illustrated on figures 3–9 of Plate 17. Detail of the center of the coiled zoarium for comparison of same in *F. archimediformis* (fig. 3). Barbed pillars are developed near the edge of the central hole from the obverse and inward of the coiling. 109

Group III

7. Columnar appendages attached to the reverse of *Fenestella stocktonensis* var. *magnolobata* n. var. (*see* Plate 7). Shows division of the appendages into several branches at a point of attachment. × 10. 82

PLATE 19.—*FENESTELLA* OF GROUP XII

Figure | Page

1–10. *Fenestella archimediformis* n. sp. Wolfcamp Series, bed 9, section 24, west end of Wolf Camp Hills, Glass Mountains, Texas.. 110

1, 2. Details of the obverse from the coiled part. × 10 and × 20.

3, 4. Details of the reverse from the distal, slightly coiled part. Outline of the basal part of zooecial chamber visible through thin semitransparent wall. × 10 and × 20.

5, 6. Top, viewed from different angles of a paratype showing three "floor levels" (1, 2, 3) of a complex zoarium which was probably broadly coiled, with the center of coiling somewhere to the right. × 2.

7. Detail of the obverse of the top "floor". × 10.

8. Detail of the obverse of the basal "floor" showing its contact with pillars, which branch out radially into four or five short clawlike branchlets near the points of contact. × 10.

9. Detail of the pillars that start from the reverse of the upper and middle "floors" and contact the obverse of the basal "floor." Detail of the latter shows carinal nodes, which are somewhat inclined distad. In the left upper corner an adnate brachiopod is attached to the *Fenestella* by the long slender spine. × 10.

10. Three pillars arising from one point on the reverse of the basal "floor." The nearly completely preserved pillar is armed with the reverted barbs. × 10.

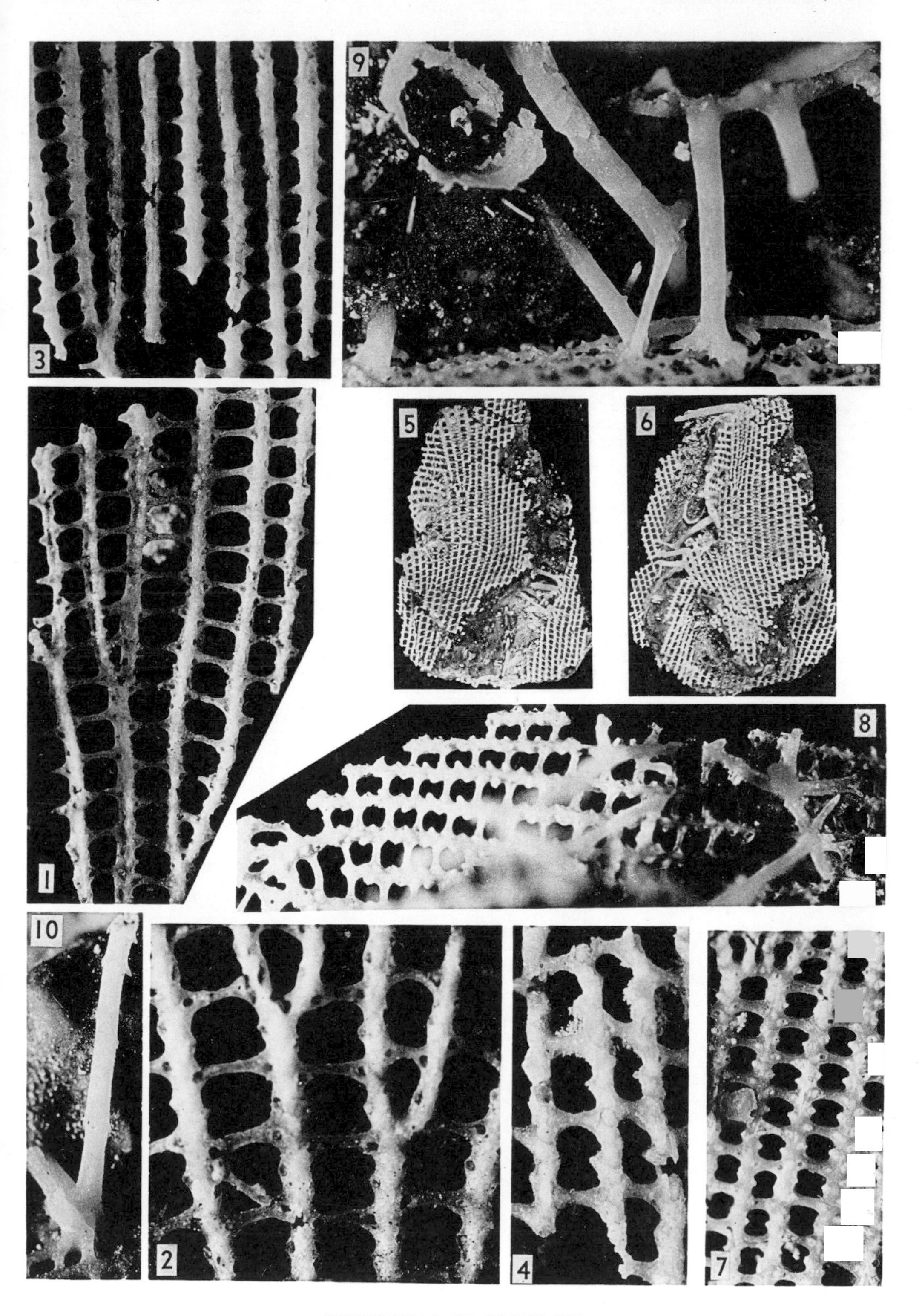

FENESTELLA OF GROUP XII

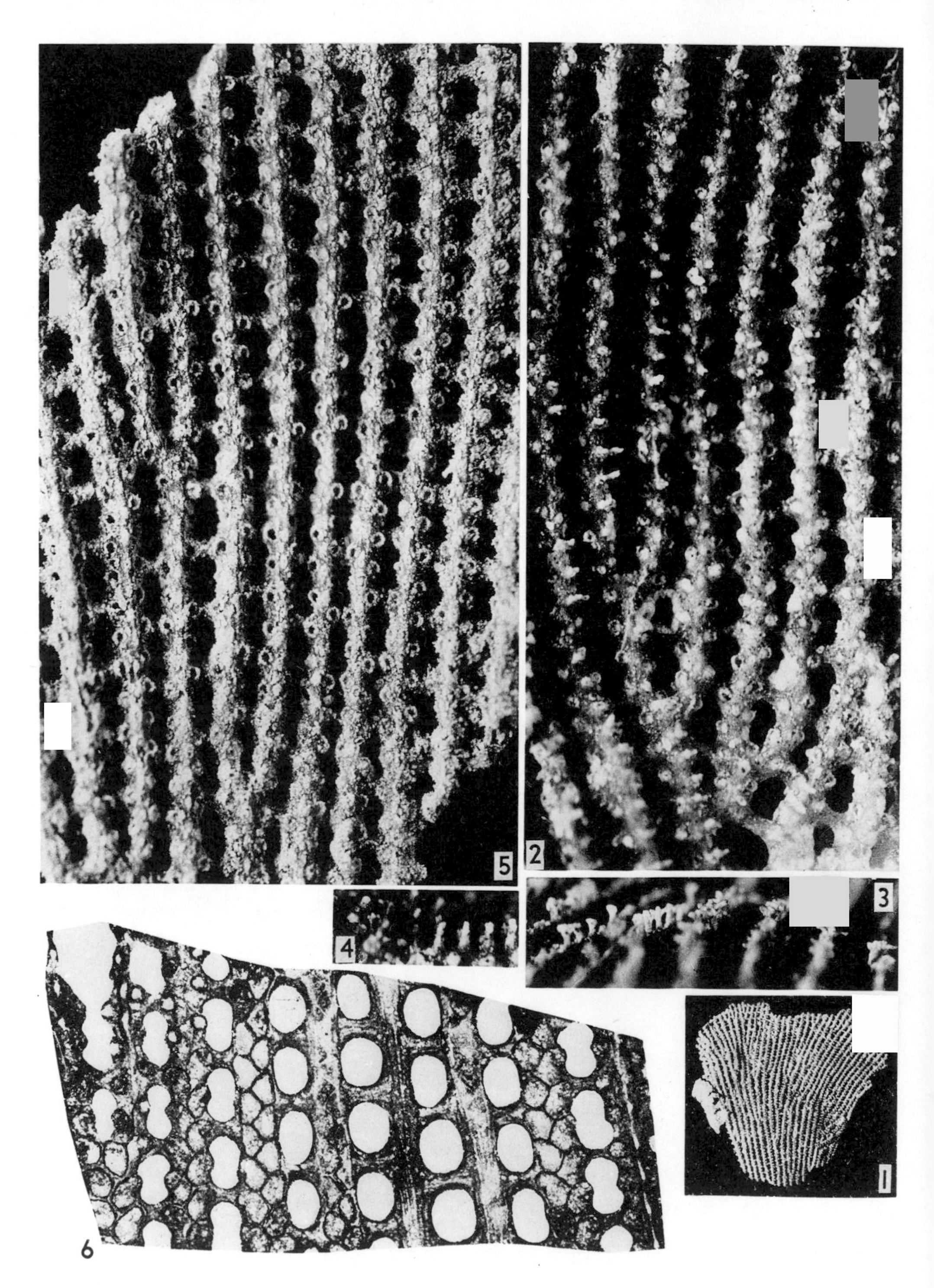

FENESTELLA OF GROUP XII

PLATE 20.—*FENESTELLA* OF GROUP XII

Figure | Page

1–5. *Fenestella* (*Cervella*) *cruciformis* n. var. Middle part of Leonard Series, bed 14, section 17, north of Leonard Mountain, Glass Mountains, Texas. 114

1. Obverse of probably distal part of a fan-shaped zoarium, with an unusually frequent bifurcation of the branches along the left part of the distal margin. × 2.
2. Detail of the zoarium in Figure 1, with unequally developed carinal nodes along some of the branches. A series of branches are given off laterally instead of by symmetrical bifurcation. × 20.

3, 4. Detail of the zoarium in Figure 1, diagonal view of the rows of the apically tripartite carinal nodes. × 20.

5. Detail of another fragment of the zoarium, with the low carinal nodes; expanded apicies destroyed or never developed. × 20.

6. *Fenestella nikiforovae* Shulga. Permian P_{1a}^{1}, Slide 278, Podcherem river, Russia (After Shulga-Nesterenko, 1936, Pl. 1, fig. 3; same as Shulga-Nesterenko, 1941, Pl. 10, fig. 4). Tangential section. × 22. 113

PLATE 21.—*FENESTELLA* OF GROUP XII

Figure | Page

1–4. *Fenestella* (*Cervella*) *cruciformis* n. var. Middle part of Leonard Series, bed 14 of section 17, north of Leonard Mountain, Glass Mountains, Texas. × 20............ 114

1. Detail of the obverse showing normal manner of bifurcation
2. Simultaneous bifurcation of two neighboring branches resulting in a gap below the two bifurcations, bridged by a long dissepiment

3–4. Detail of the reverse showing sporadic development of the wide and low nodes. The ridges of the grooved surface of the branches and dissepiments (best seen on Figs. 4, 5) are emphasized by concentration of the small tubercles along crests of the ridges.

5–6. *Fenestella nikiforovae* Shulga. Holotype, slide 565, Podcherem River, Russia (After Shulga-Nesterenko, 1936, Figs. 3 (part only), 4; same as Shulga-Nesterenko, 1941, Figs. 31, 32). × 40.. 113

5. Tangential section of the carina and the nodes of the obverse, showing larger and smaller "carinal nodes"
6. Tangential section of the secondary crust on the reverse, showing larger and smaller "capillaries," arranged in longitudinal rows (right side of sketch)

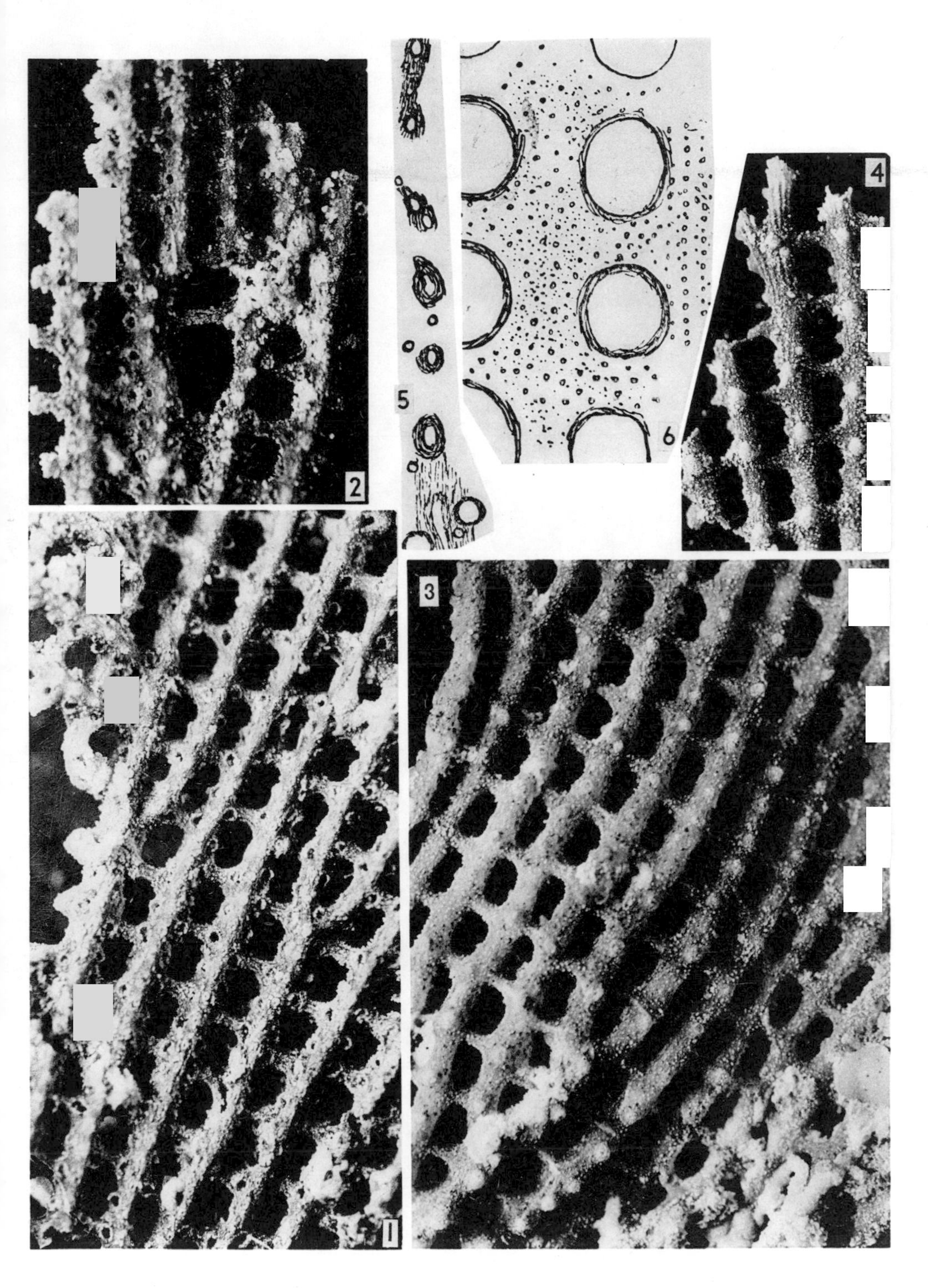

FENESTELLA OF GROUP XII

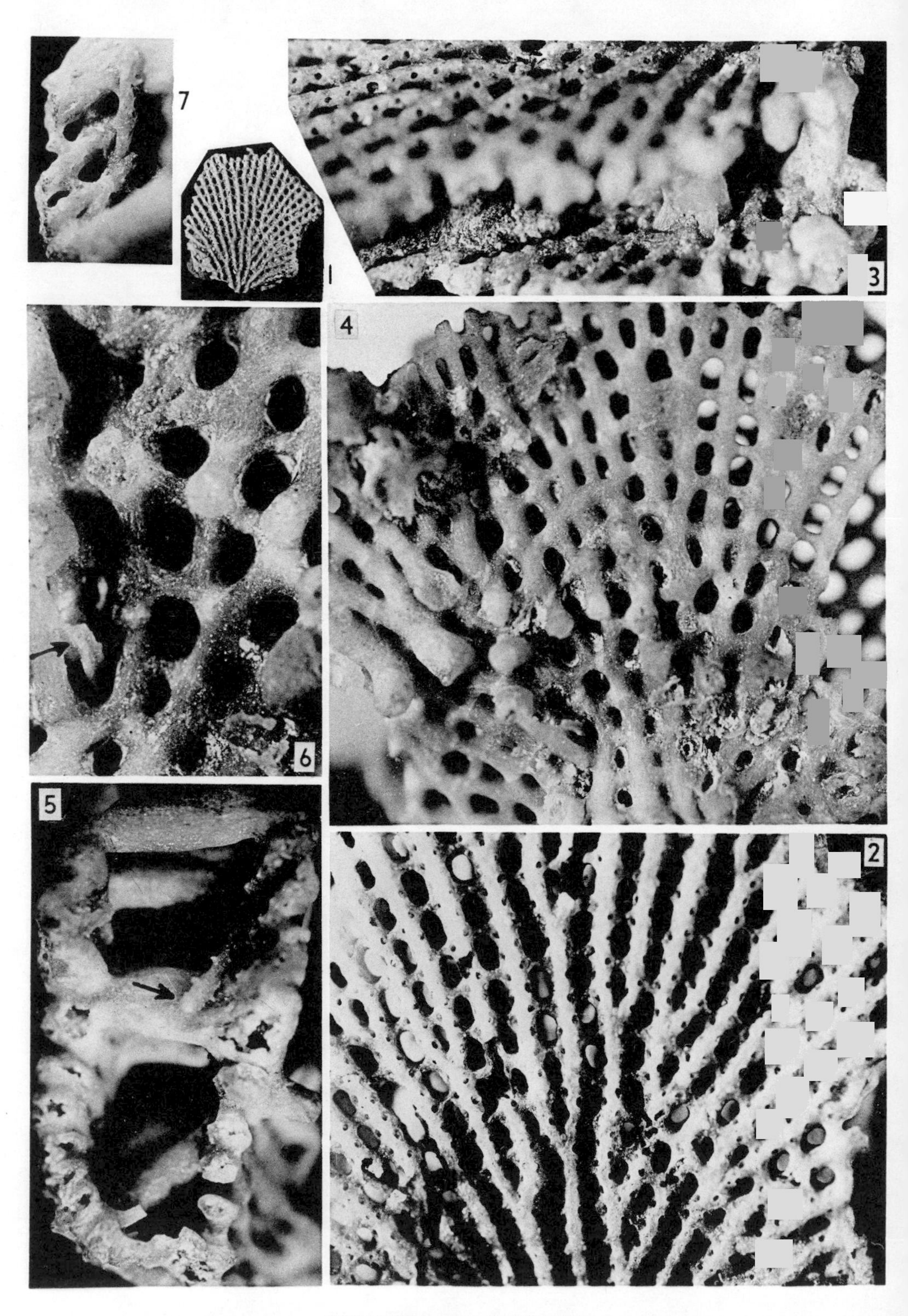

FENESTELLA OF GROUP XII

PLATE 22.—*FENESTELLA* OF GROUP XII

Figure | Page

1–7. *Fenestella parviuscula* var. *libellus*, n. var. Middle part of Wolfcamp Series, northeast of Wolf Camp, Glass Mountains, Texas. Holotype. 112

1. Top view of a "two-floor" zoarium, showing obverse of the "upper floor". × 2
2. Detail of the obverse of the "upper floor". × 2.
3. Diagonal view showing the obverse of the upper and lower "floors," connected by a series of stout columnar appendages. Where they contact the obverse of the lower floor, the columns divide into slightly spreading branches, which enter fenestrules and fuse with the sclerenchymatous encrustation on the reverse of the lower "floor." × 10.
4. Bottom view, showing the reverse of the lower "floor," covered by thick sclerenchymatous crust, from which arise the stumps of broken uprights, arranged in irregular rows. A single hook-bearing, prismatic columnar appendage, which developed diagonally from the reverse of the upper "floor," protrudes through a fenestrule of the lower "floor" (*a*). × 10.
5. Side view, showing the stout connecting uprights, a stump of slender pillar, and a distal portion of the diagonally oriented hook-bearing, prismatic column (indi cated by arrow) that is fused to the obverse of the lower "floor" by a proliferation at its tip. × 10.
6. Detail of the reverse of the lower "floor" (same as Fig. 4) showing the fibrous structure of the crust, the pillars, and the apex of a hook-bearing prismatic column (indicated by arrow) protruding through a fenestrule. × 20.
7. Diagonal view, showing the tip of the same hook-bearing pillar (*b*) that is fused to the obverse of the lower floor. × 10.

PLATE 23.—*FENESTELLA* OF GROUP XII

Figure | Page

1–3. *Fenestella tschernovi* var. *usiensis* Shulga. From the highest part (Fourth limestone) of Word group, north of junction of Road and Gilliland canyons, Glass Mountains, Texas. 116
- 1. View of the reverse. × 1.
- 2. Detail of the reverse. × 10.
- 3. Detail of the obverse; initial disk in left central part is probably *Acanthocladia guadalupensis*. × 10.

4–7. *Fenestella tschernovi* Shulga. From Leonard Series, exact locality unknown, Glass Mountains, Texas.. 115
- 4. General view of two fragments. × 1.
- 5–6. Details of the obverse of a larger and a smaller fragment. × 10.
- 7. Detail of the reverse of a larger fragment to show the replacement of the calcareous fossil by crystalline quartz. × 20.

8–11. *Fenestella shulgae* n. sp. Holotype. Lower Permian, Lipovaia Gora, near Vavilovo, western Urals, Russia.. 117
- 8. View of the reverse. × 1½.
- 9. Detail of the reverse of the lateral part of a zoarium. The striation of the reverse of the branches is locally observable; also the impression of the obverse is visible in the rock where the zoarium is broken off. × 10.
- 10. Detail of the reverse of a distal part of same zoarium, showing broad rounded nodes along the middle of the branches. × 10.
- 11. Thin section showing the outline of the zooecial chambers. × 20.

12. A group of interconnected zoaria of *Fenestella* (below), *Polypora* (above), *Thamniscus* (lower right), and a number of the columnar appendages on *Polypora*. Upper part of Leonard Series; below and to the west of Clay Slide, Glass Mountains, Texas. × 1.... 54

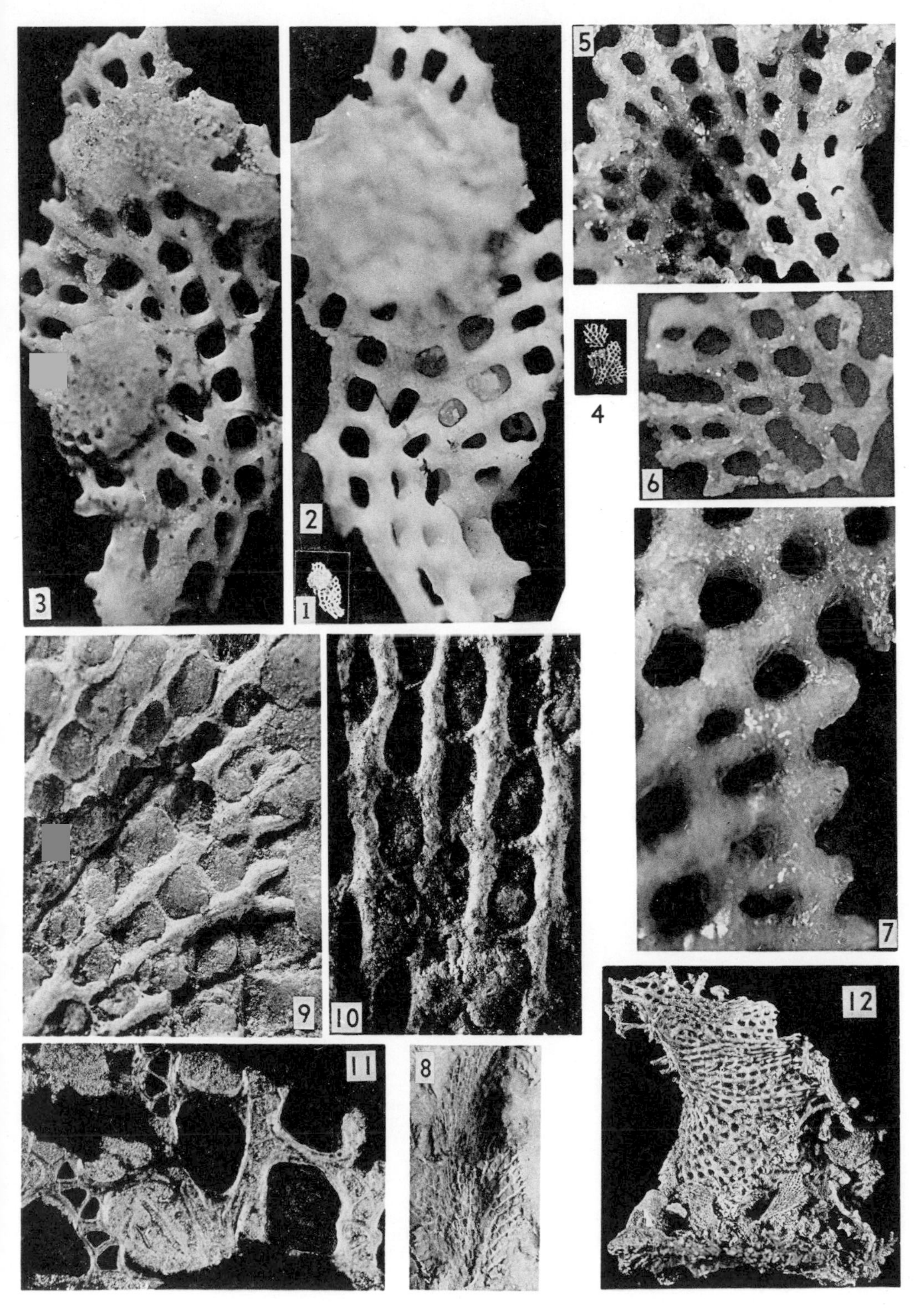

FENESTELLA OF GROUP XII

INDEX*

The index consists of five parts: Geographic Names, Stratigraphic Terms, Subject Index, Latin Names, Author Index.

GEOGRAPHIC NAMES

*Page numbers in **boldface** type indicate detailed descriptions.

STRATIGRAPHIC TERMS

SUBJECT INDEX

LATIN NAMES

AUTHOR INDEX